McGRAW-HILL PUBLICATIONS IN THE
BOTANICAL SCIENCES

EDMUND W. SINNOTT, Consulting Editor

MORPHOLOGY OF VASCULAR PLANTS

McGRAW-HILL PUBLICATIONS IN
THE BOTANICAL SCIENCES

Edmund W. Sinnott, *Consulting Editor*

ARNOLD   An Introduction to Paleobotany
CURTIS AND CLARK   An Introduction to Plant Physiology
EAMES   Morphology of the Angiosperms
EAMES   Morphology of Vascular Plants: Lower Groups
EAMES AND MACDANIELS   An Introduction to Plant Anatomy
HAUPT   An Introduction to Botany
HAUPT   Laboratory Manual of Elementary Botany
HAUPT   Plant Morphology
HILL   Economic Botany
HILL, OVERHOLTS, POPP, AND GROVE   Botany
JOHANSEN   Plant Microtechnique
KRAMER   Plant and Soil Water Relationships
KRAMER AND KOZLOWSKI   Physiology of Trees
LILLY AND BARNETT   Physiology of the Fungi
MAHESHWARI   An Introduction to the Embryology of the Angiosperms
MILLER   Plant Physiology
POOL   Flowers and Flowering Plants
SHARP   Fundamentals of Cytology
SINNOTT   Plant Morphogenesis
SINNOTT, DUNN, AND DOBZHANSKY   Principles of Genetics
SINNOTT AND WILSON   Botany: Principles and Problems
SMITH   Cryptogamic Botany
    Vol. I.   Algae and Fungi
    Vol. II.   Bryophytes and Pteridophytes
SMITH   The Fresh-water Algae of the United States
SWINGLE   Textbook of Systematic Botany
WEAVER AND CLEMENTS   Plant Ecology

There are also the related series of McGraw-Hill Publications in the Zoological Sciences, of which E. J. Boell is Consulting Editor, and in the Agricultural Sciences, of which R. A. Brink is Consulting Editor.

FRONTISPIECE.—Gametophytes and young sporophytes of *Lycopodium:* at the left *L. clavatum;* in the center and at the right *L. obscurum.* (The gameto-phyte of *L. clavatum* is triangular and dark and lies adjacent on the left to the larger pale gametophyte near the center.)

MORPHOLOGY

OF

VASCULAR PLANTS

LOWER GROUPS
(*Psilophytales to Filicales*)

BY

ARTHUR J. EAMES
Professor Emeritus of Botany, Cornell University

McGRAW-HILL BOOK COMPANY, Inc.

NEW YORK AND LONDON

1936

PREFACE

In recent years the study of the morphology of vascular plants has made much progress: valuable information concerning the structure and life histories of both living and fossil forms has been obtained; the principles of evolutionary advance in form have become much better understood; phylogeny and classification have been placed upon a more sound basis. The important changes in interpretation and classification that these advances have brought about have, however, not been apparent to those not working in the field, and there has been in the English language no book to supply the information.

This book, it is hoped, will make more readily available the important facts and theories in this field as known and interpreted today, and will emphasize the fact that notable progress in morphology is being overlooked or neglected. It has been prepared as a textbook and is not to be considered a reference book for detailed or complete information concerning the plants discussed. In form, method of presentation, and subject matter included, it is the outgrowth of the author's experience in teaching in the field.

The viewpoint is that of broad comparative study, with the development of a natural classification and phylogenetic relationships as the goal. With this object, emphasis is placed upon the range of structure within each group. Individual forms are not treated in detail; the "type method" is of little value where phylogenetic determinations are to be made. Cytological aspects have largely been omitted, as have many details of anatomical structure. Some features, prominent in the older morphology, which are no longer believed important, are likewise omitted or receive little attention.

No system of classification is presented as a basis for the treatment of the groups; classification is built up as the groups are studied, and the goal of the study, a classification that is as closely natural as possible, is attained only at the end of the book. A scheme of classification that has been built up is better understood by the student than one that is merely illustrated. (If the teacher prefers, however, to base the use of the book from the first upon a fixed classification, the table on page 401 may be used.) Theories and principles underlying interpretations are also developed so far as possible as the treatment progresses. The text, therefore, after a brief introduction, begins abruptly with the description of groups.

The order of arrangement is that found in the experience of the author to be most satisfactory. In general the more primitive forms are discussed first, but there are marked exceptions to this order. Of these the outstanding one is that in the treatment of the lower groups living forms are considered before extinct forms. This marked departure from a normal sequence is, in the opinion of the author, of distinct advantage in teaching. The student is not required at the very beginning of his study to become acquainted with certain phases of historical geology; he is not confronted with forms whose structure and life history are poorly known; he is not confused by the complexities of the nomenclature and terminology of paleobotany.

The separation of living and fossil forms gives for most major groups two separate treatments. This also is believed helpful from the standpoint of teaching: it provides an opportunity for a review of the first presentation and for a broader consideration of the group after a background of fact and of principles has been acquired.

The treatment given the various groups is not uniformly detailed. Certain families and genera—for example, the Psilotaceae, the Ophioglossaceae, *Isoetes*, *Marsilea*, *Azolla*—require more extensive discussion than others. These groups have greater interest from the viewpoint of the book because important information about them has recently become available; because their interpretation is difficult; or because they have been superficially treated in most textbooks. In some of these cases the author has reexamined the group in the light of present-day knowledge of related groups and of morphological concepts and principles, and new facts and interpretations are presented.

The book is naturally in large part a compilation based upon literature. Reference in part to this literature is given in bibliographies which conclude each chapter, and in a bibliography for general use at the end of the book. The bibliographies contain only those references which are believed to be most useful in a book of this type.

For the sake of convenience the book has been divided into two parts, the first dealing with the lower, the second with the higher groups. The point of division has no significance from the standpoint of classification.

For illustrations the author is greatly indebted to many individuals, especially to those who have supplied photographic copies. A large part of the borrowed figures have been redrawn. The preparation of these and of the original figures is the work of Mrs. Rita Ballard Eames, whose aid has been invaluable not only in the illustration of the book but in many other features of its preparation. The original photographs are the work of Mr. W. R. Fisher. To all these the author desires to express his sincere appreciation and thanks.

ARTHUR J. EAMES.

ITHACA, NEW YORK,
   April, 1936.

CONTENTS

INTRODUCTION

Morphology deals with form, the form of organisms and of their parts, large and small, external and internal, and with structure, the relation of parts to one another and to the whole. Morphology is thus fundamentally descriptive. The descriptive study of an organism through all stages of development and reproduction is commonly known as the study of its "life history." Some morphological studies are merely the determination of the facts of life histories. But morphology, as commonly understood today, rests on a broader basis: it is comparative in its fundamental nature, and its comparisons are considered in the light of evolutionary modification and development. It thus deals largely with underlying form and with homology. The study of form from this viewpoint is a study in phylogenetic modification, and its purpose is naturally the determination of the origin and relationships of groups of organisms. The establishment of a natural classification is therefore the goal of most morphological study today. In this book each group is treated first descriptively, then comparatively, and classification is built up as group after group is considered.

Vascular plants have always held an important place in botanical study, not only because of their prominence and their economic importance, but because they form "the top of the evolutionary tree" of the plant kingdom. The past 30 years have seen most important changes in the understanding of the evolutionary history of these plants. These changes have come about in part because of an increased acquaintance with living plants, but largely because of the knowledge of fossil forms acquired during this time. The comparative study of living forms provides a basis for theories of origin and relationship but paleobotany describes the forms which actually preceded the living ones.

The study of extinct plants has shown that vascular plants as a group go very far back in geological time, at least as far as the Upper Silurian period; that even in the earlier periods of their existence they were a diverse lot, showing no obvious relationship to one another; and that the oldest known members of some groups were highly complex in structure. The fossil record shows that the very early vascular plants were markedly alga-like; that apparently these plants arose directly from algal stocks and that bryophytes were not concerned with the origin of vascular plants. Through fossil forms the living groups can be traced back to the early groups as distinct and unrelated—or most distantly related—lines. It is thus apparent that vascular plants form no unit series or line leading directly from the lowest to the highest types. No simple phylogenetic tree can stand to express the origins and relationships of vascular plant groups; lines of relationship as now understood spread apart and the 'tree' has become shrub-like.

The establishment of these facts has wrought major changes in the classification which has long stood and which is, unfortunately, still largely maintained in textbooks. The division of vascular plants into two major groups—those whose reproduction is "by spores," the "Pteridophyta," and those reproducing "by seeds," the "Spermatophyta"—is now seen to be an unnatural one. More than 30 years ago the discovery that an ancient group of fern-like plants bore definite seeds formed a link between fern-like plants and modern spermatophytes. Since that time this link has been strongly reinforced by evidence from structural features of other types. And seeds have been found to have been present also in other lines of ancient plants. The seed habit cannot be used to separate the "vascular cryptogams" from the "phanerogams." The lines of relationship fall elsewhere: the ferns are apparently more closely related to the gymnosperms and angiosperms than they are to their so-called "allies." And these "fern allies" are among themselves a diverse lot of unrelated groups; the club mosses and the horse-tails bear probably no closer relation to one another than they do to the ferns. In place of two major groups among vascular plants there are today at least four such groups; the "Pterido-phyta" and the "Spermatophyta" have been replaced by the Psilopsida, Lycopsida, Sphenopsida, and Pteropsida.

Some of the larger living groups—especially the ferns and the conifers—have become known in sufficient detail so that progress within the groups can be followed and evolutionary principles determined. It is clear that parallel development and reduction have played most important parts in evolutionary progress. Because of a lack of appreciation of this, serious errors were made in the older classifications. For example, the Hydropteridineae (water ferns) were established and maintained as a natural group, the most advanced of the ferns; small, simple species of *Ophioglossum* were believed to be the most primitive of ferns forming a connecting link with the bryophytes.

The two families constituting the Hydropteridineae were bound together by heterospory but heterospory is now recognized as the expression of a general tendency affecting many groups; the possession of this character by two groups of ferns does not indicate relationship among these families. Further, detailed studies of ferns indicate that the two families are more closely related to different homosporous families than they are to each other. The old group Hydropteridineae is an artificial group and must be discarded.

The extent to which reduction has affected all groups of vascular plants has not been recognized. Extensive comparative studies—especially those involving vascular structure, in which evidence of lost parts is often retained long after proof in external form is gone—have shown that a large proportion of simple forms are not primitively simple but are simple through reduction. Thus, *Ophioglossum vulgatum* has long been looked upon as an extremely primitive fern, one that served as a connecting link with lower groups. It is now known that this plant is a highly specialized fern and that its 'simplicity' and 'primitiveness' are the result of reduction. Similarly *Phylloglossum* and *Isoetes* are not primitive types.

The fossil record is constantly lengthening the period of time during which the various vascular plant groups have existed. It is showing that among the members of a group at present known the older ones are in many cases the more complex. Thus the evidence derived from vascular structure (the presence of vestigial parts) and from comparative study is supported. The simpler members of any group lie under suspicion of reduction and must be considered with the greatest care before acceptance as primitive.

It has been stated that the recognition of reduction in many places is the "fad" of today in morphology. The reply can be made that only now has reduction come to be fully recognized—that only recently have the facts been accumulated which prove the existence of reduction broadly and abundantly in all plant groups. The recognition of reduced forms as such must play a most prominent part in the building of a natural classification. To claim that there is little reduction to be seen among modern forms is to admit ignorance of the available information.

Support for the revised classification has come from a new quarter. The essential completion of our knowledge of the gametophytes of the various living groups has placed the sexual generation in a position to be used in broad comparative studies. And it is found that the gametophyte strongly supports the major divisions of vascular plants which have been based on the sporophyte.

It is believed that the present interpretations and classification represent a marked advance over those of the older morphology. They are of course not to be considered in any way complete or perfect. Increase in knowledge of living plants, and especially facts obtained from the fossil record will surely bring changes, perhaps even major ones. And progress toward a natural classification is not to be made from morphological studies alone; morphology provides only one line of evidence, which must be added to and checked by that obtained from as many other fields as possible, especially taxonomy, cytology, and genetics.

MORPHOLOGY

OF

VASCULAR PLANTS

CHAPTER I

LYCOPODIACEAE   CLUB MOSSES

Among vascular plants the club mosses form a small and inconspicuous element, for, though they may be locally abundant, they are small plants and attract little attention.   In the group there are only two genera, *Lycopodium* and *Phylloglossum*. The former is large, with about 100 species, growing in arctic, temperate, and tropical lands, but chiefly in subtropical and tropical forests.   It is not found in arid regions.   *Phylloglossum* is a monotypic genus and is restricted in distribution to parts of Australasia.

LYCOPODIUM

The club mosses of northern temperate climates are chiefly low, evergreen, trailing plants of woodlands and barren fields. The common name suggests two of their characteristic features, the small moss-like leaves and the club-shaped fruiting stem tips or cones.   The bushy, upright branches of some species suggest minute pine trees, and the plants are therefore sometimes known as "ground pine."   The general appearance and the leaves and cones of these better known creeping species are fairly typical of the group.

Sporophyte

Habit.   In habit the many species vary greatly, but all are slender and weak-stemmed.   Many are prostrate, the main stems creeping on or below the surface of the ground; some are semierect or ascending, the older part of the stem becoming finally

1

FIG. 1.—*Lycopodium lucidulum.* Portions of plant showing habit; right-hand portion natural size.

horizontal (Fig. 1).   The stems of others scramble over shrubs, twining to some extent.   Many of the tropical species are epiphytes with weak, pendent branches.

Stems.   The stems, which are clothed with abundant small leaves, branch freely.   Branching in the genus is characteristi-

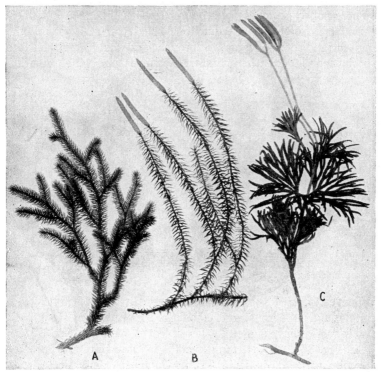

Fig. 2.—*Lycopodium.*   Habit of determinate lateral branches.   *A, L. clavatum; B, L. annotinum; C, L. complanatum* var. *flabelliforme.* × about ½.

cally dichotomous.   The successive forkings are usually in planes at right angles with one another, though this relation may be somewhat obscure.   The two branches of a forking may be equal and alike, as in typical dichotomy, and all may continue to grow indefinitely (Fig. 1); or the dichotomy may be unequal or obscure, one branch being weaker than the other, thus simulating a monopodial condition (Fig. 2,*A*).   That the stem in any species is truly monopodial is doubtful.   (In true dichotomy the apical growing region is divided symmetrically into two

parts; in monopodial branching a branch is developed laterally
from the apical meristem below the apex.)   Except in cases where
the branching is by symmetrical dichotomies, most of the
branches become lateral structures of limited growth upon a
rhizome-like or vine-like main stem (Fig. 2).   These *determinate*
lateral *branches* themselves branch freely (Fig. 2*A,C*)—chiefly
dichotomously in one plane—or sparsely (Fig. 2*B*), but their
period of growth is limited to one or very few seasons.   The
limited and often elaborate branch systems so formed are
specialized photosynthetic and fruiting structures which function
for a few years only.

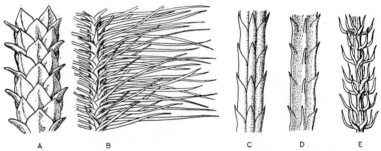

Fig. 3.—*Lycopodium.* Leaf form and arrangement.   *A, L. rufescens; B,
L. mandioccanum; C, D, L. complanatum* var. *flabelliforme*, ventral and dorsal
views; *E, L. cernuum.*   (*A, B, E,* after Pritzel in Engler and Prantl.)

Leaves.   The leaves are small—typically 2 to 10 mm long—
simple, and numerous, and cover the stem closely (Figs. 1, 2).
A few species have somewhat larger leaves, at most 25 to 35 mm
long (Fig. 3*B*).   The arrangement is in close spirals, whorls, or
opposite pairs, or is somewhat irregular; in some species it is
said to be almost without order.   Even where the arrangement is
symmetrical, it may vary from one part of the plant to another,
especially from one type of stem to another.   Where the leaf
arrangement is definite, the phyllotactic fractions are unlike those
of other vascular plants, such series as $\frac{2}{7}$, $\frac{2}{9}$, $\frac{2}{11}$ being found.
This peculiarity, and especially the irregularity of arrangement,
are of importance in considerations of phylogeny.

The leaves of the determinate lateral branch systems of some
creeping species are much specialized (Figs. 2*C*; 3*C,D*).   The
phyllotaxy is decussate, a leaf arrangement commonly recognized
as one of the highest.   The leaves are fused to the branchlets

and decurrent, and form with the stems flattened photosynthetic structures suggesting frond-like leaves (Fig. 2C). The leaves of the lateral rows are enlarged and wing-like, those of the others reduced, the lower (dorsal) row abortive (Fig. 3D). These dorsiventral branchlet systems resemble the twigs of the arbor vitae, *Thuja*, a highly specialized conifer.

Roots. The first root, developed as the young sporophyte becomes independent of the gametophyte, is short and, at least in some species, does not live long. The roots of the older plant are adventitious and arise singly or in groups acropetally along the underside of the stem (Fig. 1). Such roots are somewhat irregularly distributed and in position bear little or no relation to other organs. In some more or less erect forms, both terrestrial and epiphytic, these roots, which arise on the outside of the stele, do not at once break through to the surface but turn downward and bore through the cortex, emerging only at the base of the stem. (Similar root behavior is found in some of the ferns.)

The branching of the roots is strikingly dichotomous in some species, for example, in *L. obscurum* and *L. lucidulum* (Fig. 1), and each successive forking is at right angles to the preceding one; in other species the dichotomy is obscure. The roots do not become extensive, and no endogenous lateral rootlets arise as in seed plants. Root hairs in terrestrial forms are abundant and persist over a long period.

Anatomy. A cross section of the stem shows a central core of vascular tissue, which occupies in some species nearly half the area, in others only a small part. This vascular core is cylindrical and protostelic (that is, without a pith) with the xylem exarch. The relations of xylem and phloem are unusual and such that a complex vascular body is formed. In the simpler types the xylem forms, as seen in cross section, a star-like mass, with rays of varying number (Fig. 4A). In the bays between lies the phloem, separated from the xylem by a narrow layer of parenchyma. In more complex types (Fig. 4B) the furrows in the xylem cylinder are more numerous and less regular, and, as seen in transverse section, may break up the xylem into isolated strands. These apparently separate strands are, however, lobes of the xylem mass, which are free only at certain levels and do not represent discrete vascular bundles. The furrowing may be such as to break up the xylem core into plate-like lobes (Fig. 4D) or into a mesh-like mass with included bands of phloem (Fig. 4*C*). These more complex anatomical types are associated with the more specialized external structure. The young plant in all species has a simple, angular stele with very few protoxylem ridges.

From the ridges of vascular tissue the leaf traces extend as slender strands obliquely upward and outward through the pericycle and cortex to the leaves. One strand enters the base of each leaf and becomes the unbranched midvein.

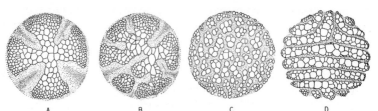

Fig. 4.—*Lycopodium*. Diagrams showing vascular structure of the stele of the stem. *A*, *L. serratum; B*, *L. lucidulum; C*, *L. cernuum; D*, *L. volubile.* (*A, C, D, after Pritzel in Engler and Prantl.*)

The stem is wholly primary in structure; no cambium arises to develop secondary xylem and phloem, and no periderm is formed. Therefore, though the stems may live many years, they do not increase in diameter. The largest ones are about 1 cm in diameter. The growing point has several apical cells.

The xylem is simple; all its conducting cells are tracheids, those of the metaxylem with scalariform-pitted walls. The phloem is also simple, consisting of sieve tubes and parenchyma cells. The sieve tubes are not ducts formed of rows of fused cells, as in many seed plants, but are elongate, tapering cells. The numerous sieve plates are scattered over the walls and not restricted in distribution to certain areas, as in higher types of plants. The slender roots are of simple structure and are usually monarch.

Reproduction. Sporangia are borne singly on the upper (*ventral*, or *adaxial*) side of the leaves near the base, in the leaf axil, or on the stem just above the leaf. The fertile leaves, or *sporophylls*, differ a great deal in the various species. In some species they are like the sterile leaves or differ from them only in their somewhat smaller size (Fig. 1). In such cases fertile and sterile regions alternate on the stem, one of each developing annually. Sporophylls of this type continue to serve as photosynthetic organs after the spores are shed.   In other species the sporophylls differ greatly from the leaves in size, shape, and color, and serve only as reproductive structures.   Such sporophylls are grouped in *cones*, or *strobili*, which are terminal on the main stem or on lateral branches (Fig. 2).   In some species the cones are sessile on the leafy stems, and the leaves pass through transition forms into sporophylls.   In other species the cones are borne on long erect stalks with distant, scale-like leaves (Fig. 2*C*). The sporangia in such cones are obviously more favorably placed

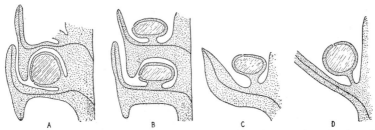

Fig. 5.—*Lycopodium*. Diagrams showing position of sporangia and point of dehiscence.   *A*, *L. inundatum*, axillary and protected; *B*, *L. cernuum*, foliar and protected; *C*, *L. squarrosum*, subfoliar and exposed; *D*, *L. lucidulum*, axillary and exposed.   (*A to C, after Sykes.*)

for spore distribution by wind.   In a few species all the leaves of the mature plant bear sporangia, that is, every leaf is a sporophyll. In these species, as in the first group, definite cones are not formed.   (The entire plant has sometimes been considered a cone.)

Sporangia.   The sporangia are large (1.0 to 2.5 mm in diameter), reniform or in some cases subspherical, yellowish when mature, and attached by a short stalk or pad-like base (Figs. 5, 6).   In the cone-bearing species they may be largely or wholly enclosed by dorsal lobes of the sporophylls above (Fig. 5*A*,*B*). When mature they open by a slit transverse to the leaf, two clamshell-like valves being formed, and the spores are scattered by the wind.   The position of the slit varies from apical to low on the outer side (Fig. 5); the opening is in the position most favorable for spore distribution in each species.

Development of Sporangium.   Sporangium initials are first evident close to the growing point, in some species as a transverse row (or two or three rows) of superficial cells on the upper surface of the young leaf near the base (Fig. 6*A*), in other species as a row or group of cells on the axis between the young leaves. At this stage in the development of the axis the limits of leaf base and internode are not defined, and, during the period of rapid growth which follows, the position of the sporangium initials may be shifted from 'leaf' (leaf primordium) to axis or from 'axis' to leaf. The mature sporangium may therefore be cauline or foliar in position, regardless of its place of origin; foliar sporangia are, however, usually foliar in origin. In most species the mature sporangia are foliar or axillary in position (Figs. 5, 6).

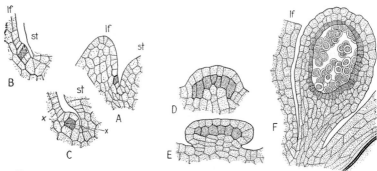

Fig. 6.—*Lycopodium Selago*. Development of sporangium. *A, B*, radial sections through base of young sporophyll, showing, shaded, one of a transverse row of sporangium initials; *C* to *E*, sections of the sporangium at a later stage; *C*, radial; *D*, in plane *x-x* of *C*; *E*, transverse; *F*, still later stage, sporocytes and tapetum developed; *lf*, sporophyll; *st*, stem. (*After Bower*.)

In the sporangium initials periclinal divisions (parallel with the surface) form an outer and an inner layer of cells (Fig. 6*C,D*). Both these layers increase greatly and build up the sporangium and its contents. The outer layer, the *primary wall cells*, by divisions both periclinal and anticlinal (at right angles to the surface) forms the wall, a layer of tissue when mature about three cells thick. The inner layer, the *primary sporogenous cells*, by divisions in various planes, forms a large number of *spore mother cells* or *sporocytes*. This method of sporangium formation, where *a group of cells, superficial in position, by periclinal division forms inner and outer cells, the inner forming sporogenous cells, the outer sterile cells only*, is called the *eusporangiate* method.

As the sporangium develops, the innermost layer of wall cells becomes specialized as a nutritive layer for the sporogenous cells, a *tapetum* (Fig. 6*F*). This layer extends also below the sporogenous cells, developing there from sterile leaf cells, and thus surrounds the sporogenous tissue.   The contents of the tapetal cells are largely used up as the sporocytes develop, and in the mature sporangium the tapetum is much shrunken or has collapsed.

Spores.   The sporocytes, by two successive divisions during one of which chromosome reduction occurs, form tetrads of spores.   The spores are tetrahedral (four-sided, like a tetrahedron, but with the base rounded or even hemispherical). They are very small (about 0.03 mm in diameter), light, with thin walls, which are smooth or pitted, or with honeycomb or

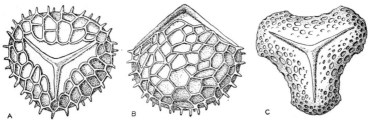

A   B   C

Fig. 7.—Spores of *Lycopodium.*   *A, L. clavatum,* top view; *B, L. complanatum,* side view; *C, L. lucidulum,* top view.   (*A, after Pritzel in Engler and Prantl.*)

net-like thickenings (Fig. 7). These thickenings are most prominent on the rounded base and may be absent on the sides. Weak *triradiate ridges* separate the three flat surfaces.   Chlorophyll is present in small amount.

Vegetative Propagation.   Reproduction occurs vegetatively by several means.   Bulbils, or gemmae, form annually on the new stem tips in some species (for example, in *L. lucidulum,* Fig. 1).   These fall to the ground or are carried a short distance by the wind and take root at once.   The morphological nature of these reproductive bodies is not altogether clear, but they seem to be the flattened tips of lateral branchlets with enlarged, winglike leaves.

Characteristically in the genus, the rhizome continues to grow indefinitely at the apex and the older part dies.   In this way, as branching regions are passed in the dying off, the original plant is broken up into a group of individuals.   In *L. inundatum* during the winter, or at the beginning of the season's growth, the entire plant dies except the tip of the rhizome which has become a resting bud.   This is essentially an annual habit.   Where the rhizome has branched, immediate multiplication of individuals is thus secured.

In tropical species and especially among epiphytes fragments of the plant body may produce new plants rather freely. Detached leaves and roots form bulbils which grow directly into young plants.

GAMETOPHYTE

The prothallia of *Lycopodium* are not so well known as are those of ferns and horsetails. They cannot readily be cultivated (only one species has matured in culture) because in most species the spores do not germinate for a very long time and the gametophytes require years to mature. Gametophytes are not commonly found wild because in many species they are subterranean, and those types found on the surface are extremely small. Prothallia of both the tropical epiphytic and the temperate terrestrial species are, however, apparently fairly common and can be found by careful search.

There are two distinct types of gametophytes. The first, which is green (except at the base) and develops on the surface of the ground, is cylindrical or ovoid with a lobed or branching top (Fig. 8*A,B,C*) and is very small, only 2 or 3 mm long. The spores in this type germinate in a few days and the gametophyte matures quickly, usually in one season, and is short-lived. The other type, which is non-green and subterranean, is tuberous and much larger, often 1 or 2 cm long or wide. In shape it is in some species like a top, or a carrot; in others it resembles a disk or a kernel of maize, and, when large and much convoluted, a walnut meat (Figs. 8, 9, and *Frontispiece*). The germination of spores in this group is long-delayed, in some species from three to five years, in others from six to eight years. The gametophyte grows slowly, requiring several years more—as many as 6 to 15— to mature, and is long-lived, living over a period of years after maturity and even nourishing young sporophytes for several years.

The first type is found chiefly in tropical species, for example, *L. cernuum*; less commonly in temperate forms, as in *L. inundatum*. The second type is characteristic of northern creeping species, such as *L. obscurum*, *L. complanatum*, and *L. clavatum*,

and also of epiphytic forms, where the gametophytes are found
under humus on tree trunks.   Between the two types there are

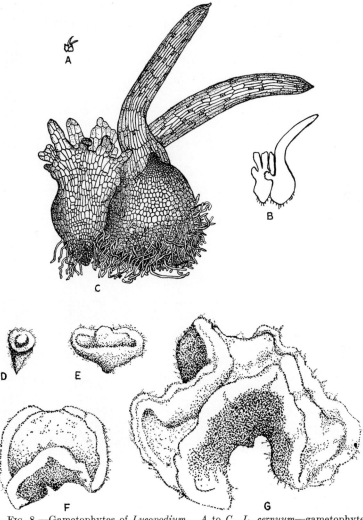

FIG. 8.—Gametophytes of *Lycopodium*.   *A* to *C*, *L. cernuum*—gametophyte
at the left, young sporophyte attached on right side; *A*, approximately natural
size; *B*, diagram of vertical section; *D* to *G*, *L. clavatum*, stages in development,
all sexually mature.   (*A* to *C after Chamberlain; D to G, after Bruchmann.*)

intermediate forms.   The gametophytes of the majority of
species are still unknown.

In both types an endophytic fungus is found in association with the tissues, occupying a definite region (Fig. 10). Though some species in the first group may be without the fungus, the

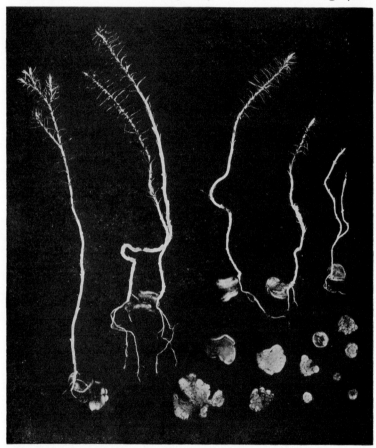

Fig. 9.—*Lycopodium obscurum.* Gametophytes (of various ages) and young sporophytes, approximately natural size.

mycorrhizal condition is a characteristic and, in subterranean types, a prominent feature.

Differences in the two types of gametophytes are emphasized by differences in their archegonia (page 16) and in the early stages of the sporophyte borne on them (page 18).

Development of Gametophyte. The germination of spores differs somewhat in detail in the different groups of species but is essentially as follows (Fig. 11): The spore swells, becoming globose, and the wall cracks along the triradiate ridge. The spore contents project through the broken wall as a conical or spherical mass. Just before the wall is ruptured, cell division

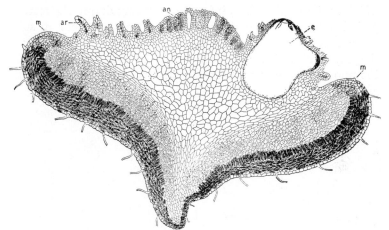

Fig. 10.—*Lycopodium* sp. Gametophyte in vertical section: *an*, antheridium; *ar*, archegonium; *e*, embryo; *m*, meristem; the deeply shaded area, the mycorrhizal region. (*After Bruchmann.*)

takes place and a small biconvex cell (*r*) is cut off at one side near the base, always under one of the arms of the triradiate ridge. This first-formed cell soon loses its contents. The second division (wall 2-2) occurs at once and divides the larger cell

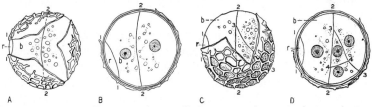

Fig. 11.—*Lycopodium annotinum.* Early stages of gametophyte. *A*, top view of opening spore with gametophyte at three-cell stage; *B*, optical section at three-cell stage, showing "rhizoidal cell," *r*, basal cell, *b*, and the apical cell of the gametophyte. *C, D*, side view and optical section after divisions have occurred in the apical cell. (*A, C, D, after Bruchmann.*)

vertically or obliquely from base to apex. Of the two cells so formed the one adjacent to the empty cell divides no further but forms a basal cell (*b*); the other becomes the apical cell of the prothallium (Fig. 11*D*). In the subterranean type a resting period of about a year ensues when the gametophyte has reached the five-cell stage, and up to this time there is no fungus associate present and no chlorophyll even in the presence of light. Further development is said to be related to the mycorrhizal association which begins at this time, infection occurring during the resting period (Fig. 12). Continued development produces a sub-globose body, which ultimately becomes top-shaped, carrot-shaped, or disk-like. The disk type is at first top-shaped, but the upper end soon expands and a dorsiventral body is built up

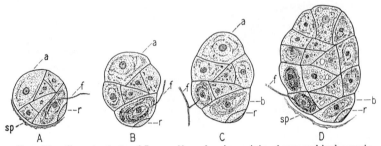

Fig. 12.—Gametophyte of *Lycopodium* showing origin of mycorrhizal associa-tion. *A, C, L. clavatum; B, D, L. annotinum; a*, apical cell; *b*, basal cell; *f*, fungus hypha; *r*, rhizoidal cell; *sp*, spore wall. (*After Bruchmann.*)

(Fig. 8*D* to *G*). Growth of this flat part is by a submarginal meristem which forms a broad, low, central cushion and a promi-nent rolled rim (Fig. 10). In age this type becomes much con-voluted (Figs. 8*G*, 9). In the radial type a crown or lobes develop at the top (Fig. 8*C*).

If the gametophyte is on or very near the surface of the sub-stratum, the crown may become green. In the subterranean types the prothallia are brownish, yellowish, or nearly colorless. They lie at various depths, from 1 to 8 cm in *L. obscurum, L. complanatum*, and *L. clavatum*, for example. The spores, per-haps, are carried down to these depths by water or by animals, but their deep position is probably in large part the result of gradual burial by the formation of humus above them during the long period of development.

The gametophytes of some epiphytic species multiply by a sort of fragmentation, and reproductive bodies of two types are formed, minute ones which rest before development and larger ones which grow at once. Vegetative propagation of gametophytes is suggestive of liverworts and mosses rather than of vascular plants in which it is rare.

Sex Organs. The gametophytes are monoecious. The numerous antheridia and archegonia are borne on the crown (Fig. 10), or at the base of its lobes or arms when these are present. On the flattened type of prothallium they are borne on the central cushion, which apparently represents the crown of the elongated radial type. In this type the first sex organs are antheridia only, which are borne in the center of, or all over, the cushion. Later

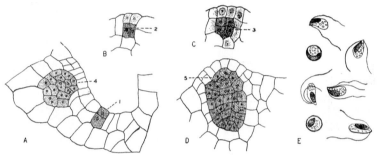

Fig. 13.—*Lycopodium clavatum.*   A to D, development of antheridium, 1 to 5, successive stages.   E, sperms and spermatocytes with mature sperms.   (*After Bruchmann.*)

both antheridia and archegonia are borne around the edges of the cushion, which enlarges as the gametophyte increases in diameter. Here the two kinds of organs are not intermingled but are borne close together in large clusters; in the green type they may be intermingled. On subterranean prothallia mature sex organs are present at all times of the year.

The antheridia (Figs. 10, 13) are somewhat indefinite structures, varying in size, shape, and number of sperms even in the same plant. They are either wholly sunken in the gametophyte or project slightly. In each antheridium a large number of spermatogenous cells is formed, the last division forming minute, cubical sperm mother cells. The many sperms have two (rarely three) cilia (Fig. 13E), and they and the sperm mother cells are much like those of mosses and liverworts and unlike those of other vascular plants.

The archegonia (Figs. 10, 14) are sunken, with only the necks protruding. Those of the subterranean type of gametophyte are slender, cylindrical structures with a long neck (Fig. 10); those of the surface-living type are short, with three or four tiers of neck cells (Fig. 14C). The venter is narrow, not much wider than the neck. The contents of the archegonium are an egg cell, a ventral canal cell, and 6 or more (even 10 to 13) neck canal cells in the long-neck form and usually 1 in the shorter form.

Development of the Sex Organs. The antheridium and the archegonium each develop from a single superficial cell. A periclinal division separates this into an outer and an inner cell (Figs. 13A, 14A). In the outer cell, only anticlinal divisions

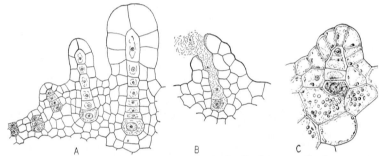

A   B   C

Fig. 14.—Archegonia of *Lycopodium*. *A, B, L. clavatum; C, L. cernuum.* *A*, stages in development; *B*, archegonium at fertilization stage; *C*, mature archegonium. (*A, B, after Bruchmann; C, after Treub.*)

occur and there is formed for the antheridium a small one-layered cover (Figs. 10, 13) and for the archegonium a neck (Fig. 14) of several tiers, each of 4 to 6 cells. The inner cell of the antheridium initial, by successive divisions, forms many sperm mother cells; that of the archegonium initial forms the egg cell, ventral canal cell, and the neck canal cells, the *axial row* of the archegonium. When the archegonium is mature the neck cells at the tip separate and the canal cells go to pieces (Fig. 14B), leaving a passage open to the egg for the sperms. The cover of the mature antheridium breaks open and the sperms are freed, to swim or be washed to the archegonium. Fertilization has not been reported.

EMBRYO

Embryo development in the species with subterranean prothallia is essentially as follows. The first division in the fertilized egg is transverse to the long axis of the archegonium (Fig. 15A). Of the cells thus formed, the outer, though it may enlarge somewhat, divides no further but forms a so-called *suspensor*. The suspensor does not serve in *Lycopodium*, as in many other plants, to push the young embryo into the tissues of the gametophyte; but, in restricting the embryo proper to the inner half of the fertilized egg, it may so function indirectly and in a very small way. The second division, at right angles to the first, divides the inner, or embryonic cell, into two, giving a young sporophyte of one plus two cells (Figs. 15*B*, 16*A*). The third division is in the plane of the page; the fourth, parallel to the first, divides the four cells formed by the second and third divisions, forming an embryo of nine cells in three tiers (Fig. 15*C*). Four segments or

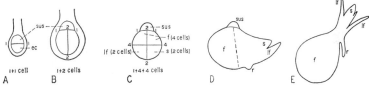

Fig. 15.—*Lycopodium.* Diagrams showing development of embryo in group with subterranean gametophytes. *ec*, embryonic cell; *f*, foot; *lf*, leaf; *r*, root; *s*, stem; *sus*, suspensor.

quadrants are obscurely evident in the body of the embryo at this stage (Fig. 16*B*). Later development shows that these quadrants seem to bear fairly definite relation to the organs of the young plant. The two quadrants next to the suspensor enlarge laterally and downward into the tissue of the gametophyte (Fig. 16*C*,*D*) and form a subspherical *foot* (Fig. 15*E*), an organ for the absorption of food from the prothallium. One of the lower quadrants forms the stem, the other the first leaf of the young sporophyte. The stem and leaf segments enlarge together laterally and upward (Figs. 15*D*,*E*; 16*D*). After a time the first root appears from the base of the enlarged leaf quadrant. The stem grows rapidly upward, with other leaves developing. The root branches but does not become extensive. The bulbous foot is deeply inserted in the gametophyte tissues and in some species is large—1.5 to 3.0 mm in diameter in *L. obscurum.* The gametophyte may support the young sporophyte, in part at least, for several years, and during this time may increase greatly in size. It may bear two or more sporophytes, formed at the same time or as far apart at least as one year.

The first root and the first erect stem are short-lived in some species, new roots arising adventitiously and a horizontal stem

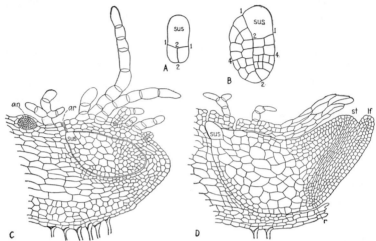

Fig. 16.—*Lycopodium clavatum.* Development of embryo. *A*, wall 1–1 separating suspensor from embryonic segment; *B*, wall 4–4 separates segments (adjacent to the suspensor) which become the foot from the innermost segments which become stem and first leaf; *C*, embryo enlarging downward and laterally in gametophyte; *D*, embryo breaking through gametophyte laterally and upward; *an*, antheridium; *ar*, archegonium; *lf*, leaf; *r*, root; *st*, stem; *sus*, suspensor. (*After Bruchmann.*)

developing from the base of the first erect one. The first leaves are scale-like (Fig. 9) and colorless and have no vascular supply. The first green leaves are often unlike later ones in form and

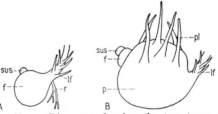

Fig. 17.—*Lycopodium.* Diagrams showing the two types of embryo. *A*, the embryo of species with subterranean gametophytes with large foot attached directly to stem base; *B*, the embryo of species with green, surface-living gametophytes with small foot and parenchymatous swelling ("protocorm") at base of stem; *f*, foot; *lf*, leaf; *p*, "protocorm"; *pl*, "prophyll"; *sus*, suspensor.

arrangement, and in many species are so closely alike that identification of young plants is difficult.

In species with green prothallia an important variation occurs in embryo development. Early stages are essentially as in the other groups. A foot is formed from the two outer segments but remains small (Fig. 17*B*) and apparently serves but little or not at all as an absorbing organ. The other two segments form a spherical parenchymatous structure which has been called a *protocorm* (Fig. 17*B*). This body is provided with root hairs and has on its upper part a few cylindrical, green, leaf-like projections, indefinite in number and arrangement. There is an associated fungus as in the gametophyte. No vascular tissue is present. Among the "leaves," or laterally, a stem tip arises (perhaps internally) and develops into a typical stem with normal leaves and adventitious roots.

DISCUSSION AND SUMMARY

The characteristically dichotomous branching of the stem gives to some species a habit suggestive rather of lower plants than of other vascular groups. Where the dichotomy is unsymmetrical or obscure (Fig. 2*A*), monopodial growth is simulated. The genus perhaps demonstrates a method of origin of monopodial from dichotomous branching.

The leaves are small and simple, with single traces and unbranched veins. They show nearly all types of arrangement. If indefinitely placed leaves represent an extremely primitive condition, a series in progressive specialization may be found from irregularity through spiral to whorled and opposite arrangement. The last type is commonly recognized in other groups as the most specialized. The first leaves of the young plant are scale-like and without vascular tissue. This suggests the origin of these simple leaves as enations, the traces and veins appearing only when the leaves are well developed.

The dichotomy of the axis, so prominent in the stem, is continued in the roots. All roots are short and without lateral endogenous rootlets; there is no general root system as in flowering plants. All roots, including the first, are adventitious. In *Lycopodium* the root therefore appears rather as a sort of secondary structure than as a fundamental part of the sporophyte body, a fact perhaps borne out by the absence of a root quadrant in the embryo.

The central cylinder of the stem, a protostele with exarch xylem, is of the type generally considered most primitive for vascular plants. The stele of *Lycopodium* is surely of a primitive type, but shows an elaboration of form, doubtless related to size and to habit and habitat, which parallels to a considerable degree the specialization in external form. A type of stele is formed which is unlike that of any other living group of vascular plants. The xylem and phloem are histologically simple and primitive.

Though the plant body shows primitive features in its anatomy, method of branching, and leaf arrangement, it shows much specialization in habit. Within the group are creeping types with rhizomes underground or on the surface, scramblers and twiners, epiphytes, and even an "annual." The determinate branch systems of the creeping types are good examples of specialization of the vegetative body. Associated with the limitation of stem growth in the formation of these units are the highest type of leaf arrangement and a fusion of leaves and stems into a single structure. Further, the leaves are specialized among themselves; in the most specialized dorsiventral branch-lets the lower row is abortive. These branch systems of restricted growth and short life are comparable in some ways to the "short shoots" of gymnosperms and perhaps also to the fronds of ferns (Chap. XVII). The plant body of *Lycopodium* is apparently a primitive one which has become much specialized along various lines as an adaptation to habitat.

The taxonomic arrangement of the species of *Lycopodium* is based largely upon the number, position, and type of sporophylls. The sporophylls of the various species can be arranged in a series of increasing complexity of structure. In one group of species the sporophylls are like the leaves, no cones being formed, and the sporangia are exposed between them; in another group the sporophylls are unleaf-like, form definite cones, and fully protect the sporangia by dorsal lobes. Intermediate stages in cone formation and sporangium protection are to be found. The species without cones are usually looked upon as primitive, and the series read as an example of increasing adaptation in sporophyll structure and arrangement to spore protection and distribution.

On an entirely different basis the type in which all leaves are fertile has been considered by some students of morphology the most primitive in the genus. This type formed the basis of a theory (now discarded) under which it was looked upon not only as a primitive lycopod but as an archaic form of sporophyte among vascular plants and therefore of great significance in the history of development of this generation (Chap. XVII). The question of primitive form in the genus can probably be answered only by the fossil record.

From the standpoint of modification of structure in evolutionary development a series may be read in two directions: modification may have increased complexity of structure or may have simplified it. That is, the simpler forms of a series may be the more primitive ones, and the series is to be read toward the complex members as representing progressive stages in advancement; or the simpler forms may represent the more advanced types of the group, and the series is to be read in the reverse direction. In the latter case the simple types are simple because of reduction not because of primitiveness. They are fundamentally more complex than the obviously complex types, because they have passed through the obviously complex stage to a more advanced condition; their simplicity is really high complexity. Evidence of the extreme reduction is often obscure or lacking, and the forms seem to be truly simple.

Comparative morphology, in its efforts to establish relationships and lines of progressive evolutionary modification, must interpret many series. Since in evolutionary advancement simple organisms have apparently given rise to complex ones, the reading of series would naturally be from simplicity to complexity. In many series the direction of advance is, however, clearly seen to be toward simplicity, that is, these are reduction series. The simplicity in these cases is false, that is, it is obscure high complexity, and the series when read toward simplicity is really being read toward greater complexity. The interpretation of simple forms—whether simple because primitive or simple because reduced—is perhaps the most difficult problem in comparative morphology. In the study of the various groups of vascular plants it will be seen that the reading of many series is toward simplicity, the simplicity of reduction; that is, structural reduction is an outstanding feature of evolutionary progress in vascular plants.

In different species of *Lycopodium* the sporangium varies in position from the adaxial surface of the leaf to the leaf axil and to the axis close above the axil. In this genus there are, therefore, both cauline and foliar sporangia and also intermediate forms. Which condition is primitive is uncertain, but the series suggests that the foliar is secondary.

The gametophytes form a series from minute green forms to fairly large, nongreen, subterranean types. Nearly all have associated endophytic fungi. The subterranean, nongreen type, which is apparently dependent upon this mycorrhizal association for nourishment, is probably a modification of the surface-living, green type. Ontogeny shows that the dorsiventral form has been derived from the cylindrical. The green cylindrical gametophyte is, therefore, undoubtedly the primitive form in the genus. Outstanding characters of the gametophyte are simplicity, radial structure, slow growth by an apical meristem, and long life.

The variability and indefiniteness in size and shape of the antheridia suggest primitiveness, as do the biciliate, moss-like sperms. The archegonia further suggest those of the bryophytes in their long necks, narrow venters, and numerous neck canal cells; they are, however, partly sunken and not stalked as usual in the mosses.

The history of modification of the archegonium in evolutionary development among vascular plants is one of reduction. This reduction first affects the neck canal cells, which become fewer in number and are finally eliminated. The elongate archegonium of some species of *Lycopodium* with its several neck canal cells, which vary in number, stands as the most primitive among vascular plants.

The first division of the fertilized egg is transverse to the archegonium axis and separates an outer, suspensor cell from the embryonic initial. The suspensor of *Lycopodium*, as compared with that of other forms, is hardly to be considered functional. It serves merely to restrict embryonic growth to the more deeply seated half of the zygote. If considered a true suspensor, it is functionally not developed.

Of the quadrants in the young embryo the two outer develop a large foot, the others stem and first leaf. It is perhaps significant that the foot is so prominent in the embryo of this primitive group; the extent of the dependence of the sporophyte upon the gametophyte in such plants may thus be suggested. From a similar viewpoint the absence of a root quadrant may be important. Roots are essential to independence in vascular plants; the primitive sporophyte was perhaps for some time dependent by a large foot upon the gametophyte and developed roots rather late. The gametophytes of *Lycopodium* may nourish sporophytes for years, and all roots, including the first, are adventitious. In the closely related genus *Phylloglossum* no root is formed for one or more years. (This is, however, probably related to the tuberous habit of the genus.) In some vascular plant groups there is a root quadrant in the embryo; that is, in higher forms the root has become established as a fundamental organ.

The protocorm is undoubtedly a tuberous structure serving to carry the young and delicate sporophyte over an unfavorable season; it is the result, therefore, of physiological specialization and does not represent a morphologically important stage in embryogeny. Its importance lies chiefly in that it has been used as the basis of a theory relating to the origin of independence in the sporophyte of vascular plants—the "protocorm theory" (Chap. XVII). The existence of the protocorm in some species of *Lycopodium* and the similarity of the mature plant of *Phylloglossum* (Fig. 18) to this unusual structure have introduced much confusion into the morphology of these plants. The resemblance is clearly the result of adaptation to similar conditions. The bulbils which form in some species on detached leaves and roots are essentially protocorms and serve a like function.

Lycopodium is a good example of a plant in which some characters have remained primitive while others have advanced far in specialization. Closely similar forms are found among the fossils of the Carboniferous period (Chap. XV), indicating that the genus is very old and has maintained itself unchanged in essential features through an enormously long period of time. The living species thus appear to be primitive vascular plants and therefore of great importance in the study of the morphology of the group.

The recognition of this primitiveness in *Lycopodium* and the presence of certain peculiarities of structure have been the basis for theories of the origin of the sporophyte in vascular plants (Chap. XVII). These will be discussed when a broader basis has been prepared.

PHYLLOGLOSSUM

Sporophyte

Habit.   The other genus of this group, *Phylloglossum*, is similar
to *Lycopodium* in technical characters but is unlike it in habit
and general appearance.   The one species is a small plant only a

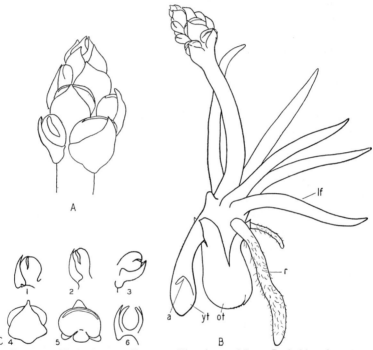

Fig. 18.—*Phylloglossum Drummondii.   A*, strobilus; *B*, habit of mature
plant; *C*, sporophylls with sporangia; 1, 2, 3, lateral views; 4, 5, views from distal
and proximal ends; 6, radial section; 1, 4, 5, 6, sporangia foliar; 2, 3, sporangia
axillary; *a*, apex of young tuber; *lf*, leaf; *ot*, old tuber; *r*, root; *yt*, young tuber.
(*After Bertrand.*)

few centimeters high (Fig. 18*B*).   An ovoid fleshy tuber bears
on its upper end a few (3 to 20) slender, quill-like leaves.   These
leaves seem to be indefinite in position but form a sort of whorl
about a growing point, which in mature specimens may develop
into an erect naked peduncle bearing a small terminal cone.
Extending from the crown of the tuber are one to three unbranched
roots and a short stalk which bears a small young tuber.

The plant is a tuberous perennial; all parts except the younger tuber die at the end of the growing period and this tuber lies dormant until the next year. In this behavior it resembles certain bulbous or tuberous angiosperms. The habit is clearly an adaptation to the climatic conditions of its restricted distribution—parts of southern and western Australia, Tasmania, and New Zealand. *Phylloglossum* in its method of annual growth is not essentially different from *Lycopodium inundatum*—sometimes called "annual"—in which all of the plant except the bud at the tip of the stem dies each season. This bud and the tuber of *Phylloglossum* are homologous structures.

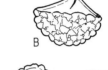

Phylloglossum has been called an "unbranched" plant, but the cone sometimes branches dichotomously and the tuber-bearing stalk is clearly a branch, for it may bear leaves and it has the vascular structure of a branch. More extensive branching is seen in those occasional or frequent plants in which two tubers are borne, each on its own stalk.

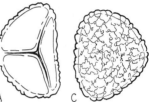

Fig. 19.—*Phylloglossum Drummondii*. Spores. *A*, top view; *B*, side view; *C*, basal view. (*After Bertrand.*)

Normally, vegetative multiplication is apparently secured only in this way, though isolated leaves may develop tubers as in some species of *Lycopodium*.

Reproduction. The cone (Fig. 18*A*) consists of a few sporophylls borne in whorls of three (or two in weaker plants). The members of the whorls (which are probably false) alternate, though not quite regularly, and those sporophylls toward the top are apparently without order. The short yellow sporophylls bear large reniform sporangia (Fig. 18*C*). In the middle of the cone the sporangia are sessile on the ventral surface of the short sporophyll petiole (Fig. 18*C* 1, 6); in the lowest whorl the sporophylls are sessile, and the short-stalked sporgangia are axillary or even definitely cauline (Fig. 18*C* 2, 3). The sporangia are yellow, with walls two or three layers of cells thick. They open as in *Lycopodium*, the valves gaping and allowing the spores to be shed gradually. A tapetum is apparently present during the development of the spore mother cells. The spores are tetrahedral, yellow, with a network of pits on the curved side (Fig. 19).

Anatomy.   The vascular cylinder of the stem differs from that of *Lycopodium* in several ways: it is not deeply furrowed or lobed; it is usually siphonostelic throughout its length; the xylem is mesarch.   The typical siphonostele of the central part of the plant (Fig. 20*B,C*) becomes a ring of strands (a dictyostele) in the upper peduncle and the cone axis (Fig. 20*D*) and breaks up and fades out in the tuber, the lower part of which lacks vascular

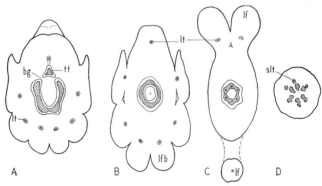

Fig. 20.—*Phylloglossum Drummondii.* Cross section diagrams showing anatomy of mature sporophyte. *A,* at top of tuber; *B,* just above *A; C,* at base of peduncle; *D,* through cone axis; *bg,* branch gap; *lf,* leaf; *lfb,* leaf base; *lt,* leaf trace; *slt,* sporophyll trace; *tt,* trace to young tuber. *(After Bertrand. D slightly modified.)*

tissue.   The simple siphonostele of the lower part of the peduncle is shown diagrammatically in Fig. 20*C.*   (This region in some less well-developed individuals is protostelic.)   Below this level, in the upper crown of the tuber (Fig. 20*B*), the similar stele is amphiphloic.   Somewhat lower (Fig. 20*A*) the stele is broken by the trace to the stalk of the young tuber, which leaves a large gap. In these figures the small simple leaf traces are seen at the point of attachment of the leaves.   A short distance below, these traces depart from the vascular cylinder without leaving gaps. At about the level of leaf-trace departure, the vascular cylinder is broken into segments which fade out abruptly below in the storage parenchyma of the tuber.   In the peduncle the simple siphonostele breaks up into a ring of bundles, from which in the cone axis depart the sporophyll traces (Fig. 20*D*), as in the case of the leaves, without forming gaps.

The tuber stalk is supplied with a large vascular strand to which in some plants are attached the traces of one or two leaves (Fig. 20A). The roots are very simple, with monarch or diarch structure.

The tuber is 'inverted'; the growing point is not apical on the base, as might be suggested by its direction of growth, but lies some distance from the tip, directed backward (upward), and is seemingly internal, appearing sunken in a furrow or slit (Fig. 18B). By the reversal of the direction of its tip, the new tuber, though developing downward, is thus oriented in the ground with its apex uppermost.

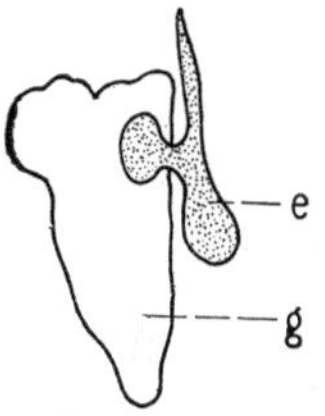

—e

—g

GAMETOPHYTE

Germination of the spores and early stages of the gametophyte are unknown. The earliest stages described suggest that development is as in the green type of *Lycopodium* gametophyte; indeed the mature gametophyte closely resembles this plant. It varies in form but is usually cylindrical, 2 to 6 mm long, with an irregular crown above a contracted region (Fig. 21). The crown projects above ground and is green: the rest of the prothallium is tuberous and has an endophytic fungus associate. Both antheridia and archegonia are borne on the crown, and both kinds of organs resemble those of *Lycopodium*. The sperms have not been described.

FIG. 21.— *Phylloglossum Drummondii.* Diagram of vertical section of gametophyte with attached embryonic sporophyte. *e*, sporophyte. *g*, gametophyte. *(Based on description by Thomas.)*

EMBRYO

Early stages of the embryo are unknown, but later stages show further similarity to that section of *Lycopodium* with green gametophytes. There is a prominent foot which remains in the position of the archegonium, and a leaf-and-stem apex which grows obliquely downward and outward and breaks through the side of the prothallium. The embryo at this stage is a short, erect, cylindrical body attached laterally by a foot to the gametophyte (Fig. 21). The upper end becomes a true first leaf with a vascular bundle; the lower end swells and becomes the first tuber. This swollen lower part has been called a 'protocorm,' comparable to the protocorm of *Lycopodium*. It is, however, clearly not this, but the tuber of the first season, for it bears a true leaf with vascular tissue. As further resembling a protocorm it has been stated that the growing point arises internally (as has been claimed also for the growing point in true protocorms), but the appearance of endogenous origin is false and is given by the inversion of the tuber tip and by its sunken position. The young plant apparently develops no root the first season—in this suggesting further resemblance to a protocorm—and only one leaf for that year and even for the second and third years.

DISCUSSION AND SUMMARY

The vegetative stem of *Phylloglossum* is a shortened, fleshy storage organ, its simple leaves crowded in a pseudowhorl. A single, *Lycopodium*-like cone is borne on a naked stalk, its sporophylls, like the leaves, in false whorls. Branching is rarely present, appearing only in the occasional dichotomy of the cone and in the formation of new tubers. The sporophylls and sporangia closely resemble those of *Lycopodium*. The sporangia may be foliar, axillary, or cauline in position, even in the same cone.

Though the vascular cylinder in some plants is in part a protostele, it is typically a siphonostele and the xylem is mesarch. Both these conditions represent stages in stelar structure more advanced than those found in *Lycopodium*. This small plant provides in its short axis examples of all the important types of steles: protostele; siphonostele, both ectophloic and amphiphloic; and dictyostele. It provides evidence that these various types are but modifications of one fundamental type since all may occur within a short distance in the axis of a single plant.

The small, simple leaf traces form no gaps in the stele. The tuber branch has a trace with a large gap and may bear leaves; these facts are evidence that the stalk is a branch and its tip a true tuber, a swollen stem tip.

The characters of gametophyte, sex organs, and embryo, so far as they are known, are those of *Lycopodium*.

The resemblances of the two genera to one another indicate close relationship; indeed the taxonomic characters used to separate them (leaf position and presence or absence of branching) seem weak. However, the siphonostelic stem and the mesarch xylem, together with extreme geophytic specialization in habit, should doubtless give *Phylloglossum* generic rank.

Phylloglossum is without doubt a reduced lycopod which has become adapted structurally to the "tuberous perennial" habit. It is not a simple and extremely primitive plant but one whose apparent simplicity is the result of specialization. Its tubers, which have been called "protocorms repeated annually," are not peculiar embryonic structures but fleshy reproductive stems, and its leaves are true leaves and not the photosynthetic lobes of a protocorm. Certainly *Phylloglossum* is not "a permanently embryonic form of lycopod" as it has sometimes been called.

As other groups of vascular plants are described and discussed, more simple forms will be seen which in their simplicity suggest primitiveness, but which also are advanced and reduced rather than archaic forms. Among these apparently primitively simple plants *Phylloglossum* has stood out from the viewpoint of primitiveness, because it has been supposed by some students not to have attained as a sporophyte the full independence secured by roots and conducting tissue, but to have remained in a pseudogametophytic stage. The problem of the primitiveness or great specialization of simple forms is one of the most difficult of all studies in comparative morphology, and such plants require the most careful examination from all angles. *Phylloglossum* provides an outstanding example of such a problem.

SUMMARY FOR THE LYCOPODIACEAE

The outstanding features of this family are a dichotomously branching stem; small simple leaves, which may be indefinite in arrangement, with unbranched midvein and small traces which leave no gaps; sporangia which are either foliar or cauline; spores of one type only; a stele which is fundamentally without pith, and xylem which is exarch or mesarch; sunken antheridia, variable in size and shape; archegonia (in part) with long necks and several neck canal cells; biciliate sperms; an embryo without a root quadrant and with a weakly developed suspensor.

Bibliography

LYCOPODIUM

BENSON, M.: The grouping of vascular plants, *New Phyt.*, **20**: 82–89, 1921.
BOWER, F. O.: Studies in the morphology of spore-producing members: Equisetineae and Lycopodineae, *Phil. Trans. Roy. Soc. London*, **185B**: 473–572, 1894.

BROWNE, I. M. P.: The phylogeny and interrelationships of the Pteridophyta, III. The Lycopodiales, *New Phyt.*, **7**: 150–180, 1908; IV. The Lycopodiales (*continued*); Selaginellaceae and Lycopodiaceae, *New Phyt.*, **7**: 181–197, 1908.

BRUCHMANN, H.: "Über die Prothallien und Keimpflanzen mehrerer europäischer Lycopodien," Gotha, 1898.

———: Die Keimung der Sporen und die Entwicklung der Prothallien von *Lycopodium clavatum, L. annotinum* und *L. Selago, Flora*, **101**: 220–267, 1910.

CHAMBERLAIN, C. J.: Prothallia and sporelings of Lycopods, *Bot. Gaz.*, **65**: 565–568, 1918. (*Review.*)

———: Prothallia and sporelings of three New Zealand species of *Lycopodium, Bot. Gaz.*, **63**: 51–64, 1917.

HILL, J. B.: The anatomy of six epiphytic species of *Lycopodium, Bot. Gaz.*, **58**: 61–85, 1914.

HOLLOWAY, J. E.: Studies in the New Zealand species of the genus *Lycopodium, Trans. and Proc. N. Z. Inst.*, **48**: 253–303, 1916; **49**: 80–93, 1917; **51**: 161–216, 1919; **52**: 193–239, 1920.

SYKES, E.: Notes on the morphology of the sporangium-bearing organs of the Lycopodiaceae, *New Phyt.*, **7**: 41–60, 1908.

TREUB, M.: Études sur les Lycopodiacées, *Ann. Jard. Bot. Buitenzorg*, **4**: 107–138, 1884; **5**: 87–114, 115–139, 1886; **7**: 141–146, 147–150, 1888.

PHYLLOGLOSSUM

BERTRAND, C. E.: *Phylloglossum Drummondii, Arch. Bot. du Nord de la France*, **2**: 70–223, 1885.

———: On the development and morphology of *Phylloglossum Drummondii, Phil. Trans. Roy. Soc. London*, **176**, II: 665–678, 1885.

BOWER, F. O.: Presidential address, Sec. K., *Brit. Assoc. Adv. Sc., Australia*, 1914.

HOLLOWAY, J. E.: The gametophyte of *Phylloglossum Drummondii, Ann. Bot.*, **49**: 513–519, 1935.

JEFFREY, E. C.: Are there foliar gaps in the Lycopsida? *Bot. Gaz.*, **46**: 241–258, 1908.

OSBORN, T. G. B.: Some observations on the tuber of *Phylloglossum, Ann. Bot.*, **33**: 485–516, 1919.

SAMPSON, K.: The morphology of *Phylloglossum Drummondii*, Kunze, *Ann. Bot.*, **30**: 315–331, 1916.

THOMAS, A. P. W.: Preliminary account of the prothallium of *Phylloglossum, Proc. Roy. Soc. London*, **69**: 285–290, 1901.

WERNHAM, H. F.: The morphology of *Phylloglossum Drummondii, Ann. Bot.*, **24**: 335–347, 1912.

CHAPTER II

SELAGINELLACEAE   SMALL CLUB MOSSES

In general appearance the Selaginellas resemble *Lycopodium* and, being as a group smaller, are commonly called "small club mosses." There is but one genus, *Selaginella*, with more than 500 species widely distributed over the earth. In spite of the large number of species, the group forms an even less conspicuous element among vascular plants of the world than does *Lycopodium*. The majority of the species occur in the tropics, chiefly on the ground in shaded, humid situations. In similar places *Lycopodium* is usually epiphytic. In cold regions and in arid parts of the world there are few species. Many species are grown in greenhouses as ornamental plants because of their delicate feathery 'fronds' which show various shades of green and are in some forms iridescent, bronze, or bluish.

SPOROPHYTE

Habit. Some species are prostrate, creeping on the ground or over logs or stones; the smaller ones, only a few centimeters long, form mats and closely resemble mosses; others are suberect or scramble or climb over shrubs with stems several meters long; many are cespitose, with dense tufts of short, frond-like branch systems. Most species are perennial; a few are small delicate annuals. Some xerophytic types of dry regions are cespitose, and the inrolling of the branches during dry periods forms a ball of the entire plant. In the presence of moisture, even after the plant is dead, the ball unfolds and the branches spread out again. Such plants are sometimes called "resurrection plants" and are sold as curiosities.

The genus as a whole is adapted to weak light conditions, though species live in all situations from the full light of desert areas to deep shade. Species of both extremes are small and moss-like, the xerophytes rigid and gray, the shade types pale and delicate.

31

All forms branch freely, chiefly in one plane, and the forking is dichotomous or pseudomonopodial. As in *Lycopodium* determinate branches are formed, and these in many species suggest fern fronds (Fig. 213). There is no relation between branching and leaf position.

In species with ascending or suberect stems prop-like structures, called *rhizophores*, grow downward from the forking regions of the stem to the ground and give rise to roots at their tips. These rhizophores provide additional root supply and perhaps give support to weak stems. Forms with ascending branch systems have probably been derived from creeping types; the usual root development from the underside of the stem is no longer possible, and the rhizophores provide the requisite rooting opportunities. The morphology of these structures has been in question, but they appear to be modified stems; normally leafless, they arise like stems and may bear leaves and even cones.

Leaves. The numerous simple leaves are small—a few millimeters long at most—vary in outline from round or oval to filiform, and are arranged in spirals, decussate pairs, or in four longitudinal rows. Spiral phyllotaxy (Fig. 22A), which is the common type in *Lycopodium*, is infrequent and is found chiefly in species of the drier habitats. In most species the branches are dorsiventral, with two rows of sublateral large leaves and two rows of smaller leaves on the upper surface (Fig. 22B to D). This four-row arrangement has been derived from decussate phyllotaxy and undoubtedly represents an adaptive modification related to light conditions. A photosynthetic system effective in shade has been formed by the displacement of the rows and the differentiation of the leaves in size. Compare this condition with that in the similar specialized branchlets in *Lycopodium* (Fig. 3C,D) where there is no displacement, and one row of leaves is abortive.

The leaves differ from those of the Lycopodiaceae in the possession of a *ligule*, a small, membranous, tongue-like projection sunken in a pit on the ventral surface near the base. The ligule develops early and is mature while the leaf is still young; in mature leaves it is shrunken and inconspicuous. Its function is unknown: it has been suggested that it may be a water-secreting or a water-absorbing structure; that by secreting water or a mucilaginous substance it may keep the growing point and young leaves moist. It is perhaps a vestigial structure, of greater importance in ancestral forms.

Roots. The first root is short-lived. All others arise, as in *Lycopodium*, adventitiously, from the underside of the stems and from the tips of rhizophores, and are thus distributed over

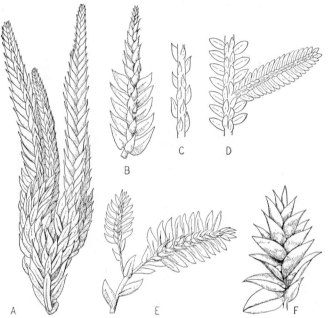

FIG. 22.—*Selaginella.* Leaf arrangement and cones. *A, S. Watsoni; B, S. umbrosa; C, D, S.* sp.; *E, S. elegantissima. F, S. apoda.*[1] (*A, B, E, after Hieronymus in Engler and Prantl; F, after Clute.*)

much of the plant. In a few species they arise close together on the somewhat enlarged stem base. Branching is dichotomous in alternate planes, but no extensive roots develop.

Anatomy. In anatomy, as in general habit, *Selaginella* resembles *Lycopodium*. The vascular cylinder is protostelic or siphonostelic, with the xylem exarch. On the whole the stele is simpler than that of *Lycopodium*, lacking the more complex arrangements of xylem and phloem. There is typically no secondary growth in the genus, though one species has been reported to show a small amount at the base of the stem. In most species the xylem consists, as in *Lycopodium*, chiefly of

[1] *S. apoda* (L.) Fernald, the older valid name, = *S. apus* Spring.

long, scalariform-pitted tracheids, but in some forms with spirally arranged leaves true vessels are present. The vessel elements are of the porous type with end walls nearly transverse (Fig. 23). Their side walls are mostly scalariform-pitted like those of the tracheids. The xylem may consist almost wholly of these vessels or may have but few among the tracheids. The elements of the phloem are closely similar to those of *Lycopodium*.

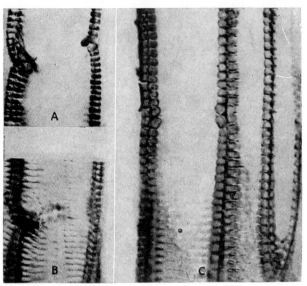

Fig. 23.—Vessels of *Selaginella*. *A*, *B*, in *S. arizonica;* *C*, in *S. rupicola;* *A* and *B* are of same segment perforation, *B* at lower focal level than *A*. (*After Duerden.*)

The leaves have a single trace, derived as in *Lycopodium*, and an unbranched midvein. The roots are also simple in structure, the stele commonly monarch.

Reproduction. Sporangia of two types are borne in the axils of sporophylls, attached either strictly in the axil or to the axis just above. In these sporangia are borne two kinds of spores—large spores, *megaspores*, and small spores, *microspores*. The sporangia which bear them are *megasporangia* and *microsporangia*, respectively, and the sporophylls subtending them *megasporophylls* and *microsporophylls*. The sporophylls form cones in all species though in some their arrangement is so lax as to suggest vegetative shoots. The cones are 3 to 60 mm long,

terete or four-angled, and borne terminally on main stems or on
lateral branchlets (Fig. 22*A,B,E*). They are usually erect,
rarely pendent or horizontal, when they may be dorsiventral
(Fig. 22*E*). In a few species the axis may grow beyond the cone,
terminating in a vegetative shoot or even in a second fruiting
region.

Sporophylls. The sporophylls differ from the vegetative leaves
more or less, but not so much as in the case of the cone-bearing
species of *Lycopodium.* In some species the sporophyll has a
basal pocket into which the sporangium fits; in others there is a

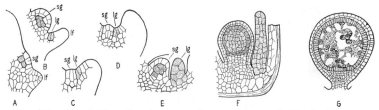

Fig. 24.—*Selaginella.* Development of sporangium. *A, B, S. Martensii;
C* to *G, S. spinosa; A, B,* radial sections of young leaf and adjacent stem showing
cauline origin of sporangium; *C* to *G,* development of foliar sporangium in longitudinal sections of sporophyll; *C, D,* early stages showing axillary origin; *C* to *F*
development of ligule; *G,* sporangium at single-tetrad stage; *lf,* leaf; *lg,* ligule;
sg, sporangium. (*After Bower, G slightly modified.*)

dorsal flap which protects the sporangium below. Cones may
consist wholly of one type of sporophyll, or both may be mingled
without order. The cones of some species are made up commonly
of microsporophylls with one megasporophyll at the base; the
cones of other species consist largely of megasporophylls, an
occasional cone showing only one or two microsporophylls. In
the genus as a whole the megasporophylls occur typically at the
base of the cone, the microsporophylls above.

Ligules are borne on the sporophylls (Fig. 24*E*), as on the
leaves. They develop early, reaching maturity before the
sporangia, and persist until the spores are shed, when they
shrivel. Their cells are mucilaginous, and it is possible that they
serve to keep the sporangia moist as they grow.

Sporangia. The sporangia are mostly reniform or obovoid,
sometimes flattened, and short-stalked (Fig. 24*F*). Commonly
the two kinds of sporangia differ greatly in size, the megasporangia being much larger, but in some forms the two are of
about the same size. The mature microsporangia appear red,

yellow, or brown from the color of the spores within their thin
walls; the megasporangia are paler, in most species green or
whitish, their spores chalky white, yellow, or orange.

The sporangium is eusporangiate in development, arising from
a small group of cells. Though it is difficult, as in *Lycopodium*,
to determine in some cases whether the initials lie on the axis
or on the leaf base, they arise in most species definitely from
cells of the axis, either in the axil or just above the axil of the
leaf (Fig. 24*A* to *D*). The sporangium is therefore usually
considered cauline. In development it follows closely that of

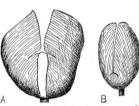

A   B
FIG. 25.—*Selaginella eryth-
ropus.* *A*, megasporangium; *B*,
microsporangium. Sporangia
empty, seen from narrow side,
showing method of opening.
(*After Goebel.*)

Lycopodium up to the time of sporocyte
formation, and both kinds of sporangia
are alike up to this stage. In those
sporangia which are to bear microspores, a few of the sporocytes degenerate; the others float free in a fluid
derived from the degenerating cells
and from the tapetal cells and form
tetrads of microspores. In those
which are to bear megaspores all
sporocytes but one usually abort.
The surviving sporocyte forms four spores which, nourished by the degenerating cell contents and the tapetal fluid,
increase enormously in size, filling and distending the sporangium. So great is the enlargement of the sporangium by
the growth of the spores that the sporophyll is in many cases
crowded out of its normal position in the cone, its tip becoming
divaricate.

The wall of the mature sporangium is thin, usually of but two
layers of cells (Fig. 26*b*). The tapetum, though losing its
contents, does not go to pieces as the spores develop but persists until the spores are nearly mature, when its cells become
flattened.

The sporangia open much as in *Lycopodium*, the upper part
splitting into two valves which gape (Fig. 25). The lower, boat-
shaped part, as it shrinks in drying, squeezes the spores out
violently, and they are shot some distance, the megaspores
6 to 10 cm, the microspores 1 to 2. The microspores are forced
out in small masses and are then probably spread by the
wind.

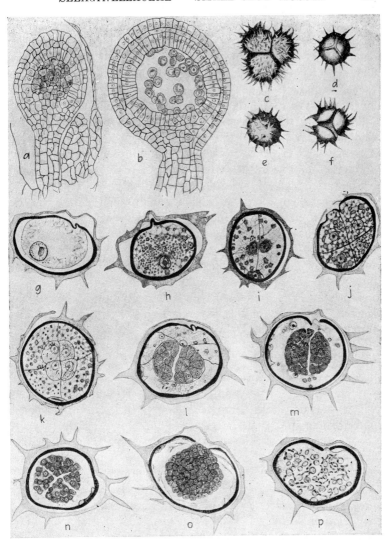

FIG. 26.—*Selaginella Kraussiana.* Development of microspores and male gametophyte. *a,* young microsporangium showing wall layers, tapetum, and sporogenous tissue; *b,* mature microsporangium with microsporocytes floating free in tapetal fluid; *c,* tetrad of microspores; *d, e,* apical and basal views of microspore; *f,* open "shell" of microspore after maturity and escape of sperms; *g* to *p,* successive stages in the development of the male gametophyte. (*After Slagg.*)

Spores. Both kinds of spores are tetrahedral, the megaspores and often the microspores showing prominent triradiate ridges and "ornamentations" of spines or other projections (Fig. 26d,e), The microspores are minute, several hundred being formed in each sporangium. The four large megaspores crowd one another and distort the sporangium which becomes knobbed or lobed.

The wall of the megaspores is very heavy and consists of a thin inner layer and a thick outer layer which is sculptured. Three distinct layers have been described, but there are perhaps not more than two in the mature spore, the third layer representing material present during development only.

An occasional sporangium shows more than 4 megaspores, from 8 to 40 having been found in several species. Under these conditions, as with the normal number, inequality in spore size may occur. The smaller spores are probably abortive. A few species show fewer than four spores: *S. rupestris* commonly has but two mature spores and sometimes but one.

Vegetative Propagation. Reproduction occurs occasionally by fragmentation, by bulbils, by rooting at the 'frond' tips, and rarely by small tubers.

GAMETOPHYTE

The microspores form male, the megaspores female gametophytes. Both are very small; the male is contained entirely within the spore wall, the female largely so. The microspores, and in some species the megaspores, germinate before they are shed, and growth of the gametophytes is completed either within the sporangium or wherever the spores have fallen when shed— on the ground, or among the leaves or sporophylls.

In the microspores the first division forms a small cell, the *prothallial cell*, at one side of the spore, and a larger one, the *antheridium initial*, which fills the remainder of the spore (Fig. 26h). The prothallial cell takes no further part in growth; the antheridium initial forms an antheridium. In the antheridium initial the first division is vertical (in the plane of the page) (Figs. 26i; 27b, 2-2). The two cells so formed are next divided transversely (Figs. 26j; 27c, 3-3). The two basal cells divide no further. Each of the upper pair is next divided by a curving wall (Fig. 27d, 4-4) which meets wall 2-2 near the middle. The two larger of the four cells formed by these last divisions are then

divided also by curved walls (Fig. 27*e*, 5-5), and two cells in the
apex of the spore are set off from a tier of four below.   In these

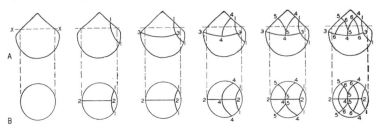

a. 1 cell   h. 2+1 cells   c. 2+2+1 cells   d. 4+2+1 cells   e. 6+2+1 cells   f. 10+2+1 cells

FIG. 27.—*Selaginella.* Diagrams showing development of male gametophyte.
A, vertical optical sections; *B*, sections at right angles to those in *A*, in plane
x-x. (*Compare with Fig. 26.*) (*Based on Slagg.*)

four cells of the middle tier periclinal divisions (Fig. 27*f*, 6-6)
form a central group of four.   The gametophyte now consists of
13 cells (Figs. 26*k*; 27*f*).   The central
four are the *primary spermatogenous*
cells, those surrounding them the sterile
jacket cells.   The spermatogenous cells
divide several times forming **128** or
256 sperm mother cells.   The jacket
cells break down (Fig. 26*l*), and the
sperm mother cells, in one or more
masses, float free in the cavity of the
spore wall (Fig. 26*m* to *p*).

The male gametophyte is partly
developed when the microspores are
shed; in various species all stages of
development from the formation of the
prothallial cell to that of the primary
spermatogenous cells have been found
at this time.   Completion of development takes place wherever the spores
may fall.   When the sperms, which are
biciliate (Fig. 28), are mature, the spore
wall cracks open along the triradiate
ridge and they are set free.

FIG. 28.—*Selaginella* sp.
Sperms. *A*, sperm just re-
leased from mother cell; *B*,
m a t u r e s p e r m . (*After
Dracinschi.*)

The development of the female gametophyte also begins in
some species while the spore still lies in the sporangium, and

even before it reaches full size. As in the case of the male gametophyte, various stages are reached at time of shedding— from that of the first division to that of archegonium-initial formation. In a few species the spores are not shed but remain indefinitely in the sporangium where fertilization takes place and the embryo develops. The young sporophyte may attain leaves and roots while still attached to the gametophyte, which is in turn held upon the mother sporophyte (Fig. 34), a condition likened to that in seed plants. On the other hand there are

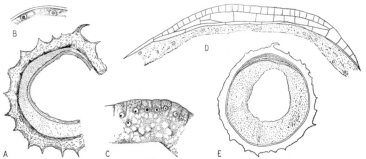

Fig. 29.—*Selaginella Kraussiana*. Development of female gametophyte. *A*, section of megaspore showing thick wall layers and thin layer of cytoplasm about a large central vacuole; *B*, portion of cytoplasmic layer with cytoplasm and nuclei increased; *C*, similar portion at later stage, nuclei multiplied and cell wall formation beginning; *D, E*, apical cushion of tissue developed. (*After Campbell.*)

species in which the spore does not germinate for some time after it has been shed.

Upon germination free-nuclear divisions occur, and the many nuclei, which are flattened, become distributed through the extremely thin peripheral layer of cytoplasm which surrounds a large central vacuole (Fig. 29*A*). As the nuclei increase in number, the cytoplasmic layer becomes thicker (Fig. 29*B*) and the vacuole smaller; ultimately the vacuole region is filled with cytoplasm. Walls develop about the nuclei in the apical region (Fig. 29*C*), and a cushion of tissue is formed there (Fig. 29*D,E*) which is gradually extended downward as the vacuole is filled with the increasing cytoplasm. In some species, wall formation ceases temporarily after the cushion has become from 3 to 10 layers thick, and the lower walls of the lowermost cells become thickened, forming a diaphragm (Fig. 30*C*) which separates the cushion from the (at first) noncellular region.

Later, the lower region also is divided into cells which are larger than those of the cushion and contain abundant food material. Development of cells here may be long delayed, even until the

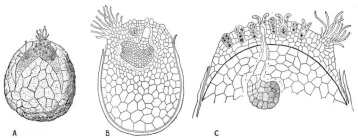

A   B   C

FIG. 30.—*Selaginella.* Mature female gametophytes. *A, S. Kraussiana; B, S. Martensii; C, S. Poulteri.* All showing apical sex organs, *B* and *C* bearing embryos; *C,* with, *B,* without, diaphragm. (*After Bruchmann.*)

embryo is developing. In other species there is no diaphragm (Fig. 30*B*); cell formation extends continuously downward and the spore is usually filled before fertilization.

Archegonium initials appear early on the surface of the cushion in the center. Mounds of tissue also develop early on the cushion under the three arms of the triradiate ridge (Fig. 31), and their growth is apparently responsible for the splitting of the spore wall, which occurs along the ridge. The cushion grows to some extent and protrudes through the gaping spore wall, the mounds developing rhizoids (Figs. 30, 31). The cushion does not usually become extensive, and even in those species in which it is best developed no chlorophyll is f o r m e d, though the spore lies in full

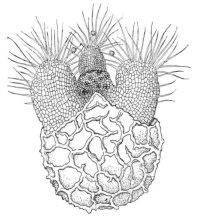

FIG. 31.—*Selaginella Galeotti.* Mature female gametophyte with apical archegonia and rhizoidal mounds with microspores caught among the rhizoids. (*After Bruchmann.*)

light. In some species the mounds are slight and the rhizoids may at times fail to develop; in others the rhizoidal mounds become extensive (Fig. 31) and with their many

rhizoids overshadow and protect the archegonial surface.   The
rhizoids serve to attach the gametophyte to the substratum
and to absorb water.   When abundant they may, by holding
water between the mounds, form a pool in which the sperms may
swim to the archegonia; they may even, it is claimed, serve to
catch and hold the microspores (Fig. 31), making fertilization
more certain.

Archegonia, varying from few to many in the different species,
are borne in the center of the cushion (Figs. 30, 31).   They are
small and simple, and are sunken in the gametophyte (Fig. 30*C*).
Development follows the usual course.   Stages are seen in
Fig. 30*C*.   When the archegonium is mature, the neck cells
separate and the neck canal and ventral canal cells go to pieces.

The sperms swim to the archegonia in dew or in rain water.
Fertilization and the development of the embryo occur in spores
which are free on the ground, or in spores still held in the open
sporangium in living, attached cones or in dead cones which
have fallen to the ground.

EMBRYO

In the fertilized egg the first division, which in most cases
is transverse (Figs. 30*B,C*; 32*A*), in others nearly vertical, forms

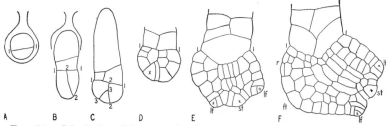

FIG. 32.—*Selaginella*.   Diagrams showing development of embryo. *lf*, leaf;
ft, foot; *r*, root; *st*, stem.   (*C to F, from Campbell, after Pfeffer.*)

a suspensor cell above and an embryonic cell below.   The
suspensor cell varies greatly in its development in the genus:
it may remain insignificant or may develop several cells (Fig. 32*B*
to *F*) and become a conspicuous part of the young embryo
serving to thrust the embryo proper down into the large-celled
nutritive tissue (Fig. 30*B,C*).   The embryonic cell by two
divisions forms a terminal and two lateral cells (Fig. 32*B,C*).

The terminal cell becomes the stem apical cell, the lateral cells two leaf apical cells (Fig. 32C to F). These form a stem tip and two embryonic leaves or 'cotyledons' (Figs. 33, 34). No quadrants are formed. There are in the young embryo no segments for foot or root. After growth by the three apical cells has formed a basal mass of tissue, a weakly developed foot is formed below one of the leaf segments (Fig. 32F). The stem apex is turned laterally, at right angles to the suspensor (Fig. 32F),

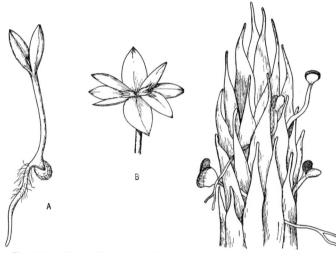

Fig. 33.—*Selaginella apoda.* Young sporophyte. *A*, showing "cotyledons" and attachment to gametophyte within spore wall. ×5. *B*, showing dichotomy of stem close above cotyledons.

Fig. 34.—*Selaginella rupestris.* Portion of cone with young sporophytes. The sporophytes are attached to gametophytes borne in megaspores retained in megasporangia. (*After Lyon.*)

perhaps by the greater growth in the foot region. The first root is formed still later, after the other parts are well defined. In early embryogeny, as in other structural features, there is much variation among the species. The relation of the first division to suspensor and embryo proper is not constant when the suspensor becomes massive. The foot may become conspicuous or may not be formed. The root appears in one group of species between the foot and the suspensor, in another between the foot and the stem tip, opposite the suspensor.

It has been found that in several species the embryos may develop apogamously—from unfertilized eggs. In these forms very few microsporangia occur, nearly all the cones being wholly megasporangiate.

The embryo plant is attached for some time to the gametophyte, still held within the megaspore wall (Figs. 33*A*, 34), and the establishment of its independence, which is accomplished rather quickly if the spore is free on the ground, may be delayed for a long time (several months, including a winter period), if the spore is held within the living cone. As the stem develops, branching soon occurs, in some species at least, the first dichotomy being directly above the cotyledons (Fig. 33*B*).

DISCUSSION AND SUMMARY

The members of this large genus are highly specialized in various structural features, and the many species show much diversity in elaboration, so that in minor ways a great deal of variation appears. In body habit adaptation has produced many types ranging from the delicate, moss-like, creeping species to the scrambling, climbing forms and to the cespitose types. The development of dorsiventral, determinate branch systems (spiral phyllotaxy having given place to decussate and this in turn to the four-rowed arrangement characteristic of the genus) is the outstanding feature of this specialization. The xerophytic species with inrolling branches and a short, spiral rhizome represent the culmination along this line. The epiphytic habit, so well developed in *Lycopodium*, is rare.

The leaf arrangement of the dorsiventral branchlets is of a type markedly different from that of the similar branchlets of *Lycopodium*, where one row of leaves is abortive and the others become fused with the stem; in *Selaginella* all leaves are retained and their size and position altered.

In the arrangement of the two types of sporophylls in the cone, all conditions are found from an irregular mingling of the two to the definite restriction of the megasporophylls to the base of the cone. The latter condition is clearly the more specialized and is found in species which in other respects also are more specialized—in anatomy, and in sporophyll form, for example.

The megasporangia show a remarkable range in spore number; from the occasional several or many to the typical four, with one as the extreme—clearly a case of reduction during specialization.

The retention of the spores within the sporangium during gametophyte development, fertilization, and embryo formation suggests seed structure, especially where but one spore of the tetrad develops.   This condition differs, however, from that in true seeds in that there are no seed coats, and a definite resting period is lacking.

Heterospory is accompanied by extreme reduction of the gametophytes and by their enclosure nearly or wholly within the spore walls.   The male gametophyte is reduced to a single vegetative cell, the prothallial cell, and an antheridium.   Reduction has apparently gone very far: a single vestigial cell represents the body of the gametophyte and one antheridium the sex organs.   The female gametophyte, though retained largely within the spore wall, is multicellular, bears rhizoids and several to many archegonia, but has no chlorophyll.   Both male and female gametophytes are dependent upon food stored in the spores.

The embryo shows a suspensor, in some species weakly developed, in others strongly.   The presence of a suspensor is perhaps correlated with the fact that the food supply lies well below the archegonium.   The first division of the zygote does not in all cases limit suspensor and embryo, for the products of either cell may enter into the later stages of suspensor or embryo. The suspensor does not appear to be of morphological importance in this group.

Selaginella resembles *Lycopodium* in many ways.   The two genera have similar methods of growth, though the former has as a whole become adjusted to the moister habitats, the latter to the drier.   Leaf type and arrangement are similar, though spiral phyllotaxy, dominant in *Lycopodium* for leaves and always present in cones, is rare in the leaves and uncommon in the cones of *Selaginella*.   The four-rowed arrangement of sporophylls, which is not found in *Lycopodium,* is characteristic of *Selaginella* and reaches an extreme in the dorsiventral type. In phyllotaxy *Selaginella* is more advanced than *Lycopodium.* Further evidence of greater specialization in habit in *Selaginella* is the presence of rhizophores.

In internal structure also, there is specialization of a high type. In the xylem, porous vessels with nearly transverse end walls are frequent.   Such vessels occur elsewhere only in the angiosperms. Many species of *Selaginella,* however, have xylem of tracheids only. It is noteworthy that the advance in specialization in the wood is uneven within the genus, and that the species in which it is greatest are among the ones considered to have the more primitive type of leaf arrangement and cone form. This condition provides a good example of the fact that advance in specialization in the structure of a group may be very uneven; a species that is far advanced in some features may lag behind in others.

Similarity to *Lycopodium* is continued in the presence of a suspensor in the embryo. But the character which ties the genera most closely together is the biciliate nature of the sperms, which are unlike those of any other vascular plants.

In spite of these features of general resemblance to *Lycopodium,* *Selaginella* stands well apart in its ligulate leaves and its heterospory. Both genera show high specialization in their gametophytes, but the specialization is of different types: in *Lycopodium* the development of a subterranean mycorrhizal form; in *Selaginella* extreme reduction in size and in number of gametes, with segregation of sex. Both types lack chlorophyll and are dependent upon food obtained in other ways.

The simple archegonia of *Selaginella* are sunken in the gametophyte and have a two-tiered neck and but one neck canal cell, all conditions representing structural advance over *Lycopodium* with its long, protruding neck and many neck canal cells.

In the development of the embryo in *Lycopodium* two segments form a prominent foot and but one leaf is developed; in *Selaginella* there is no foot segment and two leaves are formed. The embryos are alike in that they have no root segment (a fact perhaps of considerable significance), the first root appearing late from the base of a leaf segment.

Lycopodium and *Selaginella* are remarkable for their strong resemblances and their marked differences. They are undoubtedly related but not closely. *Selaginella* is in many respects more advanced. The question in classification is whether they form separate orders or should be united in one. It is generally believed that the differences are great enough to justify ordinal rank; the club mosses, therefore, form two small orders, Lycopodiales and Selaginellales, which stand more or less together, each containing a single family.

Bibliography

BOWER, F. O.: Studies in the morphology of spore-producing members—Equisetineae and Lycopodineae, *Phil. Trans. Roy. Soc. London,* **185B**: 473–572, 1894.

BRUCHMANN, H.: Vom Prothallium der grossen Sporen und von der Keimes-Entwicklung einiger *Selaginella*-Arten, *Flora,* **99**: 12–51, 1909.

————: Zur Embryologie der Selaginellaceen, *Flora,* **104**: 180–224, 1912.

DRACINSCHI, M.: Über die reifen Spermatozoiden bei den Pteridophyten (*Selaginella, Equisetum Isoëtes,* Filicinae leptosporangiatae). *Bul. Fac. de Ştiinţe din Cernăuţi,* **6**: 63–134, 1932.

HARVEY-GIBSON, J.: Contributions toward a knowledge of the anatomy of the genus *Selaginella,* Spr., *Ann. Bot.,* **8**: 133–206, 1894; **10**: 77–88, 1896; **11**: 123–155, 1897; **16**: 449–466, 1902.

LYON, F. M.: A study of the sporangia and gametophytes of *Selaginella apus* and *Selaginella rupestris, Bot. Gaz.,* **32**: 124–141, 170–194, 1901.

MITCHELL, G.: Contributions toward a knowledge of the anatomy of *Selaginella,* Spr., Part V, The strobilus, *Ann. Bot.,* **24**: 19–33, 1910.

SLAGG, R. A.: The gametophytes of *Selaginella Kraussiana,*   I. The microgametophyte, *Amer. Jour. Bot.,* **19**: 106–127, 1932.

SYKES, M. G., and W. STILES: The cones of the genus *Selaginella, Ann. Bot.,* **24**: 523–536, 1910.

CHAPTER III

ISOETACEAE   QUILLWORTS

The quillworts form among vascular plants an even less conspicuous element than the Selaginellas. All are small herbaceous plants of wet places and many grow submersed in lakes and pools. They live chiefly in cool climates and are rare or absent in tropical regions; otherwise they are distributed widely over the earth. Europe and North America have probably the larger number of species. There is but a single genus, *Isoetes*, with more than 60 (perhaps nearly 100) species. Economically the quillworts are of little or no importance: cattle may browse the grass-like leaves, and ducks and muskrats eat the fleshy "corms."

SPOROPHYTE

Habit. In appearance the plants suggest aquatic monocotyledons, such as sterile sedges or rushes. A tuft of quill-like leaves is borne on a thick flattened axis which is sunken in the soil (Figs. 35*A*, 36). All species are perennial, and the axis is a fleshy storage organ commonly called a "corm." (The term corm is inappropriate, however, since the structure is only in part a stem.) Some species are aquatic, growing on the bottom in shallow or in deep water; many are amphibious, living part of the year submersed and part emersed as the water level falls; a few live in dry soil. The submersed species are in most cases inconspicuous, though in *I. japonica* the leaves may be 1 m long, and in a Florida species the leaf tips float on the surface. The lower part of the axis is divided by a broad basal groove into two or three, rarely four, lobes, (Fig. 38*A*); in older plants the groove is deeper, extending up the sides, and the entire axis may be lobed. On the sides of the groove are many rather short roots.

Axis. The axis is covered on the top by the bases of the crowded leaves and is rough on the sides with sloughing tissues

48

(Figs. 36, 41). Its basal lobes, which are hardly evident in young plants, become more prominent as the plants grow older and the groove deepens. 'Caps' or 'shoulders' of sloughing

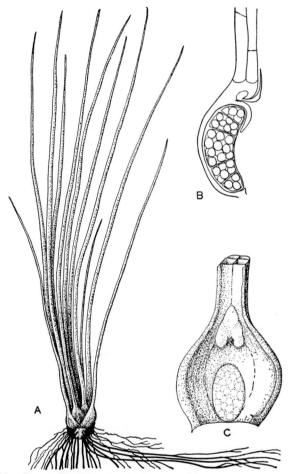

Fig. 35.—*Isoetes Engelmanni*. *A*, habit, ×⅔. *C*, face view of ventral surface of leaf base showing ligule and sporangium partly covered by the velum. *B*, longitudinal section of leaf base, showing ligule and sporangium with megaspores, trabeculae, and velum.

tissues are present on the upper margin of the axis (Figs. 36*C*; 41 *B,C*); late in the growing season these may have decayed. These shoulders include the bases of the leaves and roots of the previous season. They are more conspicuous on the younger plants, doubtless partly because of the simpler phyllotaxy of this stage, when the leaves are in two or three rows. In width the axis ranges usually from 0.5 to 2.5 cm; in some forms it may reach 4 and rarely apparently even 8 cm. Growth in length is extremely

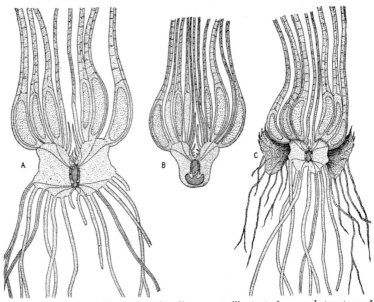

Fig. 36.—*Isoetes.* Vertical section diagrams to illustrate form and structure of plant. *A, C,* in plane at right angles to basal groove of the 'corm.' *B,* in plane of groove. *C,* showing the dead storage tissue and remains of leaves and roots of the previous year. The central core, shaded by oblique lines, is the primary vascular cylinder. Just outside this lies the cambium—shown as a line—surrounding the cylinder except at the apices. Secondary storage parenchyma makes up the greater part of the 'corm.' Through this tissue pass leaf and root traces. (*Compare Fig.* 41.)

slow and is greatly exceeded each season by that in diameter. Even though the diameter is constantly reduced by loss of the outermost layers, the axis is commonly wider than long. The apical growing points are deeply sunken by overgrowth of the surrounding tissues; the upper at the bottom of a concavity among the developing leaves, the lower drawn out in a line along the bottom of the furrow (Fig. 36*A,B*).

Occasionally a plant is found which branches dichotomously, but growth in length is so slow that the apices do not get far apart and the 'corm' itself is not divided (Fig. 37); the dichotomy is within the corm, and there are therefore two crowns of leaves. Rarely a second dichotomy occurs. The lobing of the base of the corm is an indication of dichotomy in that end of the axis also, but the arms of the groove, not the lobes, represent the branches of the axis. Adventitious branching also is reported to occur rarely. The axis, however, is clearly modified as a storage organ in a perennial herb, and branching, if ever well developed in the genus, has been nearly lost.

The morphological nature of this peculiar axis is suggested by the commonly applied terms "corm" and "rhizome," but these are inaccurate, for the axis consists of an upper leaf-bearing part, the stem, and a lower part, or *rhizomorph*, on which are borne lateral roots. Externally the limits of these parts are not evident because of the loss of the outer tissues, but in the form of the stele (Figs. 36, 41) and in the kind of appendages borne, the distinction is clear. The axis is obviously much shortened, and both leaves and lateral roots are brought close together.

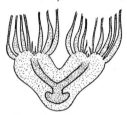

Fig. 37.—*Isoetes*. Diagram of vertical section of 'corm' showing dichotomy of stem. (*After Liebig, somewhat modified.*)

Leaves. The leaves, two to several centimeters long, are crowded in a close spiral and form a sort of fascicle. Their tips, which are straight or recurved, are linear and tapering, subterete, or three- or four-angled. Their broad, somewhat spoon-shaped bases clasp closely those next within and form a bulb-like mass (Figs. 35A, 36). These lower parts are normally buried in the soil and lack chlorophyll; they are usually white but may be dark, even black. The tips are in some species reddish. Fruiting plants bear from few to many (up to 200) leaves. The phyllotaxy is at first (in species with two-lobed axis) $\frac{1}{2}$, but passes progressively as the plant matures through $\frac{1}{3}$, $\frac{2}{5}$, and $\frac{3}{8}$, to $\frac{5}{13}$ and $\frac{8}{21}$, the commonest arrangements. Divergences of higher order are found in old plants. In amphibious and dry-soil species the leaves, with the exception sometimes of the central immature ones, die and decay at the end of the growing season. In aquatic species leaves may be present at all times, and such plants have been called evergreen.

All leaves are, at least potentially, sporophylls, for each bears a sporangium, normal or abortive, ventrally on the flattened lower

portion close to the base.   Just above the sporangium r̄ borne
a more or less triangular ligule ranging in length from 2 to
15 mm (Fig. 35*B,C*).   The ligule matures before the leaf, lacks
chlorophyll and a cuticle, and its tip early degenerates.   As in
the case of the ligule of *Selaginella*, its function is uncertain;
both absorbing and secreting functions have been ascribed to it.
On mature leaves it does not, however, become shrunken as in
Selaginella.

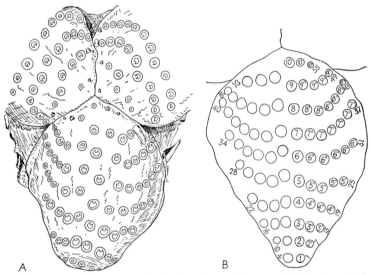

A   B

FIG. 38.—*Isoetes japonica*.   Basal view of 'corm' showing lobes of rhizomorph,
furrows, and arrangement and order of development of roots.   Roots are formed
in rows parallel with the linear meristem and are pushed outward as successive
new rows are formed; the numbers 1 to 10 indicate the sequence of development.
Within each row all are of the same age.   (The numbers around the margin
of the lobe apply to the longitudinal rows.)   (*See also Figs.* 36 *and* 39.)   (*After
West and Takeda*.)

Roots.   The rhizomorph—the lower part of the fleshy axis—
is short, thick, and increases in length very slowly.   Its apical
meristem is flattened, the apex drawn out in a line; it is therefore
wedge-shaped, or three- or four-flanged in some individuals,
and the tissues it forms are built up as two, three, or four lobes
(Fig. 38).   These lobes grow faster than the apex, which consequently is sunken in a furrow.   The numerous lateral roots
branch dichotomously a few times but are not extensive.   They
arise acropetally on the rhizomorph according to a definite geo-

metrical plan (Figs. 38, 39). As the rhizomorph increases in
length its lobes are spread slowly apart and the new roots appear
on the newly exposed surface, the sides of the groove at the base.
Each growing season new roots are formed and the older ones
(usually dead) are pushed downward and outward along the sides
of the groove—ultimately upward on the sides of the 'corm'
(Fig. 41). It thus happens that the youngest roots are those
nearest the center line of the groove and the oldest those at the
outer edges of the groove or on the rounded sides and bases of the

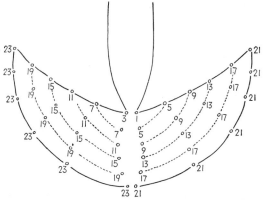

Fig. 39.—*Isoetes japonica.* Diagram (based on a bilobed specimen) showing
position and order of development of roots on rhizomorph stele. Roots with like
numbers are of same age, and sequence of numbers indicates sequence in development. (Even numbers are given to roots on other side of stele.) (*See also
Fig.* 38.) (*After West and Takeda.*)

lobes (Figs. 36, 38). The origin and position of these lateral roots
are discussed further under Anatomy.

Anatomy. The stem and rhizomorph form a continuous axis.
Their appendages are numerous and crowded. The growing
points of both rhizomorph and stem are sunken and that of the
rhizomorph is of remarkable shape. Both stem and rhizomorph
increase in diameter by secondary growth of an unusual type, and
the outer tissues are continually sloughed away. The axis is a
storage structure and its tissues are those of aquatic or semi-
aquatic plants. The structure of the axis is obviously complex
and interpretation difficult. It is therefore not surprising that
much attention has been given to it, and that there has been lack
of agreement in interpretations. It is believed, however, that
the anatomy of *Isoetes* is now fairly well understood.

Axis. The central cylinder is protostelic with a core of mingled tracheids and parenchyma, which in the stem is cylindrical and in the rhizomorph has the form of a broad plate with extended and upcurved edges (Figs. 39, 40). The stele of the entire axis has been likened in form to an old-fashioned vegetable chopper. The stele of the stem corresponds to the handle of the tool, that

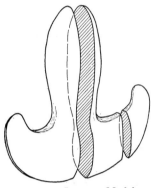

of the rhizomorph to the blade, to which (in bilobed species) it is closely similar in form. The apical meristem of the rhizomorph corresponds to the cutting edge of the tool. In detailed structure the stem and rhizomorph portions of the stele do not differ greatly; the rhizomorph, though different in structure from the stem does not have definite root anatomy. Though suggesting in position and function a root, it is certainly not a true root. Such a structure is perhaps morphologically comparable to the rhizophores of *Selaginella;* but here it is a portion of the main axis. Its stele is different in form from that of the stem and it bears lateral roots endogenously. As it is persistent, developing apically, it forms a permanent 'root' system.

Fig. 40.—*Isoetes.* Model to show form of vascular stele. The stem meristem is situated at the upper end; the rhizomorph meristem lies along the crescent-shaped lower edge, extending to the shoulders. (*Based on I. Engelmanni.*)

The line between stem and rhizome falls in the stele at the constriction just below the middle (Figs. 36, 40, 41). Externally the division of the 'corm' into stem and rhizomorph can be seen in many cases as a transverse constriction near the middle (Figs. 36, 41).

A cambium is present but is not normal in position; it arises outside, rather than inside, the primary phloem (Figs. 36, 41), which is small in amount. Its activity, further, is unusual: tissues are formed both to the outside and to the inside, but the outer tissue consists of parenchyma alone and the inner of modified vascular tissue. The parenchymatous layer is a storage tissue which is renewed each year, the exhausted layer being pushed outward and ultimately lost. The histological nature and the function of the vascular layer are still in question. It is in

some species made up of tracheids and parenchyma; in other
species it has been claimed to be wholly phloem, or phloem
mingled with xylem. The vascular elements are undoubtedly
much modified and reduced, as in many other plants of aquatic
habitats, and interpretation is rendered most difficult. Secondary growth is further unusual in that, though a considerable
amount of tissue is formed each year, the axis increases but
little in diameter year by year since the secondary vascular
tissue is small in amount and the outer tissues are being con-

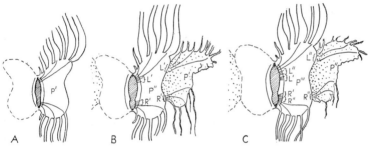

Fig. 41.—*Isoetes Engelmanni*. Diagrams of vertical sections (at right angles
to basal furrow) to show annual changes in structure. The primary vascular
cylinder is shaded with oblique lines. Just outside this lies the cambium, shown
as a line. Living storage parenchyma is unshaded. *A*, a 'corm' in late-season
condition. *B*, the same 'corm' early the following year: the parenchyma of the
previous year, *P'*, has been pushed aside by the new parenchyma, *P''*, and has
died; the traces of the leaves and roots of the previous year, *L'* and *R'* respectively,
have been ruptured near the cambium line by the forcing outward of the dead
storage parenchyma, and their ends have been widely separated. *C*, the same
'corm' in the following year: parenchyma of the third year, *P'''*, has been formed,
thrusting off that of the second year, *P''*, and the root and leaf traces of the second
year torn in two. The bases of the traces of all leaves and roots borne by the
plant persist in the vascular cylinder.

stantly lost (Fig. 41). The cambium forms a sheath about the
axis stele except at the meristematic apices and is therefore also
of peculiar form.

As the new leaves develop each year, the older ones are pushed
upward and outward over the upper surface of the stem; partly
by increase in length at the apex (primary growth), but chiefly
by the formation of secondary tissues (Fig. 41). As new roots
are formed the old ones are pushed downward and outward over
the rounded lower surfaces of rhizomorph lobes. Formation
of each new storage layer by the cambium of root and stem
crushes and crowds outward the older similar layers and stretches

the leaf and root traces which pass through them. The traces are soon broken and the outer portions carried outward with the flattened and torn tissues in which they lie (Fig. 41*B,C*) and sloughed off with them. The process of 'decortication' is a passive one, being incidental to the stretching and tearing of the exhausted and dead storage tissue. The process is analogous to that in woody plants where the formation of new secondary phloem pushes out the older layers and the cortex, rupturing the leaf traces which pass through them and ultimately bringing about the loss of these parts. In *Isoetes*, however, no periderm is formed, although the tissues along the lines of rupture become suberized.

The new roots appear on both sides of the groove, breaking their way through the tissues from a deep-seated point of origin. Overgrowth of the tissues about the rhizomorph meristem results in the bringing together and fusion of the upgrowing lobes and the burial of the apical meristem. This linear growing region lies therefore below the groove, and the new roots, which arise endogenously on its sides (like those of seed plants), must break their way through a considerable layer of tissue before reaching the surface. The roots are formed in rows roughly parallel with the linear meristem, hence in curved series (Fig. 39). New series are added acropetally as the apex grows. The members of each series are uniformly placed with relation to those of older series and so form longitudinal (vertical) rows (Figs. 38, 39). The longitudinal rows are increased in length, therefore, by each new transverse series but never become long because the older members of the rows are lost. The members of a new series are all of about the same age and constitute a row around the groove close to its base. Within this row the roots nearest the center of the axis have a longer course to the surface and hence appear later and seem to be younger than the others.

Leaf. The leaf has a median, unbranched vein, the continuation of the single, simple trace. The mesophyll is chambered with four longitudinal cavities (Fig. 35*C*), divided by many transverse diaphragms—a structure characteristic of aquatic plants. Stomata occur on the leaves of all but the permanently submersed species.

Roots. The roots, which are simple and monarch, are peculiar in that the stele is excentrically placed in a large cavity (Fig. 205), a feature of especial interest in phylogenetic considerations. Root hairs are abundant in some species.

Vegetative Propagation. Reproduction other than by spores is apparently rare. A type of budding from the stems has been reported. Aquatic and especially deep-water species are some-times aposporous, young plants taking the place of the develop-ing sporangia or forming just below them.

Reproduction. Typically a mature plant has three sets of leaves, outer ones, megasporophylls, enclosing microsporophylls, which in turn enclose an innermost cluster of immature or poorly developed leaves with abortive sporangia. These innermost leaves may survive the resting period and then become the outermost leaves of the next season; in such a case, however, they usually decay before the new leaves are mature and so are rarely seen on the outside of the sporophylls. In dry-soil species these sterile leaves may be reduced to scales or spine-like structures. The distribution of the two kinds of sporophylls varies somewhat with the species, but in most cases the mega-sporophylls are on the outside and are not mingled with the microsporophylls.

Sporangia. The sporangia are large—4 to 7 mm in length—larger than those of any other living plant. They are rounded-oblong in shape and deeply sunken in the leaf (Fig. 35*B,C*). The sunken position is the result of the upgrowth of tissue about the sporangium during ontogeny. Continuation of such growth forms a flap or fold, the *velum* (Fig. 35*B,C*), which extends over the sporangium from the sides and the upper end. The velum varies greatly in extent in different species: it may cover any part or all of the sporangium; in a few species it is absent. The sporangium walls are thin—of three or four layers of cells, one of which is a tapetum—and somewhat transparent. The megasporangia are readily identified, since the megaspores can be seen through the wall. It is reported that rarely a sporangium may bear both mega- and microspores.

The chambers of the sporangia are divided irregularly and incompletely by transverse or oblique sterile plates or bars, called *trabeculae* (Fig. 35*B*). These partitions are more numerous in the megasporangia.

The sporangium arises from a row of transverse initials, and development, though fundamentally of the eusporangiate type, is

apparently not strictly definite or uniform. The areas which
are to become trabeculae are set off from the sporogenous tissue
when this tissue is partly developed. A tapetum develops from
the inner wall layer and from the outer cells of the trabecular
bands, forming a lining layer everywhere separating sporogenous
from sterile tissues. As sporocytes and spores mature, the
tapetum gives up its contents and may collapse to some extent,
behaving much as does that of *Lycopodium* and *Selaginella*.

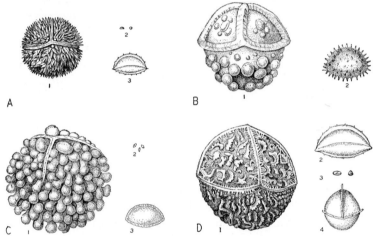

FIG. 42.—Spores of *Isoetes*. *A, I. echinospora:* 1, megaspore; 2, microspore on
same scale; 3, microspore enlarged. *B, I. velata:* 1, megaspore, 2, microspore.
C, I. Malinverniana: 1, megaspore; 2, microspore on same scale; 3, microspore
enlarged. *D, I. lacustris:* 1, megaspore, 3, microspore on same scale; 2, 4, microspore enlarged, side and end views respectively. (*After Motelay and Vendryès.*)

Spores. In the microsporangium nearly all the sporocytes
form spores and the spore number is enormous, probably much
greater than in any other living plant. In some species it is
reported to exceed 1,000,000; in others it has been estimated to
be 150,000 to 300,000. In the megasporangium a considerable
number of sporocytes produce from 50 to 300 spores. The
microspores are bilateral (in some species reported to be tetrahedral), very small (20 to 45μ long), ashy or brownish in color,
ridged longitudinally, and commonly papillose, spinulose, or
winged (Fig. 42). The megaspores are large (250 to 900μ in
diameter), tetrahedral, with prominent triradiate ridges, white,
gray, or black, and variously and conspicuously marked with

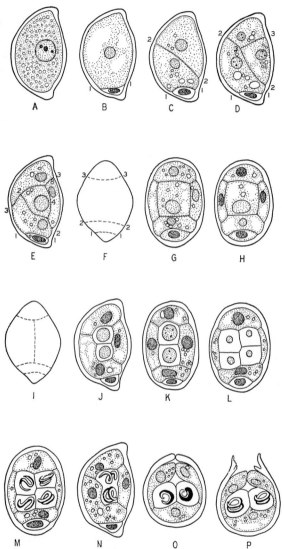

FIG. 43.—*Isoetes lacustris.* Development of male gametophyte. *A* to *E*, *J*, *N*, longitudinal sections in plane from ridge of spore to back. *F*, *I*, surface view on ridge side showing walls beneath. *G*, *H*, *K* to *M*, longitudinal sections at right angles to plane of *A*. *O*, *P*, cross sections, ridge side uppermost. *A*, mature spore. *B*, prothallial cell cut off. *C*, basal jacket cell cut off. *D*, upper jacket cell cut off. *E*, third jacket cell cut off by periclinal wall, setting off a central spermatogenous cell. *F*, surface view showing extent of third jacket cell. *G*, the central cell surrounded by the three jacket cells, the third shown on both sides. *H*, the third jacket cell has divided by a longitudinal wall. *I*, surface view showing the four jacket cells. *J*, *K*, the central cell has divided transversely forming two spermatogenous cells. *L*, the two spermatogenous cells have divided. *M* to *P*, the sperms mature. *O*, *P*, the spore wall open along the ridge, the jacket cells still intact. (*All Figs. except F and I after Liebig.*)

crests, spines, and ridges (Fig. 42). These spore markings are of much value in classification. The wall of the megaspore is thick and probably consists of several layers, the outer one siliceous.

The spores are not shed, except perhaps in dry-soil species, but are freed by the decay of the sporophylls. In the northern United States the spores mature in summer or fall and are set free in fall or winter. Distribution is by chance disturbance of the mud or by wave action. Earthworms have been reported to distribute the spores in some species, and in dry-soil species mucilage masses are formed which force the spores to the surface with the new leaves.

GAMETOPHYTE

Germination may occur as soon as the spores are shed but is apparently usually delayed until the beginning of the next growing period. As in *Selaginella*, heterospory results in dioecism among the gametophytes; both gametophytes are greatly reduced and are retained within the spore walls.

Male Gametophyte. In the microspore the first division forms a small cell, the prothallial cell, at one end, and a large cell, the antheridial cell (Fig. 43*B*). In the latter, successive divisions cut off four external "wall" cells from a "central cell" (Fig. 43). The

Fig. 44.—Sperm of *Isoetes.* (*After Dracinschi.*)

central cell forms four cells, which are sperm mother cells. The wall cells do not break down as do those of *Selaginella*, but

persist until the spore wall cracks open.   The four sperms, which
are multiciliate (Fig. 44), escape through an irregular rupture

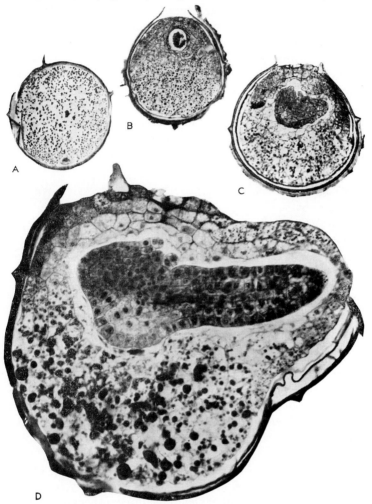

Fig. 45.—*Isoetes lithophila.*   Megaspore, female gametophyte, and embryo
in vertical section (outer spore wall removed).   *A*, spore, with nucleus in basal
position.   ×110.   *B.* Developing gametophyte with first archegonium containing young embryo.   ×110.   *C*, older gametophyte with maturing embryo in
final position.   ×120.   *D*, still older gametophyte and embryo with leaf and
root apices developing.   ×295.   (*After LaMotte.*)

in the spore wall.   The period between the beginning of germination and the setting free of the sperms is about two weeks.

Female Gametophyte. The protoplast of the megaspore has no central vacuole (Fig. 45A), and its nucleus occupies in some species a basal, in others an apical, position. The cytoplasm is rich in starch and other reserve food materials. Upon germination the divisions are free nuclear until 30 to 50 nuclei have been formed. These nuclei become distributed peripherally through the cytoplasm with the larger number in the apical region. Wall formation begins here, where the nuclei are closer together, extends slowly toward the base, following the sides, and then centripetally until the whole mass becomes cellular. So slow is wall formation in the basal region that fertilization may have occurred and embryos be well developed before wall formation is

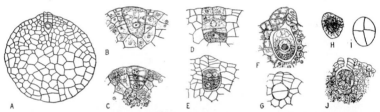

Fig. 46.—*Isoetes echinospora.* Female gametophyte and development of archegonium and embryo. *A*, mature gametophyte with first archegonium (spore wall removed). *B* to *F*, development of archegonium. *G* to *J* early stages in embryo development. (*After Campbell.*)

completed. The late-formed cells are larger and thinner walled than those of the upper region and contain more reserve food. There may be well-marked differentiation into an upper and lower region, but no diaphragm is formed.

The spore wall cracks open along the triradiate ridge, exposing below a small area of the surface of the gametophyte (Fig. 45B,C). There is, however, no immediate protrusion of gametophytic tissue as in *Selaginella.* On the exposed surface archegonia develop, perhaps in some species only two or three. The first archegonium is median (Fig. 46A), appearing early from one of the first cells formed, and, if this is fertilized, others will probably not develop. If the early archegonia are not fertilized, others may continue to form until the food supply is exhausted, a period sometimes apparently of several months. As many as 20 or 30 archegonia have been found in some species.

The number of rhizoids seems to vary greatly with the species; some forms have none or very few; others have many, distributed over the exposed surface but not in clusters as in *Selaginella*. These hairs are the only part of the gametophyte to project outside the spore wall until the embryo is well developed.

The archegonia are simple, deeply sunken, and hardly evident on the surface (Fig. 46A to F).   They form from super-ficial initials, and the course of development is the usual one: a periclinal division forms an outer and an inner cell; from the outer, by periclinal and anticlinal divisions, a neck of four tiers of four cells each is formed; from the inner, by two periclinal divi-

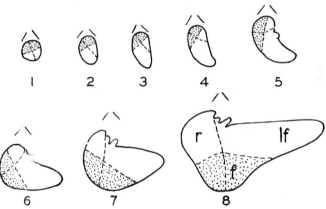

Fig. 47.—*Isoetes*. Diagrams illustrating shifting orientation of embryo during early development.   The lines above diagrams represent position of top of archegonium venter.   The dotted lines limiting regions ("quadrants") are largely hypothetical.   *f*, foot; *lf*, first leaf; *r*, root.   (*After LaMotte*.)

sions, a neck canal cell, a ventral canal cell, and an egg.   The neck canal and ventral canal cells disintegrate, and the cells of the neck spread apart.   Fertilization has not been seen.   The period of development of the gametophyte is three or four weeks.

Embryo

The first division of the fertilized egg is transverse, or somewhat oblique, to the axis of the archegonium (Fig. 46G).   No suspensor is formed and both cells enter into the embryo proper.   The first divisions form a globose body, filling the archegonium venter (Fig. 46J), in which quadrants are in some cases recog-nizable.   The relation of the quadrants to the first organs is not readily determinable, and interpretations of the orientation of the young embryo have differed greatly.   It is probable, how-

ever, that the two outer quadrants form the foot and the two
inner the first leaf and first root. As growth continues, the
rounded embryo elongates downward becoming cylindrical, and
erodes the prothallial cells below. Greater growth on one side
soon makes the embryo curved (Fig. 47, 2 to 5), and continued
uneven growth, with more rapid digestion of gametophytic tissue
below the convex side, gradually turns the embryo so that
the parts which were at first above are below (Fig. 47); the

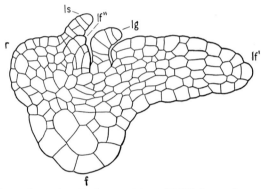

Fig. 48.—*Isoetes lacustris.* Embryo. *f*, foot; *lf'*, *lf''*, first and second leaves; *lg*,
ligule of first leaf; *ls*, leaf sheath; *r*, first root. (*After Liebig.*)

embryo is thus inverted and the foot segments are now on the
lower side adjacent to the rich storage tissue. The long axis
of the embryo is transverse to its original position and parallel to
the surface of the gametophyte. The tips elongate rapidly, one,
the faster growing, becoming the first leaf, the other the root
(Fig. 47, 8). The young leaf becomes the most prominent part
of the embryo, enlarging laterally and upward through the
gametophytic tissue (Figs. 45D; 47, 8; 48). Meanwhile there is
built up over its tip a cushion of gametophytic tissue, which,
though soon pierced by the leaf (Fig. 45D), continues to grow
and forms a conspicuous sheath (Fig. 49) covering the base of
the leaf and enclosing also the young second leaf and the stem
apex. The root tip grows through the gametophyte in the direction opposite to that taken by the leaf and is soon exserted.
There is no stem segment in the embryo (Fig. 47); the stem apex
arises late in the region between the young leaf and young root.
The foot continues to grow until the storage tissue of the gameto-

phyte is used up, when it nearly fills the spore cavity (Fig. 49). The projecting sheath and the rhizoids form the only parts of the gametophyte which protrude from the spore wall. The young sporophyte may soon become established in the soil, but it remains attached for weeks or months to the gametophyte with its enclosing spore shell. Meanwhile two to four leaves develop and there remain of the gametophyte only the upper layer and the sheath.

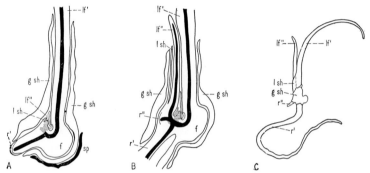

FIG. 49.—*Isoetes Engelmanni.* Young sporophyte. *C*, habit. *A, B,* longitudinal sections, *B* somewhat older than *A*. *f*, foot; *g sh*, gametophyte sheath; *lf', lf''*, first and second leaves; *l sh*, leaf sheath; *r', r''*, first and second roots; *sp*, spore wall. (*After Baldwin.*)

DISCUSSION AND SUMMARY

The fleshy storage organs of herbaceous perennials are in most cases renewed each year. The axis of the quillworts, however, is highly specialized in structure and method of growth and serves indefinitely. Yet because of an unusual type of secondary growth, it increases in size only slowly. It consists largely of temporary storage tissues. The only permanent part is a small central core (one-tenth to one-fifth the diameter of the axis) limited by the cambium. The tissues outside this are renewed each year, but the process readily escapes notice since it occurs during the early part of the growing season and the discarded tissues usually soon decay. The axis is part 'root,' part stem, and may be compared in this respect to the storage organ of the garden beet (*Beta vulgaris*). The branching of the stem, which is rare, is dichotomous, as is that of the rootlets. The rhizomorph is always dichotomously branched but the branching is hidden by the shortness of the branches and by the great amount of storage tissue formed.   Plants with a simple groove are once branched; those with three- and four-armed grooves two and three times branched. (The grooves, not the lobes, are the branches. Each arm of the groove is a branch.)   The branches of the rhizomorph are remarkable in that they curve upward.

The general appearance of the plant—its crowded leaves and roots, its corm-like stunted axis with lack of external differentiation into 'root' and stem, its very rare branching—suggests the telescoping of an originally more extended axis, which branched dichotomously to some extent at both ends.   The complex internal structure bears out this theory.   The leaves as they develop are pushed upward and outward from the sunken stem apex; the roots are similarly crowded downward and outward from the rhizomorph apex which is high up in the groove. The remarkable movements of these organs are the result of the sunken position of the meristem and of the strong activity of the cambium which pushes along the tissues in which their bases lie. The behavior of the roots seems the more peculiar because the apical meristem has the form of a bi- or triradiate wedge, and, with very slow increase in length, the marked cambial activity on its flat sides forms lobes over whose rounded lower surfaces the rootlets or their scars are carried outward.   Movement here is not so rapid as at the other end of the axis; the roots move slowly down the groove sides, then upward over the lobes; the leaves move rapidly to the edge of the axis.   The roots appear from very deep-seated origins; in addition to the penetration of tissues demanded by their endogenous origin behind the meristem, they must pierce extra tissues, since the growing point is not merely depressed but is buried by the congenital fusion of the upgrown lateral surfaces above it.

The stele is of the most primitive type, with its xylem, whose direction of development is difficult to determine, probably exarch.   The cylindrical stem stele gives off to the leaves simple traces which resemble in form and origin those of *Lycopodium* and *Selaginella*.   The remarkably compressed rhizomorph stele is in shape unlike that of other vascular plants.   Its two or three flange-like lobes grow very slowly along their basal, linear apex.   The cambium, arising anomalously outside the primary vascular tissue, clothes both stem and rhizomorph stele; it builds up additional vascular tissue in small amount on the inside, but its chief function appears to be to renew the storage tissue continually. The activity of the apical meristems provides many new leaves and roots; these can find room on an axis which increases in length and in diameter but very slowly only because the older, exhausted storage tissue and the old leaf and root bases are crowded out by cambial growth and are sloughed away. Only under such conditions would it be possible for the top of the axis to be each year completely covered with new leaves.

In contrast with *Lycopodium* and *Selaginella*, where the roots are adventitious and scattered along the stem, *Isoetes* has a definite 'root' system—a persistent basal rhizomorph with lateral endogenous roots developed successively on its new parts according to a definite plan. This condition is largely concealed by the shortness of the rhizomorph, a lack of external differentiation from the stem, and the peculiar position and shape of its apex. Because in other living vascular cryptogams there is no main descending axis, and because the presence of such a 'root' is obscure, the 'corm' has usually been considered a stem. Such a permanent 'root' system is comparable biologically at least to that of seed plants and unlike that of other vascular cryptogams.

The leaves, though much larger than those of the club mosses, are simple in form, with a single trace and unbranched midvein. The ligule is prominent and is not shrunken in the mature leaf as in *Selaginella*.

Isoetes may be likened in habit and general structure to *Phylloglossum*. In both genera crowded leaves are borne on a fleshy axis which has been shortened and modified in adaptation to the perennial herb habit. In each case branching has been almost lost and special storage tissues developed, but in ways quite different in the two genera. In *Phylloglossum* the storage organ is a tuber (stem only), which is annual, and is discarded when the food supply is exhausted; in *Isoetes* the organ is stem plus 'root' and is perennial, and the exhausted storage tissues are constantly discarded and replaced. Only secondary growth can maintain such a condition as that in *Isoetes*. The two genera provide an excellent example of morphologically different structures similarly modified and performing similar functions. They are among the most remarkable of living plants.

The sporangia are unusually large, and are definitely foliar and ventral. The two kinds are much alike in size and appearance, though in the megasporangia the large spores can be seen through the thin sporangium wall. The heterosporous condition is strongly developed, but there are many megaspores in contrast with the four in *Selaginella*. In this respect *Selaginella* may be considered more advanced. The division of the sporangia by trabeculae is an outstanding characteristic; no other living plants show this condition. The significance of this feature is uncertain. It is perhaps related to the large size of the sporangium or to the many spores: the trabeculae may serve to give support to the sporangium walls; the additional surface provided for tapetum may be of importance in supplying food to the many spores. This semipartitioning of the sporangium may be significant in the phylogenetic development of sporangia.

In the arrangement of sporophylls there is some variation, yet the dominant condition, as in *Selaginella,* is that of megasporophylls below. The fact that in a few species microsporophylls are rare suggests an approach to dioecism similar to that found in *Selaginella.*

The gametophytes closely resemble those of *Selaginella* in structure and development. They are, however, somewhat more reduced: in the female the prothallium proper does not protrude from the spore wall until very late and bears fewer archegonia; the number of sperms is reduced to four (the smallest number formed in vascular cryptogams). The sperms differ greatly from those of the club mosses in their large number of cilia. In this respect they resemble those of the ferns and some of the lower seed plants, whereas those of *Lycopodium* and *Selaginella,* with two cilia, suggest the sperms of mosses and liverworts and the motile gametes of algae.

The embryo of *Isoetes* lacks a suspensor; otherwise its early development is not unlike that of *Selaginella*. The suspensor is apparently of little morphological value. In embryos which are somewhat similar (in *Selaginella* and *Isoetes*) a suspensor may be present or absent. A relation to function is, however, evident: when a suspensor has thrust the embryo down so that it is embedded in nourishing tissues, there is a weak foot; where the embryo lies above the food-supplying cells, the foot becomes strongly developed. It has been generally believed that the two lower quadrants form the foot—apparently because the foot has been found to be below in later stages—and the two upper the first leaf and first root. On this basis the embryo of *Isoetes* has been called "inverted" as compared with that of other groups (where the foot quadrants are above) and therefore has been believed to be markedly different. The recognition of the change in orientation during early development removes this supposed peculiarity. The first leaves of the young sporophyte of the club mosses and those of the quillworts are markedly different: in *Lycopodium* they are scale-like and without traces; in *Selaginella* there are two, well and equally developed, the "cotyledons"; in *Isoetes*, one, well developed.

Habit and structure suggest that the quillworts are a group that has long lived as amphibious plants, and that the terrestrial forms have secondarily become adapted to dry soil, the aquatic forms to submersal. It is further apparent that they have been reduced from larger, more highly organized forms.

In general morphology—the abundant narrow simple leaves, spirally arranged, with a simple trace derived from an exarch protostele; the large ventral sporangia—they much resemble the Lycopodiales and Selaginellales.

The resemblance to *Selaginella* is somewhat greater because of the presence of heterospory and ligules; in fact, *Selaginella* and *Isoetes* are often included in the group "Ligulatae," standing apart from the "Eligulatae" (the Lycopodiales) in the presence of a ligule and in heterospory. Heterospory can, however, be given little weight as indicating relationship, since it is clear that this condition arises independently in unrelated groups. The sporangia of *Selaginella* are cauline and simple, those of *Isoetes* foliar and chambered. The leaves of *Selaginella* are very small and more simple than those of *Isoetes*, and the stems are long and much branched. There is little to tie the two groups together except the presence of a ligule—a single feature. *Isoetes* differs so greatly from both the Selaginellales and the Lycopodiales in its sperms, its root system, its huge, chambered sporangia, that it must be considered to stand well apart from these orders—to form an order by itself, the Isoetales. Yet it has characters which hold it nearer to these two orders than to other vascular plants. *Isoetes*, therefore, is the single representative of a family, the Isoetaceae, constituting the order Isoetales, which is probably distantly related to the club-moss orders. The relationships of the Isoetales are further discussed in Chap. XV.

Bibliography

CAMPBELL, D. H.: Contributions to the life-history of *Isoetes*, *Ann. Bot.*, **5**: 231–258, 1891.

DRACINSCHI, M.: Über die reifen Spermatozoiden bei den Pteridophyten (*Selaginella, Equisetum, Isoëtes*, Filicinae leptosporangiatae), *Bul. Fac. de Ştiinţe din Cernăuţi*, **6**: 63–134, 1932.

GRENDA, A.: Über die systematische Stellung der Isoetaceen, *Bot. Archiv*, **16**: 268–296, 1926.

LaMOTTE, C.: Morphology of the megagametophyte and the embryo sporophyte of *Isoetes lithophila*, *Amer. Jour. Bot.*, **20**: 217–233, 1933.

LANG, W. H.: Studies in the morphology of *Isoetes*, *Mem. Proc. Manchester Lit. Phil. Soc.*, **59**: 1–28, 29–57, 1915.

LIEBIG, J.: Ergänzungen zur Entwicklungsgeschichte von *Isoëtes lacustris* L., *Flora*, **125**: 321–358, 1931.

MOTELAY, L., and VENDRYÈS: Monographie des *Isoëtes*, *Actes Soc. Linn. Bordeaux*, 4 ser., **6**: 309–404, 1882.

PFEIFFER, N. E.: Monograph of the Isoetaceae, *Ann. Mo. Bot. Garden*, **9**: 79–232, 1922.

SCOTT, D. H., and T. G. HILL: The structure of *Isoetes Hystrix*, *Ann. Bot.*, **14**: 413–454, 1900.

SMITH, R. W.: Structure and development of the sporophylls and sporangia of *Isoetes*, *Bot. Gaz.*, **29**: 225–258, 323–346, 1900.

STOKEY, A. G.: The anatomy of *Isoetes*, *Bot. Gaz.*, **47**: 311–335, 1909.

WEST, C., and H. TAKEDA: On *Isoetes japonica*, *Trans. Linn. Soc. London Bot.*, 2 ser., **8**: 333–376, 1915.

CHAPTER IV

PSILOTACEAE

The Psilotaceae are a small group of plants little known generally because of their limited distribution. There are only two genera: *Psilotum*, frequent in the tropics and subtropics, reaching north in the Atlantic region to Florida and Bermuda, in the Pacific to the Hawaiian islands; and *Tmesipteris*, also in

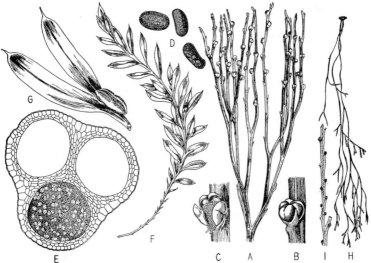

Fig. 50.—*Psilotum* and *Tmesipteris*. *A* to *E*, *P. nudum:* * *A*, habit, × about ⅔. *B*, *C*, sporangium; *D*, spores; *E*, cross section of sporangium. *F*, *G*, *T. tannensis:* *F*, habit, × about ⅔. *G*, lateral axis with sporangium. *H*, *I*, *P. flaccidum;* *H*, habit; *I*, portion of axis, × about ⅓. (*A* to *G* after *Wettstein;* *H*, *I*, after *Schimper.*)

warm regions, but restricted to Australasia and the East Indies, occurring north to the Philippine islands. Both genera are small, and specific lines are obscure: *Psilotum* has probably two well-defined but polymorphic species; *Tmesipteris* perhaps only one, but this is also polymorphic and several species have been described.

* *Psilotum nudum* (L.) Griseb., the valid older name, = *P. triquetrum* Sw.

71

SPOROPHYTE

Habit. *Psilotum* is a slender somewhat shrubby plant, 20 to 100 cm high: one species erect (Figs. 50*A*, 51*A*) and often densely tufted, the other in some forms epiphytic, lax, and drooping (Fig. 50*H*). The frequent branching is strictly dichotomous, in the lower part of the plant successively at right angles, in the upper part sometimes in only one plane. The stems are ridged (Figs. 50*A*, 52*A*) or flattened (Fig. 50*H,I*) and bear in the upper part of the plant small, awl-shaped appendages arranged irregularly, or more or less definitely in two or three rows. The stems are perennial and serve as photosynthetic organs. The plant is more or less xerophytic in structure but grows in various habitats from moist to very dry: in humus in shade; among rocks in sunny places; and even beside waterfalls. It grows well under greenhouse cultivation.

Tmesipteris, a plant of somewhat similar habit (Figs. 50*F*, 51*B*), is commonly an epiphyte with pendulous or arching stems on the trunks of tree ferns and other trees, but often occurs on the soil, especially on hummocks or mounds of leaf mold in forests. One East Indian form, "*T. Vieillardi*" (Fig. 53), grows erect on the ground. The stems are 5 to 25 cm long; branching, which is rare, is dichotomous. In contrast with the almost naked branches of *Psilotum* the stems of *Tmesipteris* are 'leafy,' bearing on the upper parts linear or elliptical leaf-like structures which are flattened laterally (at right angles to the leaf lamina of other plants) and merge into the stem by strongly decurrent bases (Figs. 50*F*, 53). In the lower part of the stem these appendages become small and scale-like. Their arrangement is more or less irregular, but two rows can often be distinguished and sometimes three, four, or five. The stem is definitely limited in growth; when mature, the axis in most cases terminates in one of the leaf-like structures (Figs. 50*F*, 51*B*). There is no clear distinction between stem and 'leaves,' especially at the tip of the branch, and the axis strongly resembles a branched and lobed thallus (Figs. 50*H*, 53).

Both genera grow in humus, and the stems merge below the surface into slender dichotomous rhizomes which branch freely and may be 1 m or more long. There are no roots. The rhizomes are mycorrhizal and are clothed with hair-like, absorbing

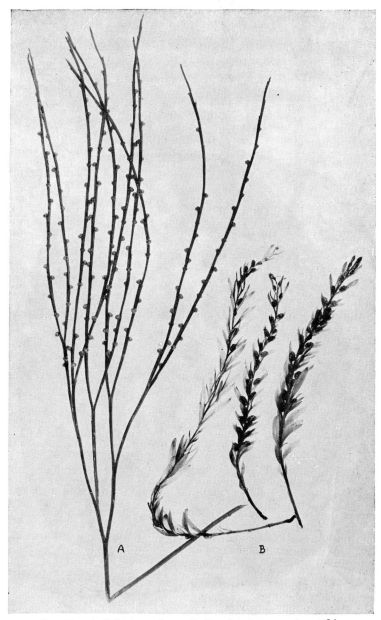

Fig. 51.—*A, Psilotum nudum. B, Tmesipteris tannensis.* ✕⅔.

Fig. 52.—Portions of Fig. 51 enlarged.

structures, or rhizoids. As the rhizomes grow, some of the tips emerge from the soil, become erect, and develop into typical 'leafy' stems. Rhizome and aerial stem are continuous and are obviously morphologically alike.

Reproduction. In both genera the more vigorous branches bear on forked appendages, near the top, large, conspicuous sporangia. These sporangia seem to be borne on the adaxial side of the appendage at the point of dichotomy (Figs. 50*B,G*; 52*B*) and are slightly raised on broad, short stalks.

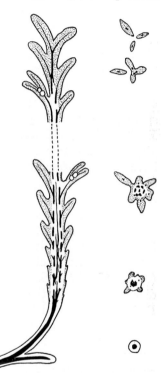

In *Psilotum* the slender branches of the fertile appendage are more or less erect and embrace the sporangium (Fig. 50*B*); in *Tmesipteris* the branches are broad lobes which resemble the sterile appendages and extend horizontally (Fig. 50*G*). Occasionally, in both genera the dichotomy of these fertile structures is repeated, each of the branches forking again once or twice, with a sporangium borne at each fork.

The fertile appendages are mostly grouped on the upper part of the stem, but fertile and sterile regions are not strictly limited and sterile appendages may occur irregularly among the fertile ones. In *Tmesipteris* the appendage which usually terminates the stem is in many cases a fertile one.

FIG. 53.—"*Tmesipteris Vieillardi.*" Habit and anatomy. The cross sections are from levels at which they are shown. Xylem is black. (*After Sahni.*)

The morphology of the fertile appendages is difficult to determine and has long been in dispute. It has been believed that the sterile appendages are leaves, and that the fertile ones are homologous structures, forked and bearing sporangia, being therefore sporophylls. It is also claimed that the sporangium-bearing structures are short fertile branches (axes), bearing two 'leaves' or lobes and terminating in a sporangium. That the axis is not definitely divided into stem and leaves is evident; also that the fertile and sterile appendages are closely similar and represent lobes or sections of the thallus-like body. These lobes range in size from the scales at the base to the fertile appendages near the top. It is apparent that the fertile and sterile appendages are homologous, varying in degree only; the fertile ones represent main divisions of the axis, the sterile ones lesser divisions. This is borne out by the anatomy, by the occasional dichotomy of the fertile lobes, and by the fact that the main axis is (in *Tmesipteris*) terminated by such a lobe. That the sporangium is terminal upon a lobe seems evident from its anatomy and ontogeny. Additional proof is found in the position of the sporangium in fossil plants with similar body structure (Chap. XIV). The tips of the fertile branches, transformed into sporangia, and therefore determinate, are upturned and, in *Tmesipteris*, have been surpassed in longitudinal growth by the appendages below. The fertile appendages are therefore not sporophylls but axes; the sporangia are axial or cauline.

The apparently ventral position of the sporangium is clearly a false one; the sporangium seems to be ventral because the axis tip is upturned and is surpassed by lower appendages.

The prominence of the sporangia is due not only to large size (those of *Psilotum* being 2 to 3 mm, of *Tmesipteris* 3 to 4 mm in diameter) but to their lobed condition. The sporangium of *Psilotum* has three lobes (in some cases two or four) (Figs. 50*B*, 52*A*), and that of *Tmesipteris* usually two lobes, which are elongate and lie parallel with the axis below (Figs. 50*G*, 52*B*). The lobes correspond to definite thick-walled chambers (Fig. 50*E*) which contain numerous spores.

Though the first stages of sporangium formation are difficult to determine, development is apparently of the eusporangiate type (Fig. 54). Large, poorly defined sporogenous masses are formed and these are separate from one another from an early stage (Fig. 54*C*). In *Psilotum* it apparently cannot readily be determined from ontogeny whether the septum between the sporogenous groups represents sterilized sporogenous tissue—as in the case, for example, of the trabeculae of *Isoetes*—or is merely vegetative tissue. In *Tmesipteris*, however, the history of development indicates that the septum and the sporogenous tissue are alike in origin; it is probable, therefore, that the original sporogenous mass is divided by a sterile septum. Further evidence is found in abnormal sporangia where there is no septum and sporogenous cells fill the partition region.

The sporangium of these genera has often been considered a synangium—a group of fused sporangia—because the chambers are so definitely separate and the lobes so prominent. But ontogeny seems to show that this compound structure is a divided sporangium rather than a synangium, and strong support is given to this opinion by the fact that the entire structure represents the fertile tip of an axis.

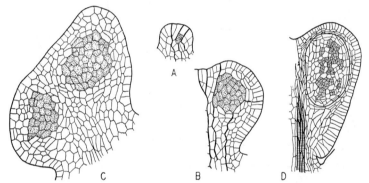

Fig. 54.—Sporangium development in the Psilotaceae. *A, B, D, Psilotum nudum,* successive stages, radial sections through loculus. *C, Tmesipteris tannensis,* radial section at early stage. (*After Bower.*)

As the sporogenous tissue matures, some of the sporocytes disorganize (Fig. 54*D*) and form a nourishing fluid in which the surviving mother cells and spores develop. Though there are suggestions of a tapetum in the irregular breaking down of the inner wall layers and outer sporogenous cells, no definite layer of such nature is formed (Fig. 54*D*). The numerous spores are formed in tetrads and are all alike, bilateral, with thin, smooth or finely reticulated walls and a line or "cleft" with thick lip-like edges along the ridge (Figs. 50*D*; 57*A,B*). The mature sporangium dehisces by a radial slit in the tip of each chamber (Fig. 50*C,G*).

Vegetative Propagation. In *Psilotum* new plants are formed by gemmae which develop freely on the rhizomes. No such reproduction is known in Tmesipteris.

Anatomy.   The axis, which in the rhizome region is protostelic, becomes siphonostelic in the region transitional to the stem, and the stem has a large pith which may be sclerenchymatous.   In *Psilotum* the xylem cylinder in the stem is sharply angled and exarch and is surrounded by rather poorly developed phloem. In *Tmesipteris* the stele is broken up into mesarch strands (Fig. 53), and some forms have internal phloem and even medullary xylem strands.   Scattered tracheids lying external to the protoxylem at the base of the stem in *Psilotum* have been called "secondary xylem," but these are perhaps centrifugally devel-

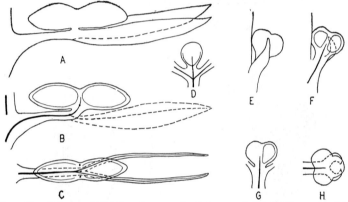

Fig. 55.—Diagrams showing form and anatomy of the fertile axes of the Psilotaceae.   *A* to *D, Tmesipteris.   E* to *H, Psilotum.   A*, side view; *B*, radial section; *C*, view from above; *D*, transverse vertical section through sporangium partition; *E*, side view; *F*, radial section; *G*, vertical section at right angles to *F; H*, view from above.

oped cells, the xylem being mesarch in this region.   The xylem elements are scalariform tracheids, with spiral tracheids in the protoxylem.

The sterile appendages of one species of *Psilotum* are without traces; those of the other species have weak strands which do not extend beyond the cortex.   In *Tmesipteris* the scale-like lobes likewise have no traces, or only weak ones which do not reach the lobe itself.   The traces of the other appendages are, however, strong.   In the fertile and sterile appendages they are similar, those of the former being larger and sometimes forming gaps in the vascular cylinder.   In *Psilotum* the trace of the fertile branch passes beyond the fork and ends in the partition between the sporangial cavities (Fig. 55F,G).   As a vestigial strand it continues in many cases nearly to the top of the sporangium. In *Tmesipteris* the strand gives off (Fig. 55*B* to *D*), just below the sporangium, branches which supply the two lateral appendages; the main strand turns upward to the base

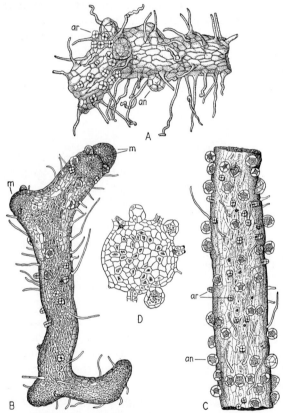

Fig. 56.—Gametophytes of the Psilotaceae. *A, Tmesipteris. B* to *D, Psilotum. A*, portion of prothallium showing sex organs. *B*, prothallium showing form, apical meristems, and distribution of sex organs. *C*, ½ of a prothallium showing form and distribution of sex organs. *D*, cross section of prothallium. *an*, antheridium; *ar*, archegonium; *m*, meristem. (*After Lawson.*)

of the sporangium where it again branches into three parts (Fig. 55*C,D*). Of these three branches the median continues upward into the sporangium partition; the lateral branches extend up the margins of the partition (Fig. 55*D*).

Gametophyte

Only in recent years have the gametophytes of this group become known, and information concerning some details of structure is still lacking. That these prothallia have remained so long unknown is due to the restricted distribution of the genera, and to the difficulty of finding the prothallia, which are small, brown, and buried in humus in the soil or on tree trunks. Though somewhat like the subterranean type in *Lycopodium*, they are elongate cylindrical structures (Figs. 56; 57*G,H*; 60) closely resembling pieces of the rhizome. They range in length up to

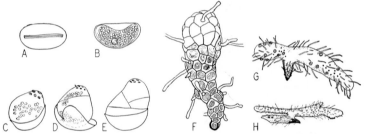

FIG. 57.—Development of gametophyte in the Psilotaceae. *A* to *E*, *Psilotum*. *F* to *H*, *Tmesipteris*. *A*, *B*, spores; *C* to *E* germinating spore and establishment of apical cell of prothallium; *F*, young prothallium just before first dichotomy; older portion mycorrhizal; *G*, prothallium after first dichotomy; *H*, much older, more branched prothallium, with one main branch broken off. (*A* to *E* after *Darnell-Smith; F* to *H* after *Holloway*.)

18 mm, in diameter to 1.25 mm, and grow by apical meristems, branching dichotomously once or more. The dichotomy is commonly irregular owing to the density of the soil or to the closeness of the tree-fern roots in which they grow. They are clothed with yellow-brown rhizoids and their cells are filled with a mycorrhizal fungus, in these respects still further resembling the rhizomes. There is no differentiation into vegetative and reproductive regions; antheridia and archegonia are borne in large numbers all over the gametophyte (Fig. 56).

Development. The spores of *Psilotum* germinate after about four months, the wall splitting along the 'cleft.' The enlarging spore contents project as a conical mound (Fig. 57*C*). The extruded portion is cut off by a transverse wall, the basal portion remaining within the spore wall as a large spherical cell (Fig. 57*D*). The apical cell divides by oblique walls (Fig. 57*E*), and

a filament is formed which soon becomes club-shaped (Fig. 57*F*).
Similar stages in *Tmesipteris* are not known, but in later development the two genera are closely similar.   An apical meristem is
established which apparently continues growth indefinitely.
Forking occurs almost at once (Figs. 57*G,H*; 60*C*), and each
branch may fork once or several times.   At this mature stage
the gametophyte closely resembles in form, color, rhizoids,
and apical meristems underground parts of the sporophyte;
only with difficulty can it be distinguished from pieces of the
rhizome without microscopic examination.

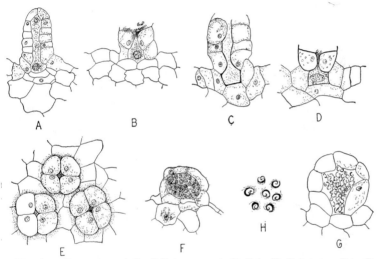

FIG. 58.—Sex organs of the Psilotaceae.   *A, B, F* to *H, Psilotum.   C* to *E,
Tmesipteris.   A, C,* mature archegonium; *B, D,* archegonium ready for fertiliza-
tion; *E,* surface view of archegonia at time of fertilization; *F,* young antheridium;
G, mature antheridium with sperms; *H,* sperms.   (*After Lawson.*)

Sex Organs.   The antheridia begin to appear early.   They are
prominently projecting, spherical bodies, with a wall of a single
layer of cells (Figs. 56*C,D*; 58*F,G*).   The archegonia are sunken,
with short projecting necks which break away at maturity
(Figs. 56, 58*A* to *E*).   The antheridium arises from a superficial
cell, which divides periclinally, separating an outer cell, which
becomes the one-layered wall, from an inner cell, which develops
the spermatogenous tissue.   The stages of development are
similar to those of the antheridia of other groups.   The sperms
are spiral and multiciliate (Fig. 58*H*).   The archegonia likewise

are formed from superficial initials and the early stages of development are as usual. Of the two cells formed by the first division of the initial, the outer forms a neck of four (in some cases five or six) tiers of four cells each (Fig. 58*A* to *E*). The inner cell divides periclinally forming the members of the

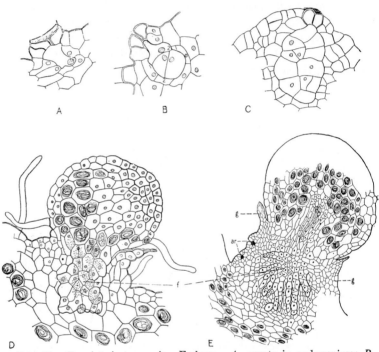

Fig. 59.—*Tmesipteris tannensis.* Embryo. *A*, zygote in archegonium; *B*, three-celled embryo; *C*, older embryo; *D*, embryo showing development of foot downward in gametophyte; *E*, later stage showing finger-like processes of the foot penetrating deeply into gametophyte. Mycorrhizal cells are abundant in both sporophyte and gametophyte. *ar*, archegonium; *f*, foot; *g*, cushion of gametophytic tissue. (*After Holloway.*)

axial row, but the details of structure here are uncertain. A ventral canal cell is reported in *Psilotum* but has not been found in *Tmesipteris*. There are probably two neck canal cells. When the archegonium is mature the upper tiers of the neck break away (Fig. 58*B,D*), leaving only the basal tier (in *Psilotum* the lower one to three tiers) which forms a shallow, slightly concave plate about the opening (Figs. 58*E*, 59*A*). (In other plant groups the cells of the neck separate and spread apart slightly when mature.) Fertilization has not been seen. In the two genera the sex organs are closely alike, though those of *Psilotum* are only about half the size of those of *Tmesipteris*.

Reproduction of the prothallium by budding has been seen in rare instances in *Tmesipteris*.

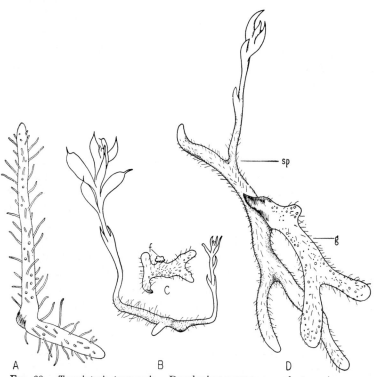

Fig. 60.—*Tmesipteris tannensis.* Developing young sporophyte. *A,* young sporophyte after first dichotomy; plant consisting merely of foot and rhizome. *B,* young sporophyte with both ends of rhizome developed as aerial stems, showing foot and lateral bud. *C,* parent gametophyte of plant shown in *B,* bearing the base of the foot. *D,* gametophyte bearing sporophyte with aerial and subterranean branches. Note similarity of gametophyte and sporophyte in size and form. *f,* foot; *g,* gametophyte; *sp,* sporophyte. (*After Holloway.*)

EMBRYO

The fertilized egg enlarges downward (Fig. 59*A*), and the first division is transverse or nearly so (Fig. 59*B*). The developing embryo is simple. Quadrants may be evident, but the first division separates an outer part which becomes axis, and an inner part, the foot. As the embryo enlarges, a cushion of gametophytic tissue is formed above it (Fig. 59*C*). This is lifted by the growing axis and finally ruptured. The foot enlarges downward (Fig. 59*D*), sending finger-like projections deep into the prothallial tissues (Fig. 59*E*). The tip of the axis branches dichotomously, in most cases, soon after it breaks through the cushion (Fig. 60*A*,*B*,*D*), and one or both parts become aerial stems (Fig. 60*B*,*D*). The division between the axis and foot remains distinct, and when the young sporophyte is no longer dependent upon the gametophyte a break occurs at this point and the foot remains attached to the gametophyte (Fig. 60*C*).

Discussion and Summary

In these genera the plant body consists of a dichotomously branching axis weakly differentiated into a subterranean, absorbing, root-like part and an aerial stem-like part with determinate lateral lobes. In *Tmesipteris* these lobes are broad and leaf-like (though unleaf-like in orientation); in *Psilotum* they are small (perhaps reduced as a result of xerophytic modification) and photosynthesis is carried on chiefly by the main axis. In both genera there are large and small lateral lobes; the larger are commonly fertile, bearing sporangia on the upturned tips. In *Tmesipteris* the main axis usually terminates in one of these sterile or fertile lobes, the apical growing point being used up in its formation.

The plant body is relatively unspecialized; there are no roots and no true leaves. Its thallus-like character is evident in its general appearance and in its laterally flattened decurrent appendages. The resemblance of the two-ranked types to algal fronds is remarkable. (These forms are however modified from the radial.)

It is often stated that the absence of roots may be due to reduction, these organs having been lost in adaptation to a mycorrhizal and epiphytic habit. Though this is possible, there is no evidence that it is so; there is no trace of roots in embryogeny or in the young plant as is the case in many such reduced plants. And the fact that there is no clean-cut distinction into stem and leaf is the best supporting evidence that roots have not yet been attained in the differentiation of the body, and that the rhizomes represent these organs. That the 'leaves' are lateral lobes of the axis is evident, especially from the fact that the main axis terminates in such a lobe. Further, the orientation of these lobes is wholly different from that of the leaves of other groups. The plant body is an extremely simple one, lacking the differentiation of that of other groups, and hence is undoubtedly a most primitive one among vascular plants.

The fertile and sterile lobes apparently represent lateral branches of the axis, of different degree. The smaller ones are 'leaves.' The larger ones—which themselves may branch once or more—which bear sporangia on their tips and may have well-defined gaps, are 'branches.' The fact that the main axis in *Tmesipteris* ends in a fertile lobe is further evidence that the lateral fertile lobes represent chief branches of the axis.

The fruiting structure is cauline and terminal. It is a radially divided sporangium and not a synangium. Its cauline nature is evident in its method of development, which is like that of the main axis, and in the fact that vascular tissue enters the center (the partitions), as in no other living plants. It is massive—crude—in structure, with walls of several cell layers and with thick partitions; it lacks the specialized nourishing layer for the sporocytes; the opening mechanism is of the simplest type. The sporangium is clearly unelaborated, except for its partitioning, and more simple than that of any other living vascular-plant group. (In only one other group (Chap. XIV) is the sporangium similar to that of the Psilotaceae in crudeness.) The spores are numerous, small, and unspecialized, as in primitive sporangia.

The gametophytes are remarkable in their resemblance to the sporophyte. They are like the rhizome in general appearance, in cylindrical form and dichotomous branching, indefinite apical growth, radial structure, rhizoids, and endophytic fungus; the rhizome, however, has vascular tissue and the gametophyte sex organs. So close a resemblance of sporophyte and gametophyte is not found elsewhere. In only one other group (the Ophioglossaceae, Chap. VI), which is also undoubtedly very primitive, does a gametophyte approaching this type occur. There are indeed resemblances in the subterranean character and mycorrhizal state, and especially in the radial form, to the gametophytes of *Lycopodium*, but in the Psilotaceae there is no segregation of fertile regions and the sex organs and sperms differ in important ways.   The lack of differentiation of the prothallium into fertile and sterile regions further suggests a most primitive state.

The antheridia are spherical protuberances, differing markedly from the sunken, rather indefinite antheridia of the Lycopodiaceae.   The sperms are multiciliate and are thus unlike those of the Lycopodiaceae and Selaginellaceae and like those of other vascular plants.   The archegonia resemble in general those of the other groups discussed.   The projecting neck is of medium length; its method of opening—by the loss of the distal tiers—is unlike that of other plants.   Unfortunately the structure of the axial row is incompletely known.   The neck canal cells are probably two, and a ventral canal cell has been reported in one genus.   The axial row is therefore probably not very different from that of other groups of lower vascular plants.

In the young embryo, only axis and foot are differentiated; in no other group is embryonic structure so simple.   The leafless and rootless condition of the mature plant is thus foreshadowed very early.   This absence of leaf and root in the embryonic stages supports other facts which indicate that these organs have not been lost in the adaptation of the plants to mycorrhizal and epiphytic habit but have not yet appeared in the differentiation of the plant body.   The simplicity of the plant body is further borne out in that early development of the axis shows that aerial stem and rhizome are homologous parts.

In two other ways the embryo is outstandingly different. It is inverted (as compared with that of the Lycopodiaceae and Isoetaceae), the foot developing from the inner, the axis from the outer of the two cells formed by the division of the fertilized egg. A unique condition exists in the breaking away of the young sporophyte from its embedded foot as it becomes independent.

These plants show many characters of marked simplicity and undoubted primitiveness.   In both generations lack of body specialization is prominent.   The sporophyte is thallus-like in many respects; the entire plant is a continuous axis, weakly differentiated.   The gametophyte is also thallus-like, an elongate, dichotomous axis, without differentiation of parts.   The resemblance of the two generations to each other is perhaps significant (Chap. XVII).   It is evident that this group is a most primitive one and that it differs in important ways from other groups.

The two genera are much alike in many ways and undoubtedly are closely related. *Psilotum* in its adaptation to xerophytic habitats is probably more specialized. The genera form a well-defined family, the Psilotaceae; and the group is so unlike other vascular plants that it must stand by itself in the order Psilotales, an order surely isolated from other living orders. In taxonomic and morphological treatments the family has often been grouped with the Lycopodiaceae; but it is evident that such a grouping is unnatural, for not only are the Psilotaceae leafless and rootless and their sporangia cauline and terminal, but the sperms are multiciliate and the antheridia superficial.

Bibliography

BERTRAND, C. E.: Recherches sur les Tmésiptéridées, *Arch. Bot. du Nord de la France*, **1**: 252–598, 1881.

BOWER, F. O.: Studies in the morphology of spore-producing members: Equisetineae and Lycopodineae, *Phil. Trans. Roy. Soc. London* **185B**: 473–572, 1894.

BROWNE, I.: The phylogeny and inter-relationships of the Pteridophyta. VII. The inter-relationships of the phyla. *New Phyt.*, **8**: 51–72, 1909.

DANGEARD, P. A.: Mémoire sur la morphologie et l'anatomie des *Tmesipteris*, *Le Botaniste*, **2**: 163–222, 1890–1891.

DARNELL-SMITH, G. P.: The gametophyte of *Psilotum*, *Trans. Roy. Soc. Edinburgh*, **52**: 79–91, 1917.

DOMIN, K.: Beiträge zur Flora und Pflanzengeographie Australiens, *Bibl. Bot.*, **20**: (85), 232–234, 1915.

FORD, S. O.: The anatomy of *Psilotum triquetrum*, *Ann. Bot.*, **18**: 589–605, 1904.

HOLLOWAY, J. E.: The prothallus and young plant of *Tmesipteris*, *Trans. Proc. N. Z. Inst.*, **50**: 1–44, 1917.

————: Further notes on the prothallus, embryo, and young sporophyte of *Tmesipteris*, *Trans. Proc. N. Z. Inst.*, **53**: 386–422, 1921.

LAWSON, A. A.: The prothallus of *Tmesipteris tannensis*, *Trans. Roy. Soc. Edinburgh*, **51**: 785–794, 1917.

————: The gametophyte generation of the Psilotaceae, *Trans. Roy. Soc. Edinburgh*, **52**: 93–113, 1917.

SAHNI, B.: On *Tmesipteris Vieillardi* Dangeard, an erect terrestrial species from New Caledonia, *Phil. Trans. Roy. Soc. London*, **213B**: 143–170, 1925.

STILES, W.: The structure of the aerial shoots of *Psilotum flaccidum* Wall., *Ann. Bot.*, **24**: 373–387, 1910.

SYKES, M. G.: The anatomy and morphology of *Tmesipteris*, *Ann. Bot.*, **22**: 63–89, 1908.

ZIMMERMANN, W.: Die Spaltöffnungen der Psilophyta und Psilotales, *Ztschr. für Bot.*, **19**: 129–170, 1926.

CHAPTER V

EQUISETACEAE   HORSETAILS

Because of unusual habit and larger size the horsetails are better known generally than the groups discussed in the earlier chapters. They are, further, to be found nearly all over the world—the only large area in which they are lacking is Australia and New Zealand—and some species, such as the field horsetail and the winter horsetail, grow along roadsides and in other places where they are commonly seen.

The group consists of a single genus, *Equisetum*, with about 25 species, most of which inhabit the cool temperate regions. The various species are plants primarily of wet places, but some, for example, *E. arvense*, the field horsetail, may grow in dry and sterile places such as the cinders of railroad embankments. Horsetails in masses, as occasionally seen in marshes and on stream banks, have an aspect unlike that of other plants.

Sporophyte

Habit. All species are herbaceous perennials, many of them evergreen. The aerial stems, which are perennial or annual, arise from much-branched rhizomes. Most species are low, less than 1 m high; the stems of the largest (*E. giganteum* of the American tropics) may reach 10 or 12 m in height but are slender, about 2 cm in diameter, and grow only where sheltered and supported by surrounding vegetation. A Mexican species is reported to have stems 2 m high and up to 10 cm in diameter but like all others lacks secondary growth.

Stems and Leaves. The outstanding vegetative characters of the horsetails are the conspicuously jointed stems and the whorled leaves and branches (Figs. 61, 62, 63). The leaves are small and simple, and fused laterally, with longer or shorter, free tips (Fig. 64*A*). Each whorl forms a sheath which is appressed to the base of the internode. The number of leaves in a whorl varies greatly with the species and with the size of

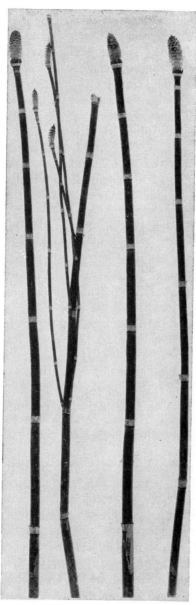

Fig. 61.—*Equisetum hyemale.* Stems with terminal cones; in one, after injury to the growing point, lateral branches have developed from dormant buds. ×½.

the stem: the larger stems have many leaves with the number indefinite; smaller stems may have as few as two or three, the number definite in some species. The leaves are mostly non-green and in many species soon become dead and scale-like. Photosynthesis is carried on by the stems, especially by the branchlets, which in some species, as in *E. sylvaticum*, are delicate and form a rather dense system.

The members of each leaf whorl alternate in position on the stem with those of the nodes above and below. The stem is markedly ridged, the ridges being of the same number as the leaves, with a leaf standing directly above a ridge in the internode below. The stem ridges therefore alternate on successive internodes as do the leaves at the nodes.

The jointed character of the stems is prominent not only because of the usually conspicuous nodal sheaths but because the method of growth is by intercalary meristems. These meristems are situated at the base of the internode where they are protected by the leaf sheaths, as in grasses, and their activity may continue for some time. Because of the presence of these meristematic regions the stems break rather readily into sections; from this character comes the name "pipes" frequently applied to these jointed plants.

The branches at a node usually equal the leaves in number, a branch developing between each two leaves (Fig. 68). The leaves develop early, and the branches, which arise at approximately the same level, break through the fused leaf bases. Because the leaf sheath is appressed, the branches appear to arise below the leaves.

The branches are markedly different from those of other groups in their whorled arrangement, the large number at a node, the abundance of branchlets, the constancy and uniformity of their development, and in their relation to the leaves.

In some species the stems are branched, in others unbranched; in still others, they are unbranched or branched. In this last group, when branches are present, they are weakly developed. In unbranched species branch buds lie dormant and buried in the nodal tissues, developing only if the terminal bud is injured (Fig. 61). It is evident from these and other facts that the branched stems represent the more primitive condition and that specialization has resulted in simplification, the compound branch systems being reduced to the unbranched stem. The freely branched stem of *E. arvense* (Fig. 62*A*) represents the primitive type within the genus, and the unbranched stem of *E. hyemale* (Figs. 61, 62*D*) the advanced.   Species like *E. limosum* (Fig. 62*C*) show a transitional condition.

Roots.   Roots occur only at the nodes of the rhizomes or stem bases (Fig. 63).   Their origin is, in many cases at least, at the base of the lateral buds (often undeveloped) and branches. They are slender and fibrous, and though they live for several years do not become long and no definite persistent system

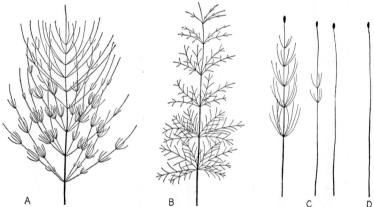

A   B   C   D

Fig. 62.—*Equisetum.* Diagrams illustrating branching habit—a reduction series. *A*, *E. arvense; B, E. sylvaticum; C, E. limosum; D, E. hyemale.*   In *C*, lateral buds may remain dormant or may develop; in *D*, the lateral buds develop only if terminal bud is destroyed.

is formed.   They arise endogenously from the bases of lateral branches or from dormant branch buds, not from the main axis.

Reproduction.   The sporangia are borne in cones, which in most species are prominent features, terminating many of the main axes, and sometimes also the lateral branches (Figs. 61, 63, 64).   In the majority of species the cones are borne on typical vegetative shoots, but in a few, such as *E. arvense,* specialization has resulted in a segregation of function among the stems (Fig. 65): some are green and sterile; others are pale and brownish or flesh-colored, and fertile.   The latter have no chlorophyll and are short-lived, withering as soon as the spores are shed.   These fertile stems are well developed below ground in the fall and expand rapidly in the spring.   In this specializa-

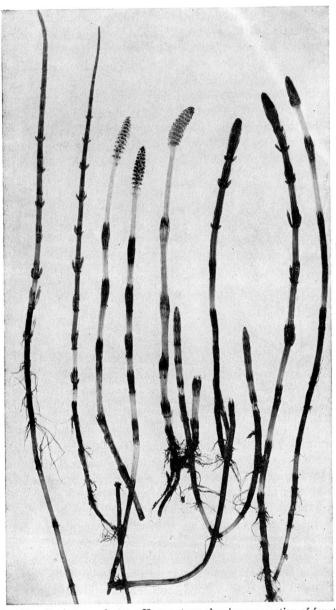

FIG. 63.—*Equisetum palustre.* Young stems showing segregation of function: those on the left, vegetative and persistent; those in the center, fertile and ephemeral; those on the right, vegetative and fertile, persistent. $\times\frac{1}{2}$.

tion of stems in function, certain species are in a transitional
state.   In *E. sylvaticum* the fertile stems are at first nongreen
and unbranched; as the cones shrivel, chlorophyll is formed and
green branches develop at the nodes.   Later these stems are like
the sterile ones except for the dead tip where the cone was borne.
In *E. palustre* (Fig. 63) three types of stems develop, often on
the same plant and at the same time—typical sterile and fertile
stems and intermediate types like those of *E. sylvaticum*.   The

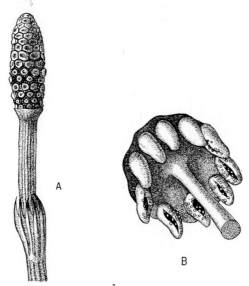

A

B

Fig. 64.—*Equisetum.   A, E. arvense,* tip of fertile stem; *B, E. telmateia,* sporangiophore with sporangia.   (*After Wettstein.*)

various species form a series in functional specialization in stems
from the type found in *E. hyemale* to that in *E. arvense* (Fig. 65).
Accompanying the elaboration of stem types is that of cone
number, position, and form.   The more primitive species bear
several or many cones on each stem; the advanced species have
on each aerial branch a single cone terminal on the main axis.
The primitive type of cone is subsessile and is apiculate, the
axis continuing beyond the spore-bearing organs (Fig. 61); the
specialized type is pedunculate with a rounded apex (Fig. 64).
The species which are primitive in both stem and cone are found
only in the tropics and subtropics.

The cone is made up of sporangium-bearing organs, *sporangio-phores*, arranged in whorls on a thick axis, the members of successive whorls alternating, though somewhat irregularly (Fig. 64). The sporangiophores (Fig. 64*B*) are stalked peltate structures projecting at right angles from the axis. Their flattened polygonal tips fit closely together and form a protective covering for the sporangia which are on the underside of the tip. The cones vary in size in the different species, the sporangiophores ranging in number from few to many. At the base of the cone in some species is a calyx-like whorl, the *annulus*, which appar-

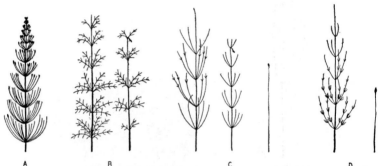

A   B   C   D

FIG. 65.—*Equisetum.* Diagrams illustrating segregation of function among branches, a series in increasing specialization. *A, E. myriochaetum;* one type of branch only. *B, E. sylvaticum;* two types of branch: one sterile, branched, green, persistent; one, when young, fertile, unbranched, nongreen—when older, becoming green, branched, persistent, resembling the sterile branches. *C, E. palustre;* three types of branch: one sterile, much branched, green, persistent; one fertile, unbranched, nongreen, ephemeral; one fertile, at first unbranched and nongreen—later branched, green, persistent (Fig. 63). *D, E. arvense;* two types of branch: one sterile, branched, green, persistent; one fertile, unbranched, nongreen, ephemeral.

ently represents a modified leaf whorl (Fig. 64*A*). The annulus is present in those species which have the more specialized cones and stems and perhaps serves to some extent as a protective structure.

Sporangia. The sporangia are elongate, sac-like structures attached in a sort of whorl on the underside of the sporangiophore near the edge, projecting horizontally toward the cone axis (Fig. 64*B*). They vary considerably in size, and the number per sporangiophore ranges from 5 to 10. The sporangium wall is delicate, only one cell layer thick when mature. When the spores are mature the sporangiophores shrink and pull apart, and the sporangia dehisce by a longitudinal slit down the side next the sporangiophore stalk.

The sporangia arise from single superficial cells around the crown of the developing sporangiophore (Fig. 66*A*). Growth in the center of the sporangiophore tip soon pushes the sporangium initials laterally and 'over the edge' so that they become inverted with reference to their earlier position (Fig. 66*A* to *F*). Development is eusporangiate, though the first division does not separate cells whose functions are strictly wall and spore formation, respectively (Fig. 66*A* to *E*). Of the several-layered tissue

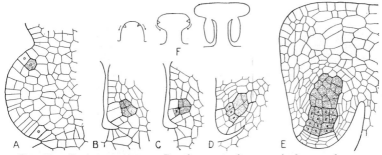

Fig. 66.—*Equisetum arvense.* Development of sporangiophore and sporangium. *A*, radial section of side of cone showing very young sporangiophore with sporangium initials around the crown, the upper divided periclinally. *B* to *E*, portions of longitudinal sections of a sporangiophore showing development of sporangium, the sporogenous cells shaded. The shaded cells marked with an *x* have been derived from the outer cell formed at the first division. *F*, diagrams showing development of sporangiophore and inversion of orientation of growing sporangium. (*A* to *E, after Bower.*)

formed by the outer cell the inner part is sporogenous like that formed by the inner cell (Fig. 66*C* to *E*); the outer part forms a wall of varying and irregular thickness (two to several layers), and the cells next the sporogenous tissue become an irregular, ill-defined, but rather thick, tapetum.

As the sporocytes are formed, the tapetal cells multiply; their walls then break down and their protoplasts fuse forming a *periplasmodium.* This cytoplasmic mass surrounds the sporocytes and in some ways behaves like a protoplast. Its nuclei divide by amitotic division. It penetrates between the sporocytes, about one-third of which go to pieces, adding to the mass of the periplasmodium.

Spores. The surviving spore mother cells form tetrads of spores which become spherical or nearly so and show no trace of a triradiate ridge. They are all alike in form and have an elaborate wall structure. The complexity of the wall is largely the result of the activity of the periplasmodium. About the one or two usual spore wall layers, the surrounding cytoplasm lays down a delicate cuticular layer and a thick *perispore*. This last layer is differentiated into narrow, spirally wound bands with flat, spoon-like tips (Fig. 67A to C). Each spore has four such bands attached at a common point. The bands are hygroscopic and unwind as the spores dry at dehiscence. They respond

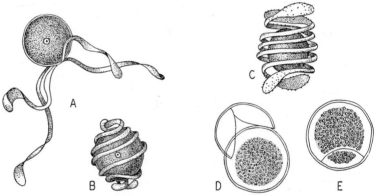

Fig. 67.—Spores of *Equisetum. A, B, E. telmateia; C* to *E, E. arvense; A* to *C*, mature spores, *A* with "elaters" uncoiled; *D, E,* germinating spores: *D,* rupture of spore wall; *E,* first division. (*A, B, after Wettstein; C* to *E, after Sadebeck in Engler and Prantl.*)

quickly to changes in air moisture and thus by coiling and uncoiling loosen the spore mass, which then projects from the shriveling sporangium. The spores when dry are light and fluffy and are carried away singly or in clusters by air currents. The projecting arms are commonly called "elaters," because they seem to aid in spore dissemination. This is an unfortunate term because the elaters of the liverworts, which serve in a similar way, are sterile sporogenous cells. The delicate spore walls have little color, but the spores contain much chlorophyll and are therefore green.

Vegetative Propagation. In some species tubers, which represent swollen internodes, form on the rhizomes and serve as reproductive structures.

Anatomy. The anatomical structure resembles that of marsh plants in the small amount of vascular tissue and the large and numerous "air chambers" (Fig. 69). In the internodes is a ring of delicate collateral bundles which at the nodes unite to form a thin collar. The bundles of the internode above arise from the collar, alternating with those below (Fig. 68). Over the internodal bundles the cortex projects in ridges. The number and position of the internodal bundles are thus evident on the outside.

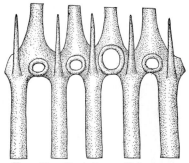

FIG. 68.—*Equisetum.* D i a g r a m showing anatomy of node. (*After Jeffrey.*)

The ridges consist of sclerenchymatous cells whose thick walls are strongly silicified and form the chief support of the stem. The name "scouring rushes" has been given to some species because these harsh, siliceous ridges make possible the use of the stems for cleaning purposes. Horsetail stems were used extensively in colonial days for scouring pewter dishes.

Prominent in the cortex are the large canals which run from node to node below the stem furrows. Between these *vallecular canals* and the epidermis lie longitudinal pockets of photosynthetic tissue. The stomata, which are sunken, lie over this tissue along the furrows. Within the bundle ring is a large pith, which is hollow except at the nodes where there are firm transverse diaphragms (Fig. 69*A*). The pith cavity and the other chambers are reduced or lacking in rhizomes and cone axes.

Each bundle (Fig. 69*C*) has three small strands of xylem: an inner one, of protoxylem, whose elements lie on the side of a large protoxylem lacuna, (the *carinal canal*), and two external lateral strands of metaxylem, lying on the 'shoulders' of the bundle. Between these outer xylem strands lies the phloem. The xylem is endarch, although there are some irregularities in order of development in the metaxylem groups. In a few species slight secondary growth has been reported to occur at the nodal ring; probably, however, there is no true cambial activity in this region and true secondary growth is absent in the genus.

(Fossil species apparently had considerable secondary vascular tissue.)

The three strands of xylem give the bundle a complex appearance, and several conflicting theories have been proposed concerning the nature of the bundle. It has been suggested that the

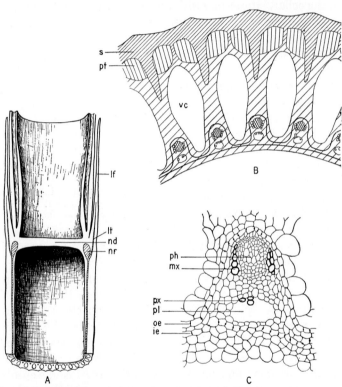

Fig. 69.—*Equisetum hyemale.* Diagrams showing anatomy of stem. *A*, nodal region split longitudinally. *B*, portion of cross section of internode. *C*, vascular bundle in cross section. *ie*, internal endodermis; *lf*, leaf; *lt*, leaf trace; *mx*, metaxylem; *nd*, nodal diaphragm; *nr*, nodal ring; *oe*, outer endodermis; *ph*, phloem; *pl*, protoxylem lacuna; *pt*, photosynthetic tissue; *s*, sclerenchymatous cortex and epidermis; *vc*, vallecular canal; *px*, protoxylem.

two outer strands represent the secondary xylem; that they are the remains of centripetal xylem (their order of development being occasionally toward the inside); and that the bundle is triple, made up of three fused strands. The bundle is, however, without doubt a simple one with endarch xylem; its apparent complexity is due to reduction, especially in the xylem where the continuity of the tissue is broken.   Plants of wet habitats normally have reduced conducting tissues.   The bundle is, further, not markedly different in general structure from the typical bundle of monocotyledons, which is also a much reduced bundle.

A variety of conditions is found in the genus as to the position of the endodermis.   The most common condition is that where the endodermis forms a simple sheath outside the bundles. Other conditions are that where there is also an internal endodermis and the outer endodermis dips in between the bundles, in some cases coming to lie against the inner endodermis in these regions; and that where each bundle is surrounded by an individual endodermal sheath.   The first condition is apparently the most primitive, the last the most specialized.   Evidence for this is derived from comparative studies of stelar structure in the genus and from the structure of the calamites, an ancient group related to the horsetails.

The leaf has a small simple trace, which is derived from an internodal bundle and passes out below the nodal ring (Fig. 68). It leaves no gap.   In the internode above, owing to the alternation of the internodal strands, there is no vascular tissue directly above the leaf trace, and these breaks have been called gaps, but the unbroken nodal ring lies between the trace and the break in the cylinder above.   There are therefore no leaf gaps.

In the cone axis the vascular tissue is less reduced; the metaxylem strands are united to form a more or less nearly complete ring, and the protoxylem lies close against or barely separated from this band.   The axis is more solid, also, because the canals are lacking.   Though the cone bears whorls of sporangiophores, its anatomy does not show intercalary meristems or other evidence of distinct nodes and internodes.

The sporangiophore has a single trace which splits radially in the flattened tip, a branch leading to the base of each sporangium.

Growth of stem and root is originated by a single large apical cell.

GAMETOPHYTE

The gametophytes are green, thalloid, branched structures which grow on wet soil in shaded places.   They are rarely found in the wild, doubtless in part because of their small size (usually only 1 to 10 mm in diameter) and their dull brownish green color, and in part because they are not sought since they can be easily grown in culture.   In *E. debile*, a tropical species,

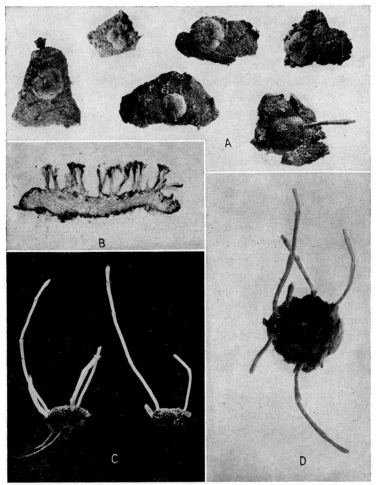

Fig. 70.—Gametophytes of *Equisetum laevigatum*.   *A*, habit, showing plants on mud.   ×1.9.   *B*, vertical section showing cushion and erect lobes.   *C, D,* mature specimens bearing several sporophytes.   (*After Walker.*)

they may be more conspicuous, reaching, when several months old, a diameter of 3 cm and becoming red when in bright light. Mature, well-developed plants of northern species resemble

"green pinheads" and consist of a rounded cushion-like base
with many erect delicate lobes (Fig. 70).   The base has an outer
meristematic rim which increases the diameter of the cushion
radially and gives rise to new erect lobes, to most of the sex
organs, and to rhizoids on the lower surface.   The vertical lobes
are irregular plate-like expanses of photosynthetic tissue, usually

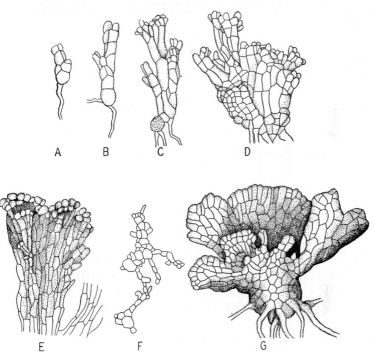

Fig. 71.—Gametophytes of *Equisetum. A* to *F, E. kansanum; G, E. telmateia; A* to *D*, early stages in development; *E*, erect lobe; *F*, cross section of
lobe; *G*, sexually mature stage.   ×36.   (*After Walker.*)

one cell thick (Fig. 71).   The base consists of large-celled tissue,
chiefly without chlorophyll.   Vigorous mature plants always
show the two well-marked regions.   Poorly developed plants—
the result of crowded conditions—are irregularly lobed and
thalloid, without an extended base and with few or no definite
erect photosynthetic lobes.   Such plants are unfortunately
those most commonly seen, since growth in culture produces
chiefly this form.   When given the most favorable growing conditions these plants will, however, develop a meristem and become

like the wild form. The larger plants may live for months, even two years or more, in culture, but the smaller ones soon die. It is evident that the normal form is seen in the wild individuals.

Development. The spores are delicate and remain alive only a few days. Under favorable conditions they germinate at once and a small cell is cut off at one side (Fig. 72). This first division is usually completed in 10 or 12 hours, in some cases even before the spherical shape of the spore is lost. Part of the many prominent chloroplastids are included in this small cell, but these are soon lost and the cell elongates, becoming the first rhizoid. The larger cell develops the body of the gametophyte. The spore wall is usually soon thrown off but may persist for a

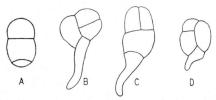

Fig. 72.—Gametophyte of *Equisetum arvense*. First stages in development. (*After Buchtien.*)

short time. The divisions which follow in the larger cell may be in any plane (Fig. 72). Under crowded conditions a short filament may be formed, and from this an elongate, branched thallus. Where the plants have plenty of room the early divisions are longitudinal and oblique, and the thicker type of gametophyte with its massive base develops.

Where the plants develop in the field and are mature they are monoecious, bearing abundant antheridia and archegonia. The gametophytes of *Equisetum* are, however, commonly said to be dioecious, the smaller plants being male, the larger female, the latter in many cases developing antheridia also in age. Such a partial dioecism does occur in the cultivated plants, but this semisegregation of the sexes is due to the unfavorable conditions under which they are grown.

Archegonia. Archegonia arise on normal young gametophytes soon after differentiation into disk and lobes occurs. They appear in the meristematic margin in regions where upright lobes are beginning to develop. The archegonia mature with the lobes

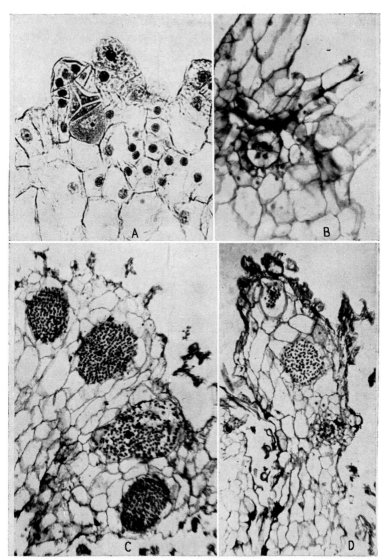

FIG. 73.—Sex organs of *Equisetum.*   *A,* mature archegonium; *B,* archegonium with embryo; *C,* mature antheridia; *D,* mature antheridia and archegonium with embryo.   (*After Walker.*)

and lie at their bases and between them (Fig. 73A, B). As the gametophyte increases in size, the archegonia become numerous and are distributed over the upper part of the thallus. If the first archegonia are fertilized, the gametophyte may cease to grow.

The method of archegonium development is essentially the same as that of the other groups studied. The mature

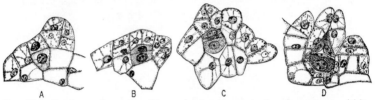

FIG. 74.—*Equisetum hyemale.* Stages in development of archegonium. (*After Jeffrey.*)

archegonium has a base sunken in the thallus and a protruding neck. The neck is short, of about four tiers of cells, with usually three cells in each tier, and the cells of the terminal tier much elongated and divaricate at maturity (Figs. 73A, 74D, 77B). In

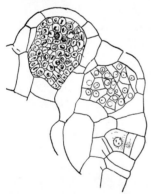

the axial row are the egg, ventral canal cell, and one or two neck canal cells; if the neck canal cells are two they lie side by side and are "boot-shaped" (Figs. 73A, 74D). It is reported that in an Indian species the number of neck canal cells may reach four and that these stand in a row.

Antheridia. After archegonia have formed in the central part of the young gametophyte, antheridia (Figs. 73C,D; 75) develop in large numbers on the marginal region. They occur chiefly on that part of the meristematic zone which is not developing upright lobes and is chlorophyll-free. Rarely they form on the photosynthetic lobes or beside the archegonia. Following antheridial development and a resting period, there is formed, if fertilization has not occurred in the first group of archegonia, a new series of archegonia. These archegonia may form among

FIG. 75.—*Equisetum telmateia.* Stages in development of antheridium. (*After Campbell.*)

the antheridia or only in certain sections of the marginal zone. Therefore, aside from the fact that archegonia appear first on normal plants, there is no definite arrangement of sex organs. On those plants which are dwarfed and on which archegonia will not appear, antheridia develop early, sometimes in considerable numbers on the tips and margins.

The development of the antheridium is similar to that in *Lycopodium.* A superficial cell by periclinal division forms an inner and an outer cell. The inner cell forms a group of spermatogenous cells of variable number, which are covered by a wall layer one cell thick, formed by the outer cell (Fig. 75). The sperms are large and multiciliate (Fig. 76) and are set free at maturity by the breaking down of the outer wall. There are usually 256 in an antheridium, and they are extruded singly through a small opening. It is commonly reported that there are two types of antheridia: the sunken type formed on massive parts of the plant, and a projecting type formed on the margin or apex of a delicate lobe. The latter type is rare or absent in normal gametophytes but is the usual form in dwarf individuals. Though much smaller and with few sperms, it is not

Fig. 76.—*Equisetum arvense.* Sperm. (*After Sharp.*)

essentially different from the sunken type. A terminal or marginal cell cuts off by oblique divisions three basal cells, much as does a tetrahedral apical cell. The terminal cell then divides periclinally, the outer cell forming a wall, the inner the spermatogenous cells. Such a development has been claimed to be like that of the higher ferns and unlike that of the other type in *Equisetum,* because the first division in the initial is not periclinal and the wall consists of very few cells. These differences are, however, apparently only superficial and the result of the fact that the small type is formed on a delicate thallus margin. The early divisions form a base on which the antheridium develops. The original marginal or terminal cell of the thallus is not the antheridial initial; the true initial is formed only after basal cells have been cut off. The other differences are merely those of size.

Embryo

The first division of the zygote is transverse. No suspensor is formed and the entire structure becomes embryo proper. Quadrants when evident are definitely unequal. Of the outer two the larger forms the stem apex, the smaller the leaf. In the lower half the larger forms the root, and the smaller may form a weak foot. In many cases the embryo is divisible definitely into only upper and lower parts (Fig. 77*C,D*); the upper becomes the stem, the lower the root. Whether, as a rule, the first leaf develops from a distinct quadrant or from the side of the stem

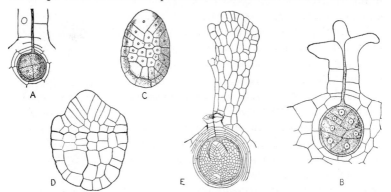

Fig. 77.—*Equisetum.* Development of the embryo. *A, C* to *E, E. arvense;*
B, E. palustre. (*After Sadebeck.*)

segment is not readily determinable. Similarly, whether a true foot is formed is difficult to ascertain. If a foot is present, it is very poorly developed and appears late—after the other parts of the embryo are well formed—as a slight swelling at the base of the root. The stem develops most rapidly; the root is slow in growth but ultimately pushes downward, piercing the gametophyte. The first leaves form a whorl, usually of three (in some cases two or four), all but the first, and in some cases this, being cut off early from the stem apex.

Several archegonia may be fertilized, and the stronger gametophytes may maintain a number of young sporophytes for some time.

Discussion and Summary

The horsetails form a group of vascular plants with unique body habit: the stems are conspicuously jointed, with intercalary meristems; the leaves are small and of the simplest type, in number often many and indefinite, and fused to form sheaths which protect the meristems; the branching is free, primitively, with the branches as numerous as the leaves and alternate with them (in no other major group of "vascular cryptogams" is there a definite and constant relation of leaf and branch, and nowhere else among vascular plants are branches alternate with leaves); the rhizome is a prominent part of the plant, and the roots are few and weak; the vascular tissues are small in amount in proportion to the size of the body; the chief supporting tissues are nonvascular and are confined to the outer cortex, a condition characteristic of many ancient vascular plants.

These plants are further remarkable for the mingling of hydrophytic and xerophytic characters found in their structure. Reduction of the vascular tissues, especially of the xylem, and the presence of intercellular chambers are characteristic of hydrophytes; reduced leaves and photosynthetic stems with sunken stomata, of xerophytes. The habitats of the various species are in accord with this structure: most of them live in moist soil—apparently the ancestral habitat—but some have become adapted to dry locations, though still maintaining an essentially hydrophytic structure.

The genus shows a remarkable series in the specialization of the sporophyte, one of simplification both in vegetative structure and in cone bearing. The primitive stem was apparently richly branched; the highest type is unbranched. The primitive type bore a terminal cone on every branch; the higher types bear cones only on the main axis, and specialization has reached a high degree in the few species in which cones are borne on branches which serve only for this purpose and are ephemeral. Transitional stages occur in both these series.

The cones likewise show a series from the sessile, slightly percrescent type to the stalked, round-tipped form with bract-like annulus.

The most advanced type in the genus has the stems annual; the fertile shoot without branches, without chlorophyll, ephemeral; the cones pedunculate, without a vegetative apex, and with a perianth-like annulus; the leaves few and definite in number.

In type of branching the horsetails are unlike other living plants. In the Lycopodiaceae, Selaginellaceae, Isoetaceae, and in the ferns, branching is fundamentally dichotomous and bears no relation to leaf position; in gymnosperms and angiosperms the branch is borne in the axil of the leaf. In the Equisetaceae the branches occur in large numbers in whorls and alternate in position with the leaves. They leave no gaps (Fig. 68).

In anatomy, as in other features, the horsetails differ greatly from other plants. The many endarch bundles uniting at the node in vascular rings, the hollow pith with nodal diaphragms, the cortical supporting tissue constitute unique gross structure. Endarch xylem is remarkable among lower vascular plants. The weak, obviously reduced bundles, the large protoxylem lacunae, and the intercalary meristems can be matched only in highly specialized groups.

The nature of the sporangiophore has long been the subject of discussion. The sporangiophore has been called a sporophyll, the morphological equivalent of the leaf; the stalk of a raised and divided sporangium; the fertile ventral lobe of a sporophyll whose dorsal sterile lobe has been lost; a lateral determinate branch bearing a whorl of sporangia; an organ *sui generis*. Whether this organ is to be considered leaf or axis in nature, or to represent an independent fundamental organ type is difficult to determine. Evidence has been produced in favor of each view, but the case has not been proved for any one. The morphological nature of the sporangiophore must perhaps remain in doubt for the present, though recent discoveries among ancient fossil plants appear to have solved the problem (Chaps. XVI, XVII).

The position of the sporangia—whether foliar or cauline, marginal or terminal, dorsal or ventral—rests on the nature of the sporangiophore. The sporangium initials are superficial cells which are in a sense marginal on the sporangiophore. Their verticillate arrangement is important in the light of the placing of leaves and branches in whorls. The indefinite number may also be considered noteworthy.

The spores are remarkable for their delicate character, abundant chlorophyll, and elaborate outer wall. It has long been supposed that, though morphologically alike, they are differentiated in function, there being two types, one developing male and one female gametophytes; that is, that *Equisetum*, though structurally homosporous, shows at least a step toward hetero-

spory. That this is not the condition has been shown in recent
years; the spores are undoubtedly all alike in respect to their
capacity for the development under favorable conditions into
monoecious prothallia.

The function of the 'elaters' has been said to be connected with
this supposed "dioecism" of the gametophytes, the entanglement
of the elater arms serving to keep several spores together during
distribution and hence to bring male and female plants together.
It is evident that these structures serve no such function. Since
the prothallia are normally monoecious no such grouping is
necessary to secure fertilization; in fact, the best developed
gametophytes in the wild are solitary. The hygrophytic
behavior of these wall projections may indeed aid in the escape
of the spores from the sporangium, but a clustering of the spores
is merely accidental.

The gametophytes of at least several species, when grown
under favorable conditions and when mature are monoecious.
When crowded, both in the wild and under cultivation, they
tend to be imperfectly dioecious.   First stages in sexual segregation may perhaps exist in this condition.   Closely similar conditions are found in some of the ferns.

The prothallia are dorsiventral with lobes and sex organs on
the upper surface, in this respect differing greatly from those of
the groups already studied, in which the gametophytes are radial,
with lobes, if present, at one end.   The ferns are the only other
group with dorsiventral prothallia, and these have sex organs on
the lower surface or on both surfaces, and lobes marginal or
lacking.

The sex organs are not markedly different from those of other
groups already discussed.   The archegonia have a short neck
with neck canal cells reduced to one or two.   The antheridia
resemble those of the Lycopodiaceae.   There are clearly not, as
commonly stated, two types of antheridia, one sunken, the other
superficial and projecting.   Those considered to be of the latter
type are superficial because of their terminal or marginal position
on delicate lobes.   Only in the Psilotaceae and in the leptosporangiate ferns do the antheridia lie above the body of the
gametophyte; massive sunken antheridia occur in the Lycopodiaceae, the Equisetaceae, and the eusporangiate ferns.

In the embryo there is no evidence of a suspensor, the first division of the fertilized egg separating parts which are fundamentally stem and root. Quadrants may be formed for leaf and foot, but these are doubtfully distinct, especially that for the foot; probably no well-defined foot exists. The first leaves resemble those of the mature plant in their whorled character.

The Equisetaceae stand well apart from other groups in many characters of sporophyte and gametophyte, and form an order the Equisetales which is in important features wholly unlike the orders already described.

COMPARISON OF LYCOPODIACEAE, SELAGINELLACEAE, ISOETACEAE, PSILOTACEAE, AND EQUISETACEAE

When the important characters of the genera thus far described are compared, strong similarities and dissimilarities appear (Table 1). The latter are outstanding, and the group is, even on the surface, a heterogeneous one.

SPOROPHYTE

In habit the various genera are herbaceous or subshrubby perennials; otherwise they have little in common except high specialization. In body structure *Psilotum* and *Tmesipteris* stand farthest apart in a lack of differentiation of the body into stem, leaf, and root. Among the genera with elaborated body, *Equisetum* differs outstandingly. Its branches are whorled; branching in the others (including that of the axis in the Psilotaceae) is dichotomous. Its leaves are also whorled; those of the others are fundamentally spiral. Its branches arise between the leaves, a condition found in no other living vascular plants. From the standpoint of general body structure there are therefore three groups among these families, and the differences between them are strong.

The leaves of all genera are alike in their simplicity of form and venation and in their single, gapless traces. They are mostly very small. The presence of a ligule (setting apart two genera) seems to provide an important difference.

In anatomy *Equisetum* again stands apart in its complex stele and its endarch xylem. Two or three genera show possible vestiges of secondary growth, but the presence or absence of secondary vascular tissue is of no importance from a phylogenetic standpoint.

The position of the sporangia accentuates the separation of the Psilotaceae and the Equisetaceae from the others and from each other. In the former the sporangium is terminal on the axis; it is also massive and chambered, with heavy walls. In the latter the sporangia are borne on sporangiophores—organs which at this point cannot readily be interpreted in terms of axis, stem, and leaf—and have delicate walls. The sporangia of the other genera are foliar, or, if cauline, are not a major part of the stem but are lateral structures borne in association with leaves.

The sporangium wall of the Psilotaceae is many-layered. Under the interpretation of the sporangium as the end of the axis, the cortex-like structure of the wall is understandable. The sporangium is of a crude, primitive type; it is still an axis tip, very little modified. Its lack of elaboration is borne out by the absence of a tapetum. These sporangium characters greatly emphasize the isolation of the Psilotaceae and reinforce those characters of body habit which speak for primitiveness.

Sporangium position, on the leaf base or on the stem near by, unites the Lycopodiaceae, Selaginellaceae, and Isoetaceae as against the other two families.

Tapetal characters not only set off the Psilotaceae but break the other genera into two groups: *Equisetum*, where the tapetum is irregular and indefinite in limit; and the other genera which have a simple uniseriate layer. *Equisetum* thus again stands by itself.

Heterospory sets *Selaginella* and *Isoetes* away from the other genera, but the possession of this feature is not evidence of relationship as will be more clear after the other groups have been considered.

GAMETOPHYTE

In the gametophyte are characters which further emphasize the prominent differences between (1) the Equisetaceae and (2) the Psilotaceae and the other groups. The dorsiventral gametophyte of the first family with its erect lobes is unlike that of any other plants. All other genera in the group under consideration

TABLE 1.—Summary of Important Characters of the Lycopodiaceae, Selaginellaceae, Isoetaceae, Psilotaceae, and Equisetaceae

	Lycopodium	Phylloglossum	Selaginella	Isoetes	Psilotum	Tmesipteris	Equisetum
Number of species	100±	1	500±	60+ (100?)	2 (+?)	1 (2+?)	25±
Type of plant	Herbaceous perennials with specialized habit; determinate branch systems	Herbaceous perennial with specialized habit (tuber)	Herbaceous perennials or annuals; determinate branch systems	Herbaceous perennials with highly specialized ("corm") habit	Herbaceous rootless perennials	As in Psilotum	Herbaceous perennials, rhizomatous
Branching	Dichotomous	(Sparse); dichotomous	Dichotomous	(Rare); dichotomous	Dichotomous	(Rare); dichotomous	Free, whorled, alternate with leaves
Leaves and leaf arrangement	Small, simple; irregular, spiral, or decussate	Small, simple; spiral (?)	Small, simple; spiral, or 4-rowed	Simple, spiral	Axis not differentiated into stem, leaf, and root	As in Psilotum	Small, simple; fused whorled
Ligule	None	None	Present	Present	....	....	None
Stele	Protostele (complex)	Siphonostele (typically)	Protostele	Protostele	Rhizome protostelic; aerial stem siphonostelic	Rhizome protostelic; aerial stem dictyostelic	Dissected siphonostele with nodal rings
Xylem	Exarch	Mesarch	Exarch	Exarch	Exarch (mesarch)	Mesarch	Endarch
Secondary growth	No secondary growth	No secondary growth	No secondary growth (vestiges?)	Anomalous secondary growth	No secondary growth	No secondary growth	No secondary growth (vestiges?)
Traces and gaps	Leaf trace small, simple	Leaf trace small, simple; no gap	Leaf trace small, simple	Leaf trace small, simple	....	....	Leaf trace small, simple, no gap
Strobilus	Present (in part of genus)	Present	Present	Present (?)	....	....	Present
Sporophylls	Like leaves, or different in size, form, color	Unlike leaves	Like or unlike leaves	Every leaf a sporophyll	....	....	Sporangiophores
Sporangia	Foliar (ventral) axillary. Homosporous	Foliar (ventral), axillary, or cauline. Homosporous	Axillary or cauline. Heterosporous	Foliar (ventral); semi-chambered. Heterosporous	Cauline, terminal, massive, 3-chambered. Homosporous	Cauline, terminal, massive, 2-chambered. Homosporous	Suspended on sporangiophores. Homosporous
Tapetum	1 layer, well defined	....	1 layer, well defined	1 layer, well defined	None	None	Irregular, several layers
Spores	Numerous, small	Similar to those of *Lycopodium*	Megaspores 4, large; microspores several hundred, minute	Megaspores 150–300, large; microspores 150,000–1,000,000	Numerous, small, bilateral	As in *Psilotum*	Numerous, small, spherical, green, with "elaters"

Prothallia	Monoecious; tuberous; green or nongreen; mycorrhizal; on surface or subterranean — Radial, short	Monoecious; tuberous; green; on surface — Radial, short	Dioecious, greatly reduced; no chlorophyll. *Male:* Wholly within spore wall; 1 vegetative cell, and 1 antheridium. *Female:* Largely within spore wall; protruding cushion with rhizoids and archegonia — ……	Dioecious; greatly reduced; no chlorophyll. *Male:* Wholly within spore wall; 1 vegetative cell and 1 antheridium. *Female:* Within spore wall; cushion with rhizoids and archegonia — ……	Monoecious; cylindrical, dichotomous; subterranean, mycorrhizal; no differentiation into vegetative and reproductive regions — Radial; elongate; dichotomous	As in *Psilotum* — As in *Psilotum*	Monoecious; cushion-like, with erect photosynthetic lobes — Dorsiventral
Sex organs	On "crown" or upper side	On "crown"	……	……	On all sides	On all sides	On upper side
Antheridia	Many; variable in size and number of sperms; sunken	Similar to those of *Lycopodium*	1; filling most of spore cavity	1; filling most of spore cavity	Many; globose, projecting	As in *Psilotum*	Many; sunken
Sperms	Many; biciliate	……	Many; biciliate	4; multiciliate	Many; multiciliate	Many; multiciliate	Many; multiciliate
Archegonia	Numerous; sunken; neck long, projecting, of several tiers	……	Several to many; sunken; neck very short, hardly projecting, of 2 tiers	Several to many; sunken; neck short, not projecting, of 4 tiers	Many; scattered, sunken; neck of 4–6 tiers, projecting, deciduous	Much as in *Psilotum*	Many; at base of lobes, sunken; neck of 4 tiers
Neck canal cells	5–10 or more; 1(2)?	……	1	1	(1?) 2	(1?) 2	2(4?)
First division of zygote	Transverse; outer cell suspensor, inner embryonic	……	Transverse; outer cell suspensor, inner embryonic	Transverse	……	Transverse	Transverse
Suspensor	Weakly developed, nonfunctional	……	Well developed but variable; not always limited by first division	None	None	None	None
Quadrants	Outer 2 become foot, inner 2 leaf and stem; root late from leaf segment	……	No definite quadrants; embryonic cell forms stem and 2 leaf apices; later, weak foot and first root	Sometimes recognizable; 2 outer form foot; 2 inner first leaf and first root	……	2 outer form axis; 2 inner large foot	2 outer form stem and leaf; 2 inner root and (?) foot

have radial (cylindrical) prothallia. (The gametophytes of the heterosporous genera have been so reduced that their original form cannot be determined.) The type and position of the sex organs divide those forms with radial prothallia. The gametophytes of the Lycopodiaceae have the sex organs restricted to one end; those of the Psilotaceae show no division into vegetative and reproductive regions. The antheridia of the latter family are wholly unlike those of the other monoecious groups. The archegonia show no fundamental differences among the families, but the deciduous necks of the Psilotaceae are a feature found nowhere else.

EMBRYO

In embryogeny no two families are alike, and no one is outstandingly different. All are alike in the position of the first wall in the zygote, an important character. The presence and extent of development of the suspensor are variable. Definite quadrants may be present, but the primary organs bear no uniform relation to them.

When the important differences are considered, it is evident that there are three major groups among these families—groups which from the evidence of living forms show little or no apparent relation to one another. On this basis the following classification is made:

Psilopsida............................ Psilotaceae

Lycopsida............................ {Lycopodiaceae
Selaginellaceae
Isoetaceae

Sphenopsida......................... Equisetaceae

The groups themselves and the basis for the classification will be better understood when the fossil members have been considered. From the study of living forms it is clear, however, that each of the three groups stands by itself. The three families of the Lycopsida show similarities which hold them together when compared with the other families, but among themselves they differ so much that no two can well be united to form an order.

The Lycopodiaceae and Selaginellaceae are alike in many features of general structure, external and internal, including sperms of a type extraordinary for vascular plants. The Selaginellaceae and the Isoetaceae are alike in the presence of a ligule and of heterospory but differ in their sperms.   Heterospory cannot be considered significant, and the presence of a ligule can hardly offset the difference in sperms.   Although in the Isoetaceae reduction is so great that general body structure can mean little when compared with that of the other families, the presence of a permanent 'root' system suggests a greater gap between the Isoetaceae and the Selaginellaceae than between the latter family and the Lycopodiaceae.   The remarkable dissimilarities in sperms bear out this difference.

The five families under discussion constitute the group of plants commonly known as "the fern allies."   That they are a markedly heterogeneous group, of three main subgroups, with little in common other than those characters formerly used in classifications which grouped them with the ferns as "vascular cryptogams" is evident; that they really have little of fundamental structure in common with ferns will be shown later.

Bibliography

BARRATT, K.: A contribution to our knowledge of the vascular system of the genus *Equisetum, Ann. Bot.,* **34**: 201–235, 1920.

BOWER, F. O.: Studies in the morphology of spore-producing members: Equisetineae and Lycopodineae, *Phil. Trans. Roy. Soc. London,* **185B**: 473–572, 1894.

BROWNE, I.: The phylogeny and inter-relationship of the Pteridophyta.   II. Equisetales, *New Phyt.,* **7**: 103–113, 1908.

DRACINSCHI, M.: Über das reife Spermium von *Equisetum, Bul. Fac. de Ştiinţe din Cernăuti,* **5**: 84–95, 1931.

HANNIG, E.: Über die Bedeutung der Periplasmodien, *Flora,* **102**: 209–242. 1911.

JEFFREY, E. C.: The development, structure, and affinities of the genus *Equisetum, Mem. Boston Soc. Nat. Hist.,* **5**: 155–190, 1899.

JOHNSON, M. A.: Origin and development of tissues in *Equisetum scirpoides, Bot. Gaz.,* **94**: 469–494, 1933.

KASHYAP-SHIV, R.: Structure and development of the prothallus of *Equisetum debile* Roxb., *Ann. Bot.,* **28**: 163–181, 1914.

MEYER, F. J.: Das Leitungssystem von *Equisetum arvense, Jahrb. wiss. Bot.,* **59**: 263–286, 1920.

PHATAK, V. G.: Recherches sur une espèce d'*Equisetum* rencontrée dans la Présidence de Bombay (Dekkan).   *Thesis.*   Montpellier, 1935.

SADEBECK, R.: Entwicklung des Keimes der Schachtelhalme, *Jahrb. wiss. Bot.,* **11**: 575–602, 1878.

SCHAFFNER, J. H.: Geographic distribution of the species of *Equisetum* in relation to their phylogeny, *Amer. Fern Jour.,* **20**: 89–106, 1930.

SCHRATZ, E.: Untersuchungen über die Geschlechterverteilung bei *Equisetum arvense, Biol. Zentralbl.*, **48**: 617–639, 1928.

SHARP, L. W.: Spermatogenesis in *Equisetum, Bot. Gaz.*, **54**: 89–118, 1912.

WALKER, E. R.: The gametophytes of *Equisetum laevigatum, Bot. Gaz.*, **71**: 378–391, 1921.

————: The gametophytes of three species of *Equisetum, Bot. Gaz.*, **92**: 1–22, 1931.

CHAPTER VI

FILICINEAE   FERNS

Ferns are well known; their large leaves, commonly called "fronds," conspicuous in their feathery form and delicate nature, set them apart from other plants. They are, further, common over most of the earth and are freely cultivated as ornamental plants. The group is large—about 175 genera and nearly 8000 species—and most varied, ranging widely in habit, in leaf form, and in reproductive structures. It is, moreover, not homogeneous but is made up of distinct subgroups, which, though all "ferns" in a broad sense, are sharply set off from one another and obviously not closely related. There are three major groups: the Ophioglossales, adder's-tongue ferns; the Marattiales, marattiaceous ferns; and the Filicales, "true ferns," or leptosporangiate ferns. The Hydropteridales, water ferns, have been commonly set apart as another distinct group; but these unusual ferns are now recognized as extreme forms of the last group and therefore do not constitute a distinct and major group. The first two groups are small, and each consists of a single family; the third is large and made up of several families. Because of important differences in structure and life history the first two groups and the more important families of the third are considered separately. The group of ferns as a whole is discussed further in Chap. XIII.

OPHIOGLOSSACEAE   ADDER'S-TONGUE FERNS

The adder's-tongue ferns form a small group, in many ways unlike other ferns. There are only three genera: *Ophioglossum* (Fig. 78); *Botrychium*, grape ferns, moonworts (Fig. 78); and *Helminthostachys* (Fig. 79); with about 60 species divided nearly equally between the first two genera, the third being monotypic. All are perennial herbs of small or moderate size, some of them evergreen, living in forests and open places in tropical and

117

temperate climates. Two tropical species of *Ophioglossum* are epiphytes. As a group these ferns are more or less fleshy in all parts, and many of them are xerophytic. *Botrychium* and *Ophioglossum* are widely distributed over the earth; *Helmintho-stachys* is restricted to the Indo-Malayan region.

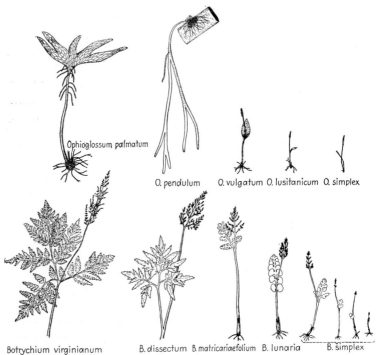

Fig. 78.—Ophioglossaceae. Habit sketches, showing reduction series in two genera. (*Ophioglossum palmatum* and *O. pendulum* after Bitter in Engler and Prantl; *O. vulgatum* and *O. lusitanicum* after Wettstein; *O. simplex* after Bower; *Botrychium Lunaria* and *B. simplex* in part after Luerssen.)

SPOROPHYTE

Habit. A short erect rhizome is characteristic of the group. In *Helminthostachys* the stem, though erect in the young plant, soon becomes horizontal; also in *Ophioglossum pendulum*, an epiphytic species, the rhizome is not erect. True branching, which is dichotomous, is rare. At the top of the rhizome is borne a succession of leaves, in most species only one being formed in a growing season; hence, since the leaves, at least in temperate regions, do not usually live more than a year, a single leaf commonly represents the plant as seen above the ground.   When the plant is fruiting, the large yellow sporangia borne on special leaf parts are conspicuous.   In some species even very small, young individuals fruit.   The largest member of the group is the epiphyte *O. pendulum,* whose linear leaves are commonly 1.5 m long and are reported to reach 2.7 m.   This is probably the only species which is cultivated; it is occasionally grown in gardens and about houses in the tropics because of its ornamental, pendent, snake-like leaves.   The name adder's-tongue ferns, given because of the resemblance of the fertile leaf segment of *Ophioglossum* to a snake's tongue, is particularly appropriate when applied to this species.   The smallest species in the family are only a few centimeters high and inconspicuous. In these the rhizome is very short, hardly more than a plate, and the leaves are small with the sterile lobe greatly reduced or lacking (Fig. 78).

Leaves. The leaf, which is never large as compared with that of ferns in general, shows great variety in form and structure.   It is, however, always divided into an adaxial (or ventral) fertile segment and an abaxial (or dorsal) sterile segment.   The leaves of *Ophioglossum* are simple or lobed, sometimes dichotomously forked; those of *Botrychium,* though in some small species simple, are typically pinnately compound or decompound, with a definitely fern-like aspect; those of *Helminthostachys* are ternately compound.   The first genus has reticulate venation; the other two open dichotomous venation.   The family as a whole is glabrous, but one species of *Botrychium* and the buds of some others have short simple hairs.

The phyllotaxy is spiral except in *Helminthostachys,* where the leaves are in two rows on the dorsiventral rhizome.

At the base of the leaf are thin, sheathing 'stipules.'   These enclose the bud so that each unfolding leaf breaks through the stipular sheath of the preceding leaf.   After the leaf has decayed the remains of the sheaths persist about the bud.   The leaf may take up to five years to develop—three or four years in the bud with expansion in the fourth or fifth season; the bud, therefore, contains the developing leaves of the next few seasons.   Slow growth in early stages is characteristic of the leaf of this group in contrast with the condition in other ferns. In its vernation also, which is not circinate, the leaf differs markedly from that of other ferns.

In the axils of the leaves are dormant buds which develop only when the apical bud is destroyed. This condition is similar to that in species of *Equisetum*, and suggests that these forms, like the unbranched horsetails, are not fundamentally unbranched plants but have been derived from branching types.

Roots. The roots are thick and fleshy and prominently mycorrhizal. They are usually simple, though in some cases branched sparsely, in either a monopodial or dichotomous fashion, and do not become extensive. They have no root hairs. Apparently in most cases there arises on the rhizome below each leaf a single root; hence, though the roots persist for several years, there are rarely more than a few.

Reproduction. *Fertile Segment or "Spike."* The fertile segment is simple and linear in *Ophioglossum* (Figs. 78, 79*A*) and pinnately compound or decompound in *Botrychium* (Figs. 78, 79*C*). In *Helminthostachys* an elongate main axis bears numerous short fertile lobes ("sporangiophores") (Fig. 79*F,G*). Such a structure suggests a spike, as does also the fertile segment of *Ophioglossum;* hence the term *fertile spike* has come to be applied in the genus as a whole. The term is, however, unsatisfactory. In *Botrychium* the subdivisions of the segment are arranged in normal fern-like fashion, pinnately in one plane (Figs. 78, 79*C*); in *Helminthostachys* they stand close in poorly defined rows on the margins (Fig. 79*F,G*). Until the spores are mature these fertile segments are green, but there is no lamina except the minute terminal lobes of *Helminthostachys* and *Ophioglossum*. The fertile segment is usually attached in the central or upper part of the leaf, but in some species of *Botrychium* it is so low down as to appear to arise from the rhizome.

Nearly all leaves of mature flourishing plants bear fertile segments; in some species very young plants are fertile, the first leaf to appear above ground bearing sporangia, and even the earlier, reduced, subterranean leaves show abortive fertile segments. Plants are sometimes found fruiting while still attached to the gametophyte. After the spores have been shed, the fertile segment (in some species) shrivels and the leaf in its later stages may therefore appear not to have been fertile.

Sporangia.   The sporangia are large (0.5 to 3.0 mm in diameter), with a massive wall: spherical and borne on short thick stalks in *Botrychium* (Fig. 79*C* to *E*); ovoid and sessile, or nearly so, in *Helminthostachys* (Fig. 79*G*); subspherical and fused with the leaf in *Ophioglossum* (Fig. 79*B*).   They stand in marginal rows except in the second genus where they are clustered and

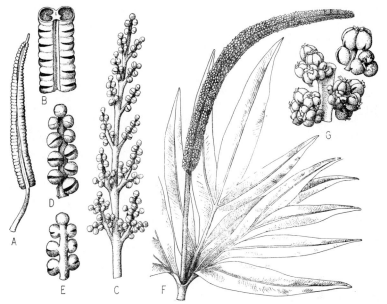

FIG. 79.—Ophioglossaceae. *A, B, Ophioglossum palmatum,* fertile spike and portion of spike; *C* to *E, Botrychium Lunaria,* fertile spike and portion of spike from ventral and dorsal sides; *F, G, Helminthostachys zeylanica,* top of leaf and part of fertile spike enlarged. (*A to C, E after Bitter in Engler and Prantl; D, after Luerssen; F, after Hooker; G, after Bauer.*)

somewhat irregularly arranged.   In *Botrychium* the fertile segment and its branches have not only marginal but terminal sporangia.   In *Ophioglossum* the sporangia are said to be sunken in the leaf tissue or to be fused in a synangium along the leaf margin.   The sporangia of the three genera seem at first sight to be borne in different ways.   The short fertile lobes of *Helmintho-stachys* appear, however, to represent contracted leaf segments; their compound nature is evident and the clustering is therefore false, and the sporangia are undoubtedly marginal as in the other genera.   In *Ophioglossum* the fertile segment and the two marginal rows of sporangia are intimately fused. Terminal sporangia occur only in *Botrychium*.

The sporangium is eusporangiate. Although a single initial plays a prominent part in the development—the sporogenous tissue and the central section of the wall being formed by this cell—the products of adjacent initials enter into the mature sporangium, forming the sides of the massive wall and the stalk (Fig. 80). Development is much as in other eusporangiate types. The first (periclinal) division of the central initial separates an outer cell (Fig. 80*A*, already divided periclinally),

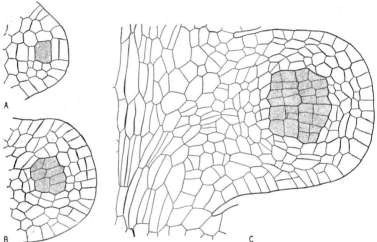

Fig. 80.—*Botrychium daucifolium.* Stages in development of sporangium. (*After Bower.*)

which forms walls only, from an inner cell which develops the sporogenous tissue. But this first division does not always sharply limit these regions, as shown in Fig. 80*B,C*; the sporogenous tissue may be added to from segments derived from the outer cell.

In early stages of ontogeny the sporangium closely resembles the leaf segments and even the stem tip; the similarity is carried further in the presence of stomata on the stalk and side walls of the sporangium.

An ill-defined tapetum of several layers and of variable thickness is formed from cells surrounding the sporogenous tissue. This disorganizes as usual, its cytoplasm forming a fluid in which

the sporocytes float.   Spores are formed by all of the sporocytes.
Dehiscence is by a long slit (Fig. 79B,D,G), which forms through
a region of somewhat smaller and weaker cells.   This slit is
called "terminal" in *Botrychium,* "lateral" in *Ophioglossum,*
and "longitudinal" in *Helminthostachys,* but it is clearly in the
same position—terminal—in all; the opening in *Ophioglossum* is
lateral only to the fertile segment; in *Helminthostachys* the
sporangia are turned backward toward the main axis in the
contraction of the segment.   There is no special opening apparatus of unequally thickened cells—an annulus—as in the true
ferns.   When mature the sporangia become yellow or brown.

Spores.   The spores are borne in very large numbers, from
1500 to 15,000 in each sporangium.   They are tetrahedral in
origin but become subspherical with triradiate markings.   The
wall is thick and sculptured with pits or irregular tuberculate
projections.   In mass the spores, which are nearly colorless,
appear pale yellow.   In a few species pale chloroplasts are
present.

Vegetative Propagation.   In some species of *Ophioglossum,* for
example, *O. vulgatum,* buds arise on the roots and in this manner
large colonies may be formed.   In the other genera there is
apparently no vegetative propagation.

Anatomy.   The plant body is soft and somewhat fleshy
throughout, with no sclerenchymatous tissue such as is characteristic of true ferns.   Hard outer layers are lacking, and the
vascular bundles are of simple structure without accompanying
sheaths of specialized tissue.   For these reasons the veins of
the leaves are in most cases not visible externally.

In *Botrychium, Helminthostachys,* and some species of *Ophioglossum* the young plant is protostelic, but a prominent pith is
soon developed.   This pith is at first mixed—that is, it contains
tracheids scattered among the pith cells—and its structure
suggests that the pith in this group is intrastelar in origin.   The
leaf traces are large single strands and form prominent gaps
in the stele.   In part of the genus *Ophioglossum* the stele is
complex, being broken up into many strands; in these forms the
leaf trace is also complex, consisting of several bundles.   The
xylem is mesarch in *Helminthostachys* and endarch in the other
genera.   In *Botrychium* weak cambial activity slowly builds
up a thin cylinder of secondary tissues (Fig. 81).   The tracheids

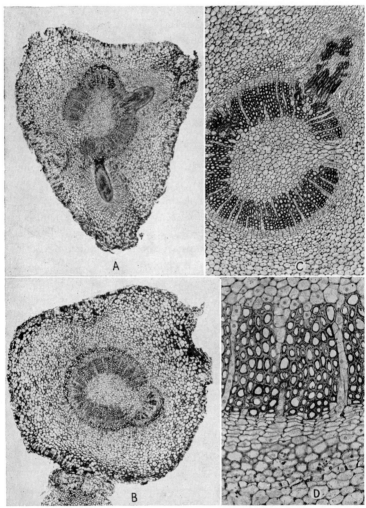

Fig. 81.—*Botrychium virginianum.* Cross sections of rhizome. *A*, showing root traces departing (at right and below), leaf trace departing (above), and leaf gap (at left); *B*, showing leaf trace departing (at right) and forming gap; *C*, central cylinder enlarged showing secondary vascular tissues with root trace departing (above) and leaf gap (at right); *D*, portion of vascular cylinder enlarged to show secondary vascular tissues and cambium. (*After Wright.*)

are in general unlike those of other ferns.   Those of *Helmintho-stachys* and *Botrychium* have pits with round or oval outline, round aperture, a broad border, and a definite torus; those of *Ophioglossum* are scalariform with narrow-bordered, torus-less pits.

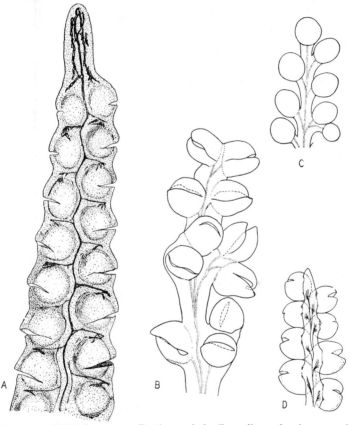

FIG. 82.—Ophioglossaceae. Portions of fertile spikes, showing vascular supply to sporangia.   *A, Ophioglossum pedunculosum; B, Botrychium simplex; C, B. virginianum; D, B. dissectum.   (A, B, D after Goebel.)*

An external endodermis is present in most forms, and in some there is also an internal one.   In *Botrychium* internal phloem may be present in older plants.

In *Botrychium* and *Ophioglossum* vascular strands extend to the base of the sporangium.   In *Botrychium* the vascular tissue of the segment ends close below the sporangium (Fig. 82 *B* to *D*). In *Ophioglossum* lateral vascular strands extend between the sporangia, but their tips turn at right angles and lead to the sporangia (Fig. 82*A*).   In no other ferns are sporangia supplied with vascular tissue.

The anatomy of the fertile leaf segment in *Botrychium* is of especial interest since it provides the best evidence of the nature of this structure.   From the more or less crescent-shaped bundle of the leaf axis (Fig. 83, 1) there is cut off on each side just below the fertile segment a small bundle (Fig. 83, 5, 6).   These two lateral bundles (Fig. 83, 7, 8) turn upward and pass together up

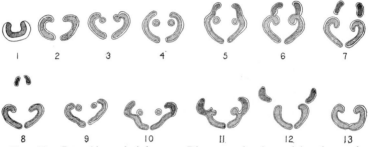

FIG. 83.—*Botrychium virginianum.*   Diagrams showing origin of vascular supply of fertile spike and of first pair of vegetative pinnae; successive sections in acropetal order.   Petiole oriented with adaxial side upward; xylem shaded, phloem clear.   5 to 8, the formation and departure of the two traces to the fertile spike; 10 to 12 the formation and departure of the traces to the pair of pinnae directly above the fertile spike, one trace to each pinna.   (*Modified, after Chrysler.*)

the stalk of the fertile segment, each supplying the lobes and sporangia of one side.   At the successive pairs of sterile pinnae above the fertile segment, two lateral strands are formed in the same manner (Fig. 83, 10 to 12) and one supplies each pinna. Frequently in some species the fertile segment is double with its halves separate or partly fused; in such cases each bundle supplies one half.   From the anatomical structure it is apparent that the fertile segment consists of a pair of pinnae raised erect and fused. The leaf, therefore, is not divided into ventral and dorsal segments; such a division apparently exists because of the raising of a part of the horizontal leaf into the vertical plane.   Closely similar conditions exist in other ferns, especially in *Anemia* (Fig. 123) where only the fusion of the two raised pinnae is lacking to complete the similarity of the fertile segments to that of *Botrychium.*

In the other genera the vascular structure of the fertile segment is more complex, and it is evident that this condition is derived and specialized. This conclusion is in line with other evidence that *Botrychium* is the primitive genus, and that the 'spikes' of *Helminthostachys* and *Ophioglossum* are reduced from the more leaf-like type of *Botrychium.*

The roots, which are fleshy and mycorrhizal, are in most cases monarch or diarch but may have several strands of xylem and phloem.

GAMETOPHYTE

The prothallia of all the genera are subterranean, fleshy, mycorrhizal structures resembling in many ways those of *Lycopodium.* They are pale in color, gray, yellowish, or brownish. In some species they may be densely covered with rhizoids, in others smooth or papillose. Rhizoid-bearing types apparently may become smooth in age. In *Ophioglossum* there are apparently no rhizoids at any stage. Though usually found several centimeters below the surface, they may develop above ground; when growing thus in light, small amounts of chlorophyll may be formed.

In *Botrychium* the mature gametophyte is a short-cylindrical, ovoid, or flattened tuber, in the various species ranging from 1 or 2 mm to 10 and 20 mm in length. Those of *B. virginianum* (Figs. 84, 86*J,K*) are among the largest and are apparently frequent where the plant occurs. Careful search will usually result in the finding of them as well as those of other species. In *B. dissectum* (Fig. 85) the prothallia are mostly smaller and flattened, resembling in form a kernel of maize. (Some reach a size of 6 to 8 by 14 to 18 mm.) Such gametophytes, when without young sporophytes, can be separated on general appearance from young prothallia of *Lycopodium clavatum* and *L. obscurum* only with difficulty. In *Helminthostachys* the sexual plant is more complex in form, consisting of a short, erect, cylindrical body which is irregularly lobed below (Fig. 86*G*).

In *Ophioglossum*, where the prothallia range from ovoid to linear and stellate (Fig. 86*C* to *F*), the cylindrical form is outstanding. In *O. vulgatum* the slender, elongate, rarely branching gametophyte may attain a length of 6 cm, and much resembles pieces of the root. In *O. pendulum* there may be free branching in several directions (Fig. 86*F*). Apical growth appears to be continued almost indefinitely, and it has been concluded from

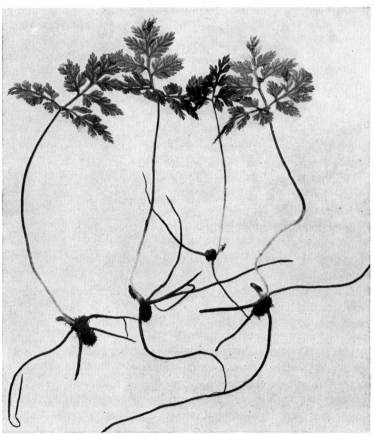

Fig. 84.—*Botrychium virginianum.* Gametophytes with young sporophytes. Natural size.

observations on its rate that the prothallia may live for 20 years or longer. In *Botrychium* the gametophytes in many cases live for several years after embryos form, meanwhile increasing in size. The prothallia of *Helminthostachys*, on the other hand, are apparently short-lived, possibly annual.

The branching is dichotomous or irregular (Fig. 86C,F,G). In some species adventitious buds appear in abundance; these are set free, and the branches may also break away, so that vegetative propagation apparently occurs freely.

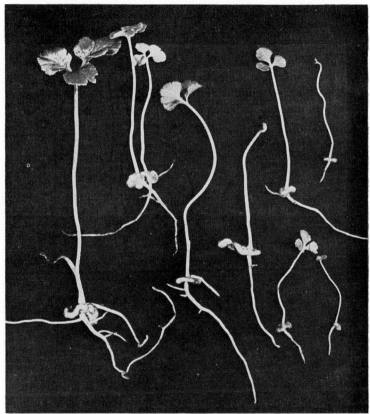

Fig. 85.—*Botrychium dissectum.* Gametophytes with young sporophytes. Natural size. (*Botrychium dissectum* Spreng., a valid older name, = *B. obliquum* Muhl.)

As in underground gametophytes generally, an endophytic fungus is prominent, occupying chiefly the inner layers.

Development. Little is known about the early stages of gametophyte development in this group. Spore germination in *Ophioglossum* may take place in a few days, be delayed for a month or more, or even for one, two, or more years, the different species varying greatly in this respect. The spore contents enlarge, and the wall bursts along the triradiate ridge. The first division is transverse; the next is vertical in the basal cell. Few

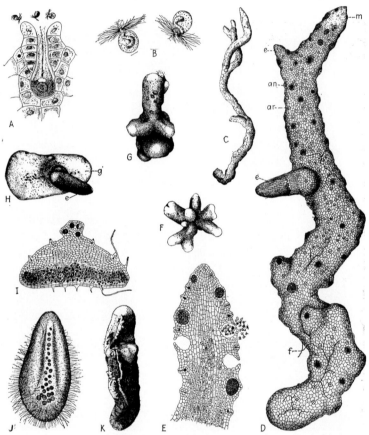

Fig. 86.—Gametophytes of the Ophioglossaceae. *A* to *E*, *Ophioglossum vulgatum; F*, *O. pendulum; G*, *Helminthostachys zeylanica; H* to *K*, *Botrychium virginianum. A*, mature archegonium with sperms; *B*, sperms; *C, D, F*, to *H*, *J, K*, mature prothallia; *E, I*, longitudinal and cross sections of prothallia, respectively; *an*, antheridium; *ar*, archegonium; *e*, embryo; *f*, fungus hypha; *m*, meristem. (*A* to *E*, *after Bruchmann; F, G, after Lang; H to K, after Jeffrey.*)

other stages have been observed, and the method of develop-ment beyond this is insufficiently known. Growth in culture beyond the three-cell stage is difficult, and it has been claimed that only infection by the mycorrhiza-forming fungus enables the plant to continue growth.   It is apparent that growth in early stages, as in later ones, is slow.

Sex Organs.   The sex organs are numerous and scattered, in the case of the cylindrical types usually over the entire surface (Fig. 86*D*); in the flattened species, on the upper surface (Fig. 86*H* to *J*).   The gametophytes of *Botrychium* are monoecious; those of the other genera in most cases also bear both types of

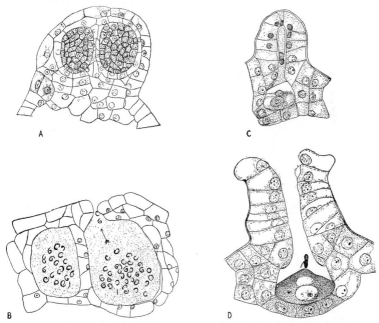

Fig. 87.—*Botrychium virginianum.*   *A*, 3 antheridia showing stages in development; *B*, mature antheridia with sperms swimming in a gelatinous fluid; *C*, mature archegonium; *D*, archegonium open for fertilization, with sperm.   (*After Jeffrey.*)

sex organs, but poorly developed individuals apparently may have antheridia only.

Antheridia.   The antheridia are much like those of *Lycopodium* and *Equisetum.*   They are large, sunken or slightly projecting (Figs. 86*D,E*; 87*A,B*) and contain many multiciliate sperms (Fig. 86*B*) which resemble those of true ferns.   Their development is also much as in the above-named genera.   The outer wall is one or two cells thick in *Botrychium.*

Archegonia. The archegonia are of the usual type in structure and origin. The neck projects strongly in *Botrychium*, having seven or eight tiers of cells (Fig. 87*C,D*) but is somewhat shorter in the other genera, and sunken (Fig. 86*A,E*). The ventral canal cell is inconspicuous and apparently disintegrates early, and the one neck canal cell has two nuclei.

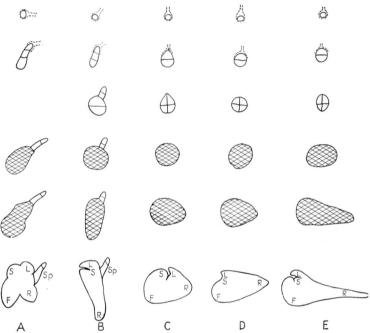

Fig. 88.—Embryogeny of the Ophioglossaceae. *A, Helminthostachys zeylanica; B, Botrychium dissectum; C, B. virginianum; D, B. Lunaria; E, Ophioglossum vulgatum. F,* foot; *L,* leaf; *R,* root; *S,* stem; *Sp,* suspensor. *(A, based on Lang; B, on Lyon; C, on Jeffrey; D, E, on Bruchmann.)*

EMBRYO

There are two types of embryogeny in the group: in *Helminthostachys* and the species of one section of the genus *Botrychium* there is a suspensor; all other forms whose embryogeny is known lack this structure. In all cases, however, the first division is transverse to the long axis of the archegonium.

In the first type (Fig. 88, cols. *A, B*) the fertilized egg enlarges downward, and transverse divisions form a row of two or three

cells, the lowermost cell becoming the embryo proper.   In this
cell transverse division again separates outer and inner parts.
Although this division apparently does not sharply limit regions
from which the four primary organs arise, the inner cell usually
develops the foot and the outer the stem and leaf.   The root
arises from near the center, but from which segment it is difficult

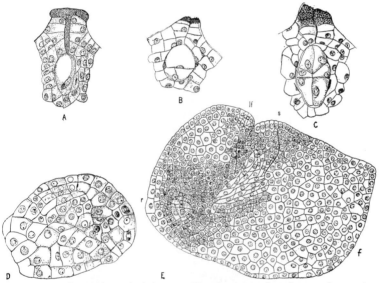

Fig. 89.—*Botrychium virginianum.*   Development of embryo.   *A*, zygote;
B, first division in embryo; *C* to *E*, later stages; *f*, foot; *lf*, first leaf; *r*, root; *s*,
stem.   (*After Jeffrey.*)

to determine.   The embryogeny of these forms is still incompletely known.

In the other type (Fig. 88, cols. *C* to *E*) the fertilized egg does
not become greatly elongated.   The first division is transverse
or nearly so (Fig. 89*B*).   The two cells so formed are then
divided vertically (Fig. 89*C*) and the outer four next transversely.
Divisions are then irregular, and definite segments, if formed, are
difficult to distinguish.   (In *Ophioglossum*, at least, a tracing of
the organs to definite segments has been found impossible.)
The cells of the inner half apparently all enter into the formation
of a foot.   From the outer half come root, stem, and leaf
(Fig. 89*E*).   In both genera the organs are slow in developing,
the root being distinguishable first and forming the most con-

spicuous part of the young sporophyte. In *Ophioglossum,* development of stem and leaf may be so long delayed that a root more than 1 cm long may be formed before there is evidence of the other organs, and the second root may be well developed before the first leaf appears outside the gametophyte. The first leaf in some forms seems to arise from the young stem and not

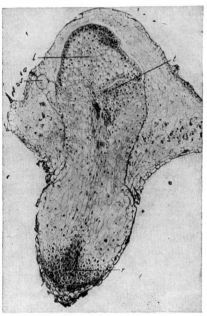

Fig. 90.—*Botrychium dissectum* ("*Sceptridium obliquum*"). Vertical section through prothallium with young sporophyte. The root has broken downward through the gametophyte; the first leaf is about to break through upward. *a,* archegonium neck; *l,* first leaf; *s,* suspensor; *t,* stem apex. (*After Lyon.*)

directly from a segment. Apical cells are not initiated early, as in true ferns.

The embryo becomes large before breaking out through the tissues of the prothallium, the growth of the cells about the archegonium forming a prominent cushion over the young sporophyte. At least in some species several years may pass before the first leaf appears above ground, and in some the first few leaves are scale-like and are never expanded. Slow development is characteristic throughout all stages of the plant.

In the radial type of prothallium the embryo breaks through gametophytic tissue near the position of the archegonium, the root appearing first (Fig. 86*D*), and the embryo is attached to the side of the prothallium; in the flattened type the root pushes downward through the prothallium and breaks out through the lower surface, the leaf and stem later breaking through the cushion on the upper surface. The latter type thus definitely pierces the gametophyte (Fig. 90) and stands "erect"; the other type is apparently oriented variously, from "oblique" to "horizontal." Orientation with respect to the first division of the zygote is, however, such that in all cases the stem-root axis of the embryo is along the long axis of the archegonium, that is, is *erect*. Distortion of form by the early and strong development of the root brings about an apparently horizontal position in some forms. This erect orientation is in strong contrast with that of true ferns in which the embryo is *prone*, its axis transverse to the long archegonium axis.

Summary and Discussion

These ferns form a group sharply distinct from other living ferns. Though possessing many features of habit and structure which are definitely fern-like, they stand by themselves in other important respects.

There is much evidence that they are primitive among ferns, but that as a group they are specialized to a high degree. The three genera form a rough series in reduction and simplification, with *Botrychium* as the most primitive and *Ophioglossum* as the most advanced.

Within each of the large genera there exists a series in reduction and simplification (Fig. 78). The modifications run parallel in the two genera and seem to be related to mycorrhizal habit.

The rhizome is in most cases short and unbranched; where branching is present, it is of the primitive dichotomous type. The presence of dormant buds is evidence that these plants have been derived from larger, freely branched forms.

The leaf, which, like the stem, shows evidence of dichotomy, is fern-like in *Botrychium* and *Helminthostachys*. In *Ophioglossum* the blade has been greatly simplified and shows stages in reduction; the sterile segment is typically small and simple and in most extreme species (*O. simplex*) has disappeared (Fig. 78). The genus *Botrychium* shows steps in reduction from the large, decompound leaf of *B. virginianum* to the smaller, simpler blade of *B. simplex*, thus itself possessing nearly as complete reduction as the more specialized *Ophioglossum*. The plants are strongly mycorrhizal, their roots fleshy and prominently modified in relation to this habit. The reduction of the leaf blade is doubtless connected with this condition, as is the case with many plants with fungus associates. In the case of the most extreme reduction (*O. simplex*), nutrition seems to be dependent upon the mycorrhizal relation since the leaves are represented only by fertile segments.

The leaf venation of the different genera shows further evidence of the specialization: *Botrychium* and *Helminthostachys* have dichotomous, open venation; *Ophioglossum* has reticulate venation. The first type is without question a primitive type of venation, with the second derived from it (page 161). Comparative structure in other groups provides excellent evidence of this fact, and the fossil record supplies proof—reticulate venation being unknown among the older fossil plants.

The leaf is unlike that of other ferns in its slow growth, soft character, noncircinate vernation, and stipular sheaths. The uniformly semifleshy character of the plant is emphasized by a lack of the chaffy emergences found in advanced ferns and by the nearly complete absence of hairs.

The presence of a fertile segment, "attached ventrally," seems further to set these ferns apart from others. This segment is, however, morphologically not a ventral structure but represents fused lateral leaf lobes. The condition where one part of the leaf is fertile and the rest sterile is common in ferns; only the fusion of lobes in an erect position is to be considered characteristic of this group. The ventral position is false, and therefore a division into dorsal and ventral lobes is only apparent. Nowhere among living plants are leaves so divided.

The fertile leaf segment itself shows a series in simplification and specialization. In the larger species of *Botrychium* the fertile part of the leaf is in form not unlike the sterile; in other smaller species, in which the whole plant is clearly reduced, the segment is much more simple with few and very short, sometimes no, branches in juvenile forms. Simplification has resulted in the loss of the lateral parts or in their fusion with the central axis. In *Helminthostachys* the spike-like structure of the fertile segment has probably been formed by the contraction and reduction of the lateral segments and their close grouping on the main axis. The major clusters correspond apparently with the main branches of the segment in *Botrychium*. The minor segments (inappropriately called 'sporangiophores') still show evidence of compound pinnate structure. In *Ophioglossum* the fertile segment is of the simplest structure—a lobe with two lateral rows of sporangia—and clearly represents the extreme in reduction of this segment in the family. Evidence of branching is lost, unless the small lateral bundles be considered vestiges of lateral lobes, and there is further specialization in the fusion of the sporangia with the leaf lobe.

The morphological basis of the division of the leaf into "dorsal and ventral segments" was for a long time not understood. A condition so remarkable provided grounds for much discussion and played a most important part in the development of theories of the origin and elaboration of the sporophyte generation of vascular plants (Chap. XVII). Briefly, according to one theory, the supposedly ventral fertile spike represents an enlarged and highly elaborated ventral sporangium and suggests derivation from *Lycopodium* or some similar plant; according to another theory, the simpler type in the family, represented by *O. vulgatum*, is a most simple and most primitive vascular plant showing relation to the bryophytes—the 'spike' being a segmented sporangium, the sterile segment an expanded photosynthetic lobe of the sporangium base. On the basis of anatomical and other evidence it is now understood, however, that the leaf is not divided horizontally, and the true nature of the fertile segment seems determined; there can be no connection with plants with ventral foliar sporangia. It is also clear that the simple types in the family are the most specialized and not the most primitive and cannot, therefore, form a connecting link with nonvascular plants.

The fact that nearly all leaves bear fertile segments, that in some species even the first leaves bear such parts, suggests that the leaf of this type of plant was from the first, as part of a vascular plant, made up of fertile and sterile parts, that is, was dimorphic in its segments (Chap. XVII).

The sporangia are remarkable for their large size, great number of spores, massive walls with stomata, and lack of special structural modification for dehiscence. Of much importance also is the fact that in *Botrychium* sporangia terminate the branches of the fertile segment and stand along the margins (page 125). It is significant further that the vascular bundles of the segment lead through the stalks to the sporangium base. (Elsewhere among living vascular cryptogams, only in the extremely primitive Psilotaceae does the sporangium have a vascular supply.) The sporangia are therefore terminal and marginal on the leaf divisions; all may perhaps be considered terminal, the marginal ones being terminal on reduced, minor, lateral divisions. In *Ophioglossum* lateral vascular strands run out between the sporangia and from their course appear at first not to supply these structures, but they are bent backward at right angles at their tips and reach the sporangium bases. This bundle course definitely suggests that the sporangia are indeed sunken in the leaf or fused to its margin; that the vascular supply is as in *Botrychium;* that in the process of simplification of the fertile segment the sporangia have been brought backward and inward against or into the leaf tissues. The sporangia of *B. simplex* (Fig. 82) show in their position how this change may have occurred. The "lateral" dehiscence of *Ophioglossum* is really terminal as in *Botrychium*. In *Helminthostachys* dehiscence is likewise terminal; the smaller end of the somewhat elongate sporangium, through which the break occurs, is apparently the apical part, turned backward in the specialization of the "sporangiophores."

The sporangia of *Ophioglossum* may well be fused not only with the leaf segment but at least in their outer part with one another along the margin; the limits of their massive walls and bases cannot be distinguished and a synangial condition may exist, as is often stated.

There is strong resemblance of the sporangia to leaf lobes in the massive structure, growth by a group of apical cells, continuity of tissues with leaf segments, stomata, and vascular supply. In *Botrychium* at least the sporangia seem to take the place of the leaf lobes, particularly at the tips.

All these features are considered evidences of primitiveness, since evolutionary specialization in the sporangium is clearly toward reduction in size, in number of spores, in thickness of wall, and toward elaboration of means of spore dispersal.

The roots persist for some time, but there is no permanent or extensive root system with one or more main roots, as in *Isoetes* and seed plants. The occasional appearance of dichotomy in these organs emphasizes the occurrence of this feature, at least at times, throughout the plant body—root, stem, leaf, venation—and provides another line of evidence for the primitiveness of the group.

In histological structure this group is unlike other ferns and nearly all other vascular plants; the absence of strong supporting and protecting tissues (as compared with other ferns) throughout the plant body is remarkable.

In stelar structure there is a range from the primitive protostele (in young plants) to complex dictyosteles. The leaf traces are large as compared with those of the groups already discussed and further, have large gaps. Endarch xylem (mesarch in one genus) is unusual for ferns; and secondary vascular tissue, though small in amount and slow in growth, is not found elsewhere among living ferns.

The mycorrhizal condition is even more prominent in the gametophyte than in the sporophyte. In all forms the prothallia are tuberous and subterranean. Since gametophytes may develop on the surface and show small amounts of chlorophyll, it is apparent, as in the case of *Lycopodium*, that the subterranean condition is derived.

Though the gametophytes of the three genera differ considerably in detail, they are much alike in essential points. In *Ophioglossum* and *Helminthostachys* the general form is cylindrical: in the first genus slender, in the second stout; in both usually branched. In *Botrychium* the prothallia are unbranched and thick-ovoid, or short and dorsiventrally flattened. In all, growth is by apical meristems, and the *Botrychium* type has undoubtedly been derived from the cylindrical type by loss of branching and the reduction of the apical growth.

These three genera show, as do the species of *Lycopodium*, progressive stages in the specialization of the gametophyte— from elongate, cylindrical to shortened, flattened types. *Ophioglossum* and *Helminthostachys* show the more primitive types, though *Botrychium* within itself shows stages from fairly elongate to the maize-kernel and convolute, 'rolled-margin' shape. A remarkable similarity exists between prothallia of some species of *Botrychium* and those of some species of *Lycopodium*. In both cases the gametophytes are of the highest type in the genus, and the similarity is undoubtedly the result of parallel development. It is clear that at least in these two groups specialization has resulted in the reduction of the large, elongate type of prothallium and the formation of a small, short, flattened type, which in age becomes convolute.

There are resemblances in the more primitive type (Fig. 86*C,D*) to the prothallia of the Psilotaceae (Figs. 56; 57*G,H*; 60*D*) in form, branching, method and rate of growth, vegetative propagation, and distribution of sex organs. These features may be especially significant. The resemblance of this gametophyte to the root of the plant parallels the resemblance in the Psilotaceae of the gametophyte to the rhizome. Such resemblance of gametophyte and sporophyte in groups that are surely primitive is perhaps also highly significant (Chap. XVII).

Slow and long-continued apical growth is characteristic of the gametophytes—another resemblance to *Lycopodium*. Thus long life, large size, apical growth, and cylindrical shape are common to three certainly primitive groups and are therefore probably primitive characters of the gametophyte. They suggest an ancestral condition where the two generations were more alike in form and length of life. Other probably primitive characters are the long life of the gametophyte after the development of an embryo—sporophytes several years old, and fruiting, can be found attached to normal gametophytes—and the bearing of a number of embryos (though the advanced type of the *Botrychium* gametophyte usually has but one, and rarely more than two). Contrast these conditions with those in the advanced ferns (Chap. XIII). Both these characters—the long life after embryos are formed and the bearing of several embryos—are found also in the gametophytes of the Psilotaceae and the Lycopodiaceae, two other archaic groups.

The presence of many widely scattered sex organs is probably also a primitive feature. It is characteristic of the Psilotaceae, the most primitive living vascular plants. The restriction of these organs in the more specialized species of *Botrychium* to the upper surface is certainly an advanced condition, probably the result of a biological response to the flattened form. (In subterranean dorsiventral types the sex organs are on the upper side, in surface-living dorsiventral types they are on the lower side; in each case the position is apparently biologically most favorable for fertilization.)

In a general way the sex organs resemble those of *Lycopodium* and *Equisetum*. The antheridia are large and sunken, and their outer walls are one- or two-layered. The archegonia are of the usual type and rather deeply sunken. The sperms are many in each antheridium and like those of true ferns and *Equisetum* in number of cilia. The archegonia vary in length of neck and in the extent to which they are sunken, but, though the neck is long and projecting in *Botrychium*, there is but one neck canal cell. Progress in reduction of the axial row has reached the stage of one neck canal cell, though the presence of two nuclei suggests that these forms are not far from the two-cell stage. In the other genera, though the neck is much shorter and sunken, there is also but one neck canal cell. In all genera the axial row is therefore similarly reduced, though the neck itself remains long in *Botrychium*.

In embryogeny diverse conditions are found. The differences lie chiefly in the presence or absence of a suspensor and an apparently varied orientation of the rest of the embryo. This variation in regard to the suspensor is perhaps hardly to be expected since in other groups early stages are more constant. The embryogeny of vascular plants in general presents evidence that the formation of a suspensor is possibly a primitive feature. If this is so, the Ophioglossaceae show stages in advancement to the suspensorless condition. The presence or absence of a suspensor seems, however, to be probably of little or no morphological significance; it is doubtless a matter primarily of correlation with embryo position, form, and orientation in relation to nourishment.

The tracing of the various organs of the embryo to definite segments is difficult or impossible in this group. The development of all organs is very slow and late, with the root appearing first. This retarded development falls in line with the general slowness of growth throughout both generations and contrasts strongly with development in other ferns. Slow development of mature sporophyte as well as of embryo and gametophyte is characteristic of those living vascular plants which seem to be most ancient—Psilotaceae, Lycopodiaceae, Ophioglossaceae.

Within the family, *Botrychium* is clearly the primitive genus and *Ophioglossum* the advanced. In the gametophyte, however, in contrast with the sporophyte, the first genus is most advanced and the second least so. This is an excellent example of a condition constantly observed, one which should be always kept in mind, that a group of plants may be far advanced in some features or stages and unspecialized in others. Among the structural features of any plant various stages of evolutionary modification may be found, and these may lie anywhere within the range of advancement; in general, high specialization in one character is accompanied by similar advance in others, but some or all of these other characters are often only fairly advanced and may even be primitive.

It has been suggested that a section of the genus *Botrychium* should be raised to generic rank (*Sceptridium*) on the basis of the presence of a suspensor, the perforation of the gametophyte by the embryo, and the low point of division of the leaf into fertile and sterile segments. The relative position of the fertile segment is surely not of generic significance; the possession of a suspensor is sometimes a variable character even within a species (page 153); and the perforation of the gametophyte by the embryo is related to the flat shape of this structure. There seems, therefore, to be no basis for the erection of a new genus.

The three genera of this group, although unlike in appearance, are surely closely related. They form a small compact family, the Ophioglossaceae, a family so markedly unlike other ferns in many critical features that it must be considered to form a separate order, the Ophioglossales. Among the ferns these forms are surely a very primitive group.

Bibliography

BAAS-BECKING, L. G. M.: Origin of the vascular structure in the genus *Botrychium*, with notes on the general anatomy, *Rec. Trav. Bot. Nieul.*, **18**: 333–375, 1920.

BOWER, F. O.: "Studies in the Morphology of Spore-producing Members. II. Ophioglossaceae," Dulau and Co., London, 1896.

———: *Ophioglossum simplex*, Ridley, *Ann. Bot.*, **18**: 205–216, 1904.

BRUCHMANN, H.: Ueber das Prothallium und die Keimpflanze von *Ophioglossum vulgatum* L., *Bot. Ztg.*, **62**: 227–247, 1904.

———: Über das Prothallium und die Sporenpflanze von *Botrychium Lunaria* Sw., *Flora*, **96**: 203–230, 1906.

CAMPBELL, D. H.: "The Eusporangiatae," Carnegie Institution of Washington, Washington, 1911.

CHRYSLER, M. A.: The nature of the fertile spike in the Ophioglossaceae, *Ann. Bot.*, **24**: 1–18, 1910.

JEFFREY, E. C.: The gametophyte of *Botrychium virginianum*, *Trans. Canad. Inst.*, **5**: 265–294, 1896–1897.

LANG, W. H.: On the prothalli of *Ophioglossum pendulum* and *Helminthostachys zeylanica*, *Ann. Bot.*, **16**: 23–56, 1902.

———: Studies in the morphology and anatomy of the Ophioglossaceae. II. On the embryo of *Helminthostachys*, *Ann. Bot.*, **28**: 19–37, 1914.

———: On a suspensor in *Helminthostachys zeylanica*, *Ann. Bot.*, **24**: 611, 1910.

LYON, H. L.: A new genus of Ophioglossaceae, *Bot. Gaz.*, **40**: 455–458, 1905.

WRIGHT, G.: Pit-closing membrane in Ophioglossaceae, *Bot. Gaz.*, **69**: 237–247, 1920.

CHAPTER VII

MARATTIACEAE   MARATTIACEOUS FERNS

The Marattiaceae are a small group of ferns which have many characters in common with the Ophioglossaceae, but which more closely resemble true ferns. There are seven genera and about 145 species. All are tropical plants occurring mostly in humid

Fig. 91.—*Angiopteris evecta.* Habit. (*After Wettstein.*)

forests, where occasionally some of the larger species form prominent elements of the vegetation. The smaller forms are not conspicuously different in appearance from some true ferns, and, as they are scarce and occur chiefly in mountain forests in inaccessible regions, some of them (*Archangiopteris, Macroglossum,* and *Protomarattia*) have been discovered only in recent years. The large genera are *Angiopteris, Marattia,* and *Danaea;* the first widely distributed in the eastern, the last in the western tropics; *Marattia* in both hemispheres. The other genera belong in the Malayan region, from southern China and Formosa to northern Australia.

SPOROPHYTE

Habit. These ferns are perennials and range from rhizome types with fronds a few decimeters high (resembling similar types among temperate-climate ferns) to huge forms which are among the largest of ferns. The latter—species of *Angiopteris* and *Marattia*—are stately, magnificent plants, in habit resembling large tree ferns with a very short trunk (Fig. 91). The fronds are circinate in development, and the sporangia are borne on the dorsal side of normal leaves; the plants, throughout, much more closely resemble true ferns than do the members of the Ophioglossaceae.

Some of the larger species are occasionally grown in greenhouses for their beautiful habit and the interest in them as members of a rare group. It is reported that the fleshy trunks and stipules are sometimes used as food.

Leaves. The leaves, though simple in some of the smaller species, are typically pinnately compound. The cycad-like leaves of *Macroglossum* may reach a length of 4 m and the twice pinnately compound leaves of species of *Angiopteris* and *Marattia*, with stalks as thick as a man's arm, may be 5 or 6 m long. In all the genera there are thick fleshy stipules, which, with the base of the petiole, persist after the leaf has fallen and form a fleshy case about the stem. The base of the petiole and a pair of stipules from one of the large species somewhat resemble in size and shape a horse's hoof. In some species there are near the base of the petiole and of the pinnae swollen 'joints' (Fig. 92*B*) which apparently serve as regions of orientation. As the leaf falls or decays, it breaks at these points. Characteristically the leaf is glabrous, but in some forms there are hairs or small scales. The venation is of the open dichotomous type except in *Christensenia* (*Kaulfussia*) where it is netted. On erect stems the leaves are spirally arranged; in the rhizome types they are more or less definitely two-ranked.

Stems. In the smaller forms the stems are chiefly dorsiventral rhizomes; in the larger species they are erect tuberous trunks. These fleshy stems with their persistent sheath of stipules and petiole bases may reach a height of 1 m and a diameter nearly as great. Stems of such shape appear to be half-buried in the soil, and the crown of huge leaves seems to come from the ground

(Fig. 91).   Branching is occasional in the rhizome types but does not occur in the large tuberous trunks.

Roots.   The number of roots varies in the different genera, there being one, two, or several on the stem below each leaf.

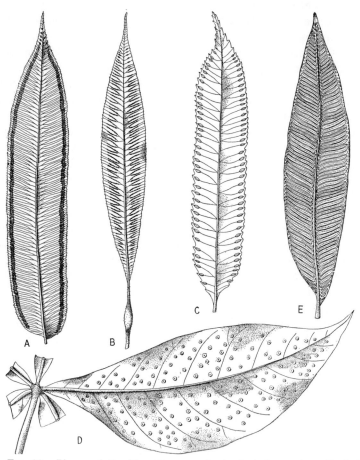

Fig. 92.—Pinnae of the Marattiaceae.   *A, Angiopteris crassipes; B, Archangiopteris Henryi; C, Marattia fraxinea; D, Christensenia aesculifolia; E, Danaea elliptica.   (After Bitter in Engler and Prantl.)*

They are stout, mycorrhizal, in some genera branching freely, in others sparsely.   In origin they are endogenous and may pierce the fleshy stipules in their course.   Their root hairs are unusual in that they are several-celled.

Vegetative Propagation. Where the stipules join the petiole, there are on the margins dormant buds. Ultimately the stipules are shed from the trunk with the petiole base—in some cases many years after the leaf has fallen—and the dormant buds may then become active and form new plants. Because of the presence of these buds the stipules are sometimes used as cuttings in propagation.

Anatomy. In structure these ferns are more or less fleshy throughout. With the exception of *Christensenia* they are not, however, wholly lacking in hard tissues, as are the Ophioglossaceae, for small amounts of supporting tissue may occur as hypodermal layers in the leaves and may be present with the stem bundles. In amount, type, and distribution of mechanical tissues this group is, however, unlike true ferns; in the possession of large mucilage ducts they are further unlike other ferns.

In the young plant the stem is protostelic; as it becomes older the stele becomes an amphiphloic siphonostele. This structure is retained in the rhizome types when mature. In the large forms a dictyostele of a most complex type is formed, the many bundles, of varied size, lying roughly in concentric zones. The leaf traces are large, and in the species with complex steles are themselves complex in structure and origin. In all cases they form large gaps.

The tracheids in their pitting are scalariform, resembling those of true ferns, and are unlike those of the Ophioglossaceae. A very weak development of secondary xylem is reported to occur in *Angiopteris*.

The stems of older plants lack an endodermis, though this layer is present in young plants.

The mechanical support of the large soft stems is to a large extent provided by the thick sheath of leaf bases and roots. In this respect these ferns resemble tree ferns and cycads. In other groups support is secured in other ways: the stems of conifers and angiosperms are supported chiefly by their woody cylinders; those of the horsetails and the larger (fossil) club mosses by a sclerenchymatous cortex; the short underground stems of the Ophioglossaceae with their solitary leaves require little or no support.

Reproduction. The sporangia are large, with massive walls and a broad base, and are arranged in sori on the dorsal side of

leaves which in most species do not differ otherwise from the
sterile ones.   The sporangia lie along the backs of the veins
(Fig. 92), as in many true ferns, not at the ends as in the Ophioglossaceae.   In the sori the sporangia are arranged in a row and
form linear or circular groups.   Various degrees of fusion among
the sporangia occur in the group: in three genera the sporangia

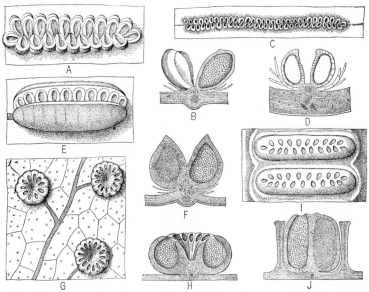

Fig. 93.—Sporangia and synangia of the Marattiaceae.   *A, B, Angiopteris
crassipes;* sorus in face view and section.   *C, D, Archangiopteris Henryi;* sorus
in face view and section.   *E, F, Marattia fraxinea;* synangium in face view and
section.   *G, H, Christensenia aesculifolia;* synangium in face view and cross
section.   *I, J, Danaea elliptica;* two synangia in face view, one in section.
*(From Engler and Prantl; A, B, E, G, I after Bitter; C, D after Christ and Giesen-
hagen; F, H, J after Hooker-Baker.)*

are free or nearly so (Fig. 93*A,C*); in four, definite synangia are
formed.   In the synangial types the sporangia are closely united
in a firm mass, as in *Marattia* (Fig. 93*E*) and *Christensenia*
(Fig. 93*G*).   In size the sori range from small clusters with
three to five sporangia to elongate groups up to 3 cm in length
with more than 100 sporangia.   Stomata are frequent on the
sporangial and synangial walls.

The synangia are themselves elaborately specialized structures.
The sporangia form chambers in the hard, fused walls and open

by slits or pores into a central furrow or on the lower surface (Fig. 93*G* to *I*). The synangium may form a closed capsular structure (which may even be raised upon a stalk) with a definite two-valved dehiscence. In such cases the openings of the sporangia are enclosed except when the valves are open. In the more specialized synangia the fusion is so complete that there is little or no external evidence of the individual sporangia.

There is no typical indusium. A few hairs or scales are found in some species about the margins of the sorus (Fig. 93*B,D,F*),

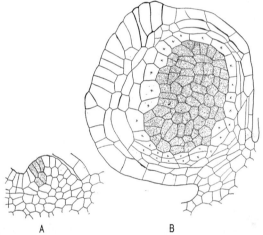

A   B

FIG. 94.—*Angiopteris evecta.* Stages in sporangium development. *A*, early stage showing cells derived from superficial initial; *B*, nearly mature stage, with annulus, sporocytes (shaded), and tapetal cells (marked *x*) differentiated. (*After Bower.*)

and in *Danaea* the sori are sunken in the leaf so that folds of tissue extend up about the synangium and slightly overarch it (Fig. 93*I,J*).

The sporangia are eusporangiate, and all those in a sorus mature together. The sporogenous mass, with that section of the wall immediately above it, arises usually from a single superficial cell (Fig. 94*A*). Development follows no uniform course. The rest of the wall is formed from cells surrounding the single initial. The wall becomes several layers thick, the cells adjacent to the sporogenous tissue becoming a tapetum of one or two layers. The sporocytes are numerous and all develop spores. The spore number is therefore large, from 1450 to 7500. Both

tetrahedral and bilateral types occur.   The mature sporangia
open by slits on the inner side, or by pores near the apex.   The
openings form in thin areas on drying and are widened by the
collapse and shrinkage of the surrounding tissue; there is an
annulus only in *Angiopteris* and *Macroglossum*.   (The structure of the sporangium wall in *Archangiopteris* is apparently
unknown.)   In *Angiopteris* an arch of cells with slightly thickened walls extends from side to side across the top of the sporangium.   By the contraction of these cells and of those in the wall
of the sporangium away from the center of the sorus, the wall
toward the center, which is only one to three layers of cells thick
outside the tapetum, is torn open.   In *Macroglossum* the annulus
is represented by a transverse row of about six cells whose walls
show hardly any additional thickening.   These genera, in which
the sporangia are free, may, therefore, be said to have poorly
differentiated and therefore doubtless primitive types of annulus.
In the synangial genera an annulus obviously could not function.
In the most specialized synangia—those in some species of *Danaea*
—dehiscence and spore distribution are features of synangial
rather than sporangial structure.

GAMETOPHYTE

The prothallia are deep-green, surface-living, thalloid plants.
Though of somewhat varied form, they are chiefly cordate or
oblong in outline (Fig. 95H to K).   In structure they tend to be
massive and, though green, are mycorrhizal.   They are long-
lived, continuing to grow for at least two years and apparently
often for several years, attaining meanwhile a length of more
than 3 cm, when they much resemble thalloid liverworts.   They
remain active long after the sporophyte has become independent.
Adventitious buds may develop and form separate prothallia.

The spores germinate a few days after shedding.   For the first
month, growth consists of enlargement to several times the
original size, with the formation of abundant chlorophyll.   The
first division, which is "transverse," then occurs, and a first
rhizoid is formed (Fig. 95B).   There is then formed a cluster of
cells, one of which is an apical cell, and a plate-like structure
develops immediately (Fig. 95G).   Later growth is by a series
of marginal initials, and divisions in many planes produce a

thallus several cell layers thick with a projecting cushion on the
ventral surface.   Old elongate prothallia may branch dichoto-

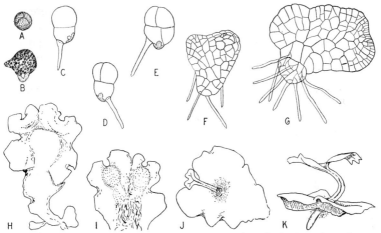

Fig. 95.—Gametophytes of the Marattiaceae.   *A* to *G, Angiopteris pruinosa;*
stages in development.   *H* to *K, Marattia Douglasii;* mature prothallia.   *J, K,*
with young sporophytes.   (*A to G, after Jonkman; H to K, after Campbell.*)

mously (Fig. 95*I*); in such plants the cushion becomes a rib-like
structure.

Sex Organs.   The prothallia are monoecious, with archegonia
usually only on the cushions, but with antheridia scattered over

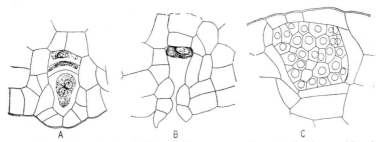

Fig. 96.—*Marattia Douglasii.   A, B,* mature archegonia (on lower side of
prothallium); *C,* antheridium (on upper side of prothallium).   (*After Campbell
"Mosses and Ferns" by permission of The Macmillan Company, publishers.*)

both surfaces.   (Archegonia are reported to occur rarely on the
upper surface.)   The antheridia (Figs. 96*C*, 97*D*) are large and
sunken, resembling those of the Ophioglossaceae.   In development they are also similar to those of this family.   The sperms

are of the fern type with many cilia. Their number is variable but large, as many in some cases as several hundred. The archegonium is similar to that of *Ophioglossum* but has a shorter, broad neck, in most cases of two to three tiers, and is almost

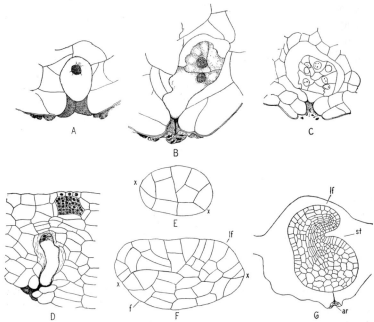

Fig. 97.—Embryogeny of the Marattiaceae. *A* to *C*, *Danaea jamaicensis;* *D* to *G*, *Angiopteris.* *A*, archegonium with zygote; *B*, archegonium with 3-celled embryo; *C*, archegonium with older embryo; *D*, section of prothallium showing (on the upper side) an antheridium and (on the lower side) an archegonium with 2-celled embryo, the outer cell a suspensor; *E* to *G*, later stages in the development of the embryo; *G*, the first leaf about to break through the gametophyte above. *ar*, archegonium; *f*, foot; *lf*, leaf; *st*, stem; *x-x*, line separating segments delimited by first division. (*A* to *C*, *E* to *G*, after Campbell; *D*, after Land.)

completely sunken (Fig. 96*A,B*). There is one large neck canal cell with two nuclei, which in some cases are separated by traces of a division wall. The ventral canal cell (except in *Danaea*) is also large and conspicuous.

EMBRYO

The fertilized egg increases greatly in size, and the first division is transverse to the archegonium axis (Fig. 97*B*). Quadrant segments are obscure, and the young organs are not definitely traceable to these (Fig. 97*E* to *G*). It is evident, however, that the stem, root, and first leaf arise from the half of the young embryo in the base of the archegonium.   There is no definite foot formed, although the other half is often considered to represent this organ.   The embryo in these forms is thus reversed in orientation as compared with that of the Ophioglossaceae.   The root appears late and is endogenous in origin.   The developing leaf and stem grow upward through the tissue of the prothallium (Fig. 95*J*,*K*).   Differentiation of the embryonic organs is slow and late, as in the Ophioglossaceae.   Only one sporophyte is normally formed on a prothallium.

In *Danaea*, *Macroglossum*, and in some individual cases in *Angiopteris evecta* (Fig. 97*D*) the fertilized egg elongates before division, and a suspensor of one, two, or several cells is formed (Fig. 97), much as in *Botrychium dissectum*.   In *Macroglossum* the suspensor becomes large and thrusts the embryo laterally for some distance.   The development of a suspensor in this family is therefore inconstant, as it is in the Ophioglossaceae.

DISCUSSION AND SUMMARY

The Marattiaceae are a small and fairly uniform group, of rather restricted distribution, which resemble both the Ophioglossaceae and the true ferns.   In habit and general appearance they are like the latter; in important structural features they are similar to the former.

The leaves in their circinate vernation and generally pinnate form resemble those of true ferns; but in the presence of stipules they are like those of the Ophioglossaceae.   The stipules of the adder's-tongue ferns are, however, of a somewhat different type, being thin and sheathing rather than fleshy and paired.

Anatomically the Marattiaceae occupy a position rather intermediate between the Ophioglossaceae and the true ferns. In their generally fleshy structure they are like the former group, but the presence of some hard tissues is suggestive of the latter. Their vascular structure is not markedly different from that of either group, though in some forms it is exceedingly complex. In the presence of abundant large mucilage canals, they are unique among ferns.

The large, massive-walled sporangia with very many spores and eusporangiate development resemble those of the Ophioglossaceae but, unlike them, are borne in sori on the underside of the leaves and on the back of veins rather than at their ends. The presence of stomata on the walls of the sporangia is another character of similarity in these two groups and may be significant (Chap. XVI). Normally the entire leaf is fertile; there is no division into fertile and sterile segments. The sori are characteristically synangial and display a series in fusion of sporangia (page 148). Specialization of the synangium has progressed far: the rosette-like structure with apical pores represents one extreme of elaboration; the box-like, stalked structure with mechanically opened valves another.

The various genera of the family provide a series in soral structure from the free to the completely fused sporangial state. This series has been read in both directions: when read toward the fused forms, it is believed to show progress in specialization of the sorus along synangial lines; when read toward the free forms, it is believed to show stages in the segmentation of an original large, solitary sporangium to form a sorus. The weight of evidence favors the view that the series is one of progress to synangy: the synangial genera are the most specialized in other features, especially of leaf structure; there are no known forms among fossil fern-like plants in which a large sporangium shows evidence of division. (Evidence of such division in the Psilotaceae and Isoetaceae cannot be considered of much value here.)

Though the sporangia may be to some extent protected by the presence of a few hairs or scales at the base of the sorus, or by sinking in the leaf tissue, they lack an indusium of the type characteristic of the higher ferns; as in the primitive Ophioglossaceae the sori are naked. Where the sporangium wall is massive and firm, protection is not so important as where it is thin and delicate. Furthermore, aggregation in a synangium gives greatly increased protection. An annulus is found only where the sporangia are free and is then of a simple unspecialized type. The tapetum is derived as in the Ophioglossaceae, not from sporogenous cells, but from surrounding tissue, and all the sporocytes form spores so that the spore number is large.

The gametophytes are of the usual fern type, but thick and massive. They are long-lived and persist after the sporophytes are independent, resembling in this the prothallia of *Lycopodium* and the Ophioglossaceae. Such a condition is doubtless primitive. Though richly green, they have an endophytic fungus. In development they are thalloid from the first; there is no filamentous stage as in many true ferns. The sex organs are borne on both surfaces in contrast with the true ferns where they are on the ventral surface only, and with the Ophioglossaceae where in the flattened forms they are on the dorsal surface.

The antheridia in their large size and sunken position resemble those of the Ophioglossaceae, Equisetaceae, and Lycopodiaceae. They are obviously of a primitive type. The archegonia resemble those of the Ophioglossaceae but in their shorter broader necks are perhaps slightly more advanced. The neck

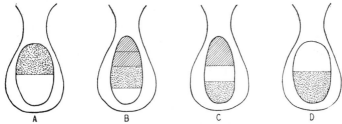

FIG. 98.—Embryogeny of eusporangiate ferns. Diagrams to show relation of early divisions to first organs. *A, Ophioglossum; B, Helminthostachys; C, Angiopteris; D, Marattia.* (Suspensor, cross-hatched; leaf and stem, dotted; foot, clear.)

canal cells are at essentially the same stage of reduction, but the ventral canal cell is more prominent than in the other group.

The embryogeny bears many resemblances to that of the Ophioglossaceae. The first division of the fertilized egg is transverse to the long axis of the archegonium. The organs of the young embryo are very slow in appearing and cannot be traced to particular segments. The embryo is erect. (That of true ferns is prone.) It is, however, reversed in orientation (Fig. 98); the stem and first leaf develop from the inner part of the proembryo (Fig. 97*F,G*). In the presence of a suspensor there is no constancy in the family, a feature of further resemblance to the Ophioglossaceae. Evidence provided by this group strengthens that from other groups, that the presence of a suspensor is probably of little or no morphological significance. The first leaf and the stem grow upward through the tissue of the gametophyte.

Since the synangial sorus is obviously a specialized form, *Angiopteris* and the other genera with free sporangia are more primitive, with *Marattia, Protomarattia,* and *Christensenia* the most specialized in this respect. The last genus stands apart also in its netted venation and in the scattered position of its rosette-like sori; both the position and the form of the sori are doubtless correlated with the advanced type of venation in this genus.

The family is definitely allied to the other fern groups in its large leaves, with large traces which form gaps, and in the position of its sporangia—dorsal (superficial) or marginal—in contrast with ventral or cauline in the groups thus far treated. It is, like the Ophioglossales, eusporangiate, and in this character differs from the Filicales, which are leptosporangiate (page 170). From both the Ophioglossales and the Filicales it is, however, well set off (Table 3, page 302); its characters are such that it cannot be placed close to either of these groups and must form an independent order, the Marattiales. Like the Ophioglossaceae it possesses many characters which are clearly primitive, and it is concluded that, like this group, it is primitive among fern-like plants. This conclusion is borne out by the fossil record. There are, therefore, among the ferns two primitive groups. The relationship of the various groups is further discussed later (Chap. XVII).

Bibliography

BITTER, G.: Marattiaceae in Engler and Prantl, "Die natürlichen Pflanzen-familien," vol. I, Pt. 4: 422–444, 1900.

BOWER, F. O.: Studies in the morphology of spore-producing members. III. Marattiaceae, *Phil. Trans. Roy. Soc. London* **189B**: 35–81, 1897.

CAMPBELL, D. H.: "The Eusporangiatae," Carnegie Institution of Washington, Washington, 1911.

———: The Structure and affinities of *Macroglossum Alidae* Copeland, *Ann. Bot.,* **28**: 651–669, 1914.

CHRIST, H., and K. GIESENHAGEN, Pteridographische Notizen, *Flora,* **80**: 72–85, 1899.

FARMER, J. B., and T. G. HILL: On the arrangement and structure of the vascular strands in *Angiopteris evecta* and some other Marattiaceae, *Ann. Bot.,* **16**: 371–402, 1902.

HAYATA, B.: *Protomarattia,* a new genus of Marattiaceae, *Bot. Gaz.,* **67**: 84–92, 1919.

JONKMANN, H. F.: La génération sexuée des Marattiacées, *Arch. Néerland. Sci. nat.,* **15**: 199–224, 1880.

LAND, W. J. G.: A suspensor in *Angiopteris, Bot. Gaz.,* **75**: 421–425, 1923.

WEST, C.: A contribution to the study of the Marattiaceae, *Ann. Bot.,* **31**: 361–414, 1917.

CHAPTER VIII

FILICALES   LEPTOSPORANGIATE FERNS

General Discussion

The leptosporangiate ferns—often called "true ferns" and "typical ferns"—make up the great mass of ferns. They differ in important characters of gametophyte and sporophyte from the two groups that have been discussed. Taxonomically they are divided into several families, and these differ so much that it is necessary to consider separately the more important ones. It is desirable, however, to discuss first the group as a whole insofar as certain features are concerned.

Like the eusporangiate types, these ferns are primarily plants of warm regions and of moist and shaded habitats. They are often abundant in temperate regions, but it is only in the tropics —as in wet mountain forests—that they may form a dominant element in the floras. The majority of the species are meso-phytes or hygrophytes, but there are many xerophytic species, some of them of an extreme type; primarily ferns are a moist-climate group. Nearly all are perennials; true annuals are very rare.

Sporophyte

Habit. These ferns are most diverse in habit; all types are found, ranging from moss-like to dendroid forms. There are delicate herbs, creepers, scrambling and climbing forms, epiphytes, and small and large trees.

Stems. The most common type of stem is the rhizome; this varies from slender, far-reaching, and much-branched to stout and unbranched, and passes into the erect dendroid stem. Branching is on the whole weak; many groups branch sparsely or not at all. In the free-growing types of rhizome, branching is frequently dichotomous; in other cases, branches arise in the leaf axils, beside or below the leaf base or from it abaxially, or without relation to leaves or to other branches. The various

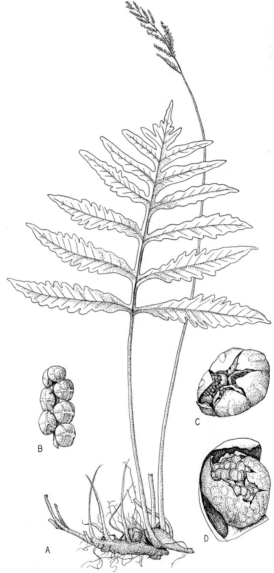

FIG. 99.—*Onoclea sensibilis.* *A*, habit; *B*, pinna of fertile frond; *C*, lobe of fertile pinna enclosing cluster of sori; *D*, sorus with indusium and portion of pinna. (*A, after Diels in Engler and Prantl: B to D, after Bauer.*)

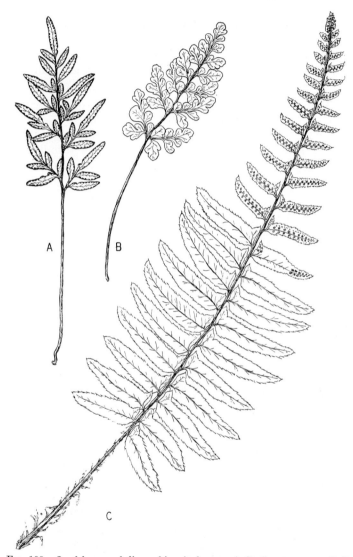

Fig. 100.—Leaf form and dimorphism in ferns. *A, B, Cryptogramma Stelleri,* fertile and sterile frond; *C, Polystichum acrostichoides,* frond with distal portion fertile, proximal sterile. *(Redrawn from Slosson, "How Ferns Grow," by permission of Henry Holt and Company, publishers.)*

habital types are not restricted to families, though some of them are characteristic of certain groups.

Leaves.   The leaves as compared with the stem and with the plant as a whole are large, as in ferns generally, and show great variety in size, form, venation, and texture.   They range in length from a few millimeters to several meters, often with a width nearly as great.   In form the "compound" frond is considered typical, but simple types are common in nearly all groups.   In the divided or dissected type the frond is commonly pinnate, though palmate and pedate division is frequent.

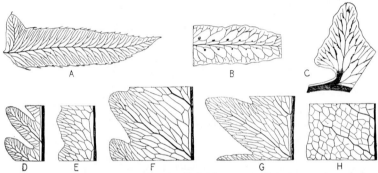

FIG. 101.—Leaf venation in ferns.   Series from open dichotomous to complex netted.   *A, Polystichum acrostichoides; B, Polypodium Swartzii; C, Camptosorus rhizophyllus; D. Woodwardia virginica; E, W. areolata; F, G, Onoclea sensibilis; H, Drynaria* sp.   (*A, C, E, G, redrawn from Slosson, "How Ferns Grow," by permission of Henry Holt and Company, publishers.*)

Dichotomous forking is characteristic of some families and is occasional in others.   Simple leaves range in outline from linear to oval and reniform, and there are many angular and odd shapes.   Species with leaf shape unusual for the group—such as those with grass-like leaves—hardly resemble ferns at all at first glance.   The largest leaves are of the compound type, but simple leaves may be large also, in some cases reaching 2 m or more in length.   The typical leaf, compound or simple, has a prominent, stout, or rigid petiole (Figs. 99, 100); sessile leaves are rare among ferns.   Comparative study indicates that the large compound leaf is primitive, and that the simple and smaller forms have been derived from such leaves by reduction and simplification; that dichotomy is primitive, and that from this have been derived the pinnate and other types of division.

Venation.   In venation a series exists from the open dichotomous type to the reticulate (Fig. 101).   This series represents
an undoubted line of progressive specialization in the vascular
skeleton of the leaf, the dichotomous type being primitive and
the more complex netted the most advanced.   Evidence that
this is the correct interpretation is based not only on comparative
studies of living plants but also on the fossil record.   The
reticulate condition is derived by the fusion of the veinlets and
the loss of free vein tips.   In the earlier stages the fusions are
few (Fig. 101*B* to *D*); in later stages the fusions are numerous,
and smaller vein islets occur within the larger (Fig. 101*H*).

Texture.   In texture there is a range from the filmy condition
—where the blade, except at the veins, is only one cell layer thick
—to the heavy, leathery blades of some of the xerophytes.
Filmy leaves occur chiefly in ferns of rain forests.   It was
formerly believed that filmy leaves indicate primitiveness by
their simplicity of structure, their resemblance to moss leaves,
their small size, and the moist habitat in which they are found.
The filmy character is, however, clearly the result of adaptive
modification and does not indicate primitiveness.   It occurs in
several families but reaches high development in only one.   This
character provides a good example of parallel development, or
homoplasy, the independent development of similar structure in
distantly related or unrelated organisms.

Dimorphism.   Leaf dimorphism is of frequent occurrence.
In one type two forms of vegetative leaves are found, as in the
staghorn fern, *Platycerium*, an epiphyte, where one form is basal
and clasping and serves to hold humus about the rhizome, and
the other form is green and erect.   The more common type of
dimorphism is that between vegetative and reproductive leaves.
In many species the majority of leaves serves both vegetative and
reproductive functions, or there is little difference in form between
fertile and sterile leaves.   In many other species fertile and
sterile leaves are wholly different in form and in other ways, as
in the cinnamon fern, *Osmunda cinnamomea* and the sensitive
fern, *Onoclea sensibilis* (Fig. 99).   Between these extremes in
form and in segregation of function, all intermediate conditions
exist: there are those transitional types in which sporangium bearing is restricted to a part of the leaf (Fig. 100*C*), and those in
which a leaf is, throughout, either fertile or sterile (Fig. 100*A,B*).

Ontogeny. Fern leaves develop by an apical meristem which persists for a long time; in the leaves of other plants the meristematic tip is soon lost and the leaf matures throughout, all parts of the organ, after early growth, being at any one time at approximately the same stage of development. The growing fern frond is coiled at the tip and unrolls progressively as the lower part matures. A developing leaf thus has a basal part which is mature and an upper part in all stages of ontogeny. Such continuing acropetal development is not found in the leaves of other groups. Though in most species a frond matures in one season, in a few genera three and even more years may be taken for the leaf to mature; in rare cases growth at the leaf tip is apparently indefinite, and leaves up to 30 m or more long are formed. In the climbing fern *Lygodium* the frond in appearance and behavior closely resembles the stem and leaves of other ferns (Fig. 121). Fern leaves, indeed, in method and continuity of growth differ greatly from those of other groups and closely resemble stems. That they represent branch systems, in most cases determinate and highly modified, is now clear (Chap. XVII).

Persistence. The leaves of many species of the colder regions live only through one growing season; those of others and of warm-climate species are evergreen, persisting in some tropical forms for many years. When the leaves die they may be shed by definite abscission, forming clean-cut scars (Fig. 167), or they may shrivel and decay leaving stalks or ragged stumps (Fig. 99). In some tree ferns the persistent bases form a protective and supporting armor; on underground stems the leaf bases may remain alive and serve as storage organs, as in many herbaceous ferns of the temperate regions. Dermal appendages in the form of hairs or chaffy scales (Fig. 100*C*) are usually present, and may be abundant, especially about the growing point where they serve as most efficient protective structures. Hairs undoubtedly are the more primitive type of appendage and the simple uniseriate hair the earlier form.

Phyllotaxy. The leaf arrangement is alternate, with the leaves, where the internodes are long, tending to be in longitudinal rows, most commonly two, as in the marsh fern, *Dryopteris Thelypteris* and the polypody, *Polypodium vulgare.* Spiral types are common, with approaches to the divergences found in angiosperms. A more complex spiral arrangement is found in the tree ferns and in the short-rhizome types, where the leaves stand close together around the terminal bud and form a pseudowhorl or a basket-like cluster, as in species of *Osmunda*, *Aspidium*, and the ostrich fern, *Pteretis nodulosa*.

Roots. The roots are mostly slender—fibrous or cord-like—and dark-colored. All except the embryonic root are adventitious, arising from the stem or from the leaf bases. They may be rather few but are frequently abundant, as in many tree ferns where the trunk is covered with a close-packed mass, which is said to serve in part for protection and support. Such roots apparently remain alive and perhaps functioning in the coat of humus which gathers about the trunk. The tops of certain more or less xerophytic tree ferns when cut off and set in the ground continue growth, apparently through the adaptability of these aerial roots to subterranean activities. Tree ferns as a whole, however, require special conditions for growth, and most of them are difficult to cultivate. Roots are lacking in some aquatic forms and also in some filmy types where rhizoids take their place. In none of the ferns is there a unit root system.

Anatomy. The stem shows all stelar types from simple protosteles to complicated dictyosteles. The leaf trace likewise varies from simple to complex. Large leaf gaps are formed. No cambial growth is present. The tracheids are scalariform-pitted and vessels occur rarely.

Reproduction. Sporangia are borne, usually in large numbers, on the margin or on the dorsal surface of the leaf and are therefore described as *marginal* and *superficial*, respectively. They are in the majority of cases borne in sori—to which also these terms of position are applied. The primitive position for the sorus is obviously the marginal one; the superficial position has been acquired by transfer to the dorsal surface, the so-called *phyletic slide*. That such a change of position has taken place is supported by abundant evidence from living and fossil forms. The change is, of course, primarily a phylogenetic one, but it takes place ontogenetically in some forms.

Sori. *Form.* Sori are most diverse in form, but they are commonly circular, reniform, or linear (Fig. 102). They vary greatly in size; the larger ones, however, represent two or more, that is, they are fused sori, or *coenosori* (Fig. 103). The larger linear sori, whether marginal or superficial, are usually of this type, but some elongate sori are the result of the spreading of sporangia along a vein (Fig. 102*F,G*). Coenosori may be broken up into segments, as in species of *Blechnum* and of *Woodwardia*. Thus the nature of soral clusters is often obscure, but it can usually be determined by the comparative study of related species or genera.

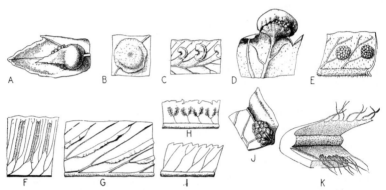

Fig. 102.—Form and structure of the fern sorus. *A, Cystopteris fragilis;* indusium lateral, scale-like. *B, Tectaria singaporiana:* indusium median, radial. *C, Nephrolepis cordifolia:* indusium lateral, reniform. *D, Saccoloma sorbifolium:* indusium 2-lipped, the (upper) ventral lip blade-like. *E, Polypodium pectinatum:* sorus naked, by loss of indusium. *F, Phyllitis Scolopendrium:* sorus compound, extended, covered by two lateral indusia. *G. Asplenium ensiforme:* sorus extended, with unilateral indusium. *H, I, Plagiogyria semicordata:* sori naked, extended along veins forming false "forked sori"; and homologous venation in sterile blade. *J, Pteris aculeata:* part of marginal coenosorus with fused ventral indusial lips forming "folded over leaf margin" or "false indusium"; the dorsal indusial lips have been lost. *K. Pteridium aquilinum:* part of marginal coenosorus (the sporangia removed), the ventral indusial lips fused into a reflexed "false indusium" the fused dorsal lips persisting as a vestigial flap. (*A to E, G to K, after Engler and Prantl: A, from Bauer: B, C, G, from Diels; D, E, from Hooker; H, I, from Mettenius; J, from Baker; K, from Luerssen. F, after Bower.*)

Receptacle. A simple and apparently a primitive type of sorus is that where the sporangia are few and arranged uniseriately in a flat cluster (Fig. 120). With specialization the number of sporangia is increased, more being added centrally and a rounded 'heap' built up (Fig. 120). For the larger number of sporangia more space for attachment is required, and the leaf surface is raised as a mound or *receptacle*. By elongation of the receptacle still further increase is possible, and sequence in development of sporangia appears. With the development of a basal meristem, elongation may go on for some time with continuous production of new sporangia basipetally. Enlargement of the receptacle may be lateral and a broader, flatter type formed.

A definite relation exists between sori and the vascular tissue of the leaf; each sorus lies usually over a vein ending or along the back of a vein. Primitively the sorus lay at the end of a vein; with the change to the dorsal position it has sometimes come to lie along the back. When the sorus is over a vein ending, the vascular bundle may extend well into the receptacle.

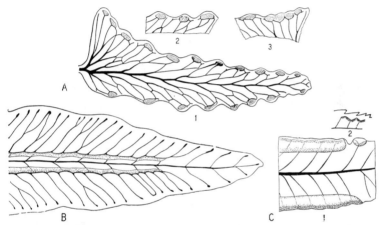

Fig. 103.—The coenosorus. *A*, *Diellia falcata* showing (1) sori solitary on vein endings and fused, and (2, 3) advanced stages of soral fusion. *B*, *Blechnum orientale*, two coenosori with continuous false indusia; the "blade" lateral to the sori is a "flange," a projection of the leaf blade proper (Fig. 104 *E*, *F*). *C*, *Pteris serrulata* showing (1) two coenosori and a solitary sorus, and (2) venation— vein tips forked and united in a sympodial marginal vein which supplies the coenosorus. (*A*, *B*, *from Bower, "The Ferns" by permission of the Cambridge University Press, publishers; C, after Goebel.*)

Where there are no definite sori, the sporangia are borne (*a*) over the surface of slender leaf divisions, as in *Osmunda* (Fig. 113*A*); (*b*) solitary, along or close to the margins of narrow leaf segments, as in *Schizaea* and *Anemia* (Figs. 122, 123); (*c*) over a large part or all of the dorsal leaf surface, as in *Acrostichum*. The first condition is sometimes called the *tasseled*, the last the *acrostichoid*. The tasseled and the solitary arrangements appear to be primitive; the acrostichoid represents the highest soral condition, the soral limits being lost and the sporangia dispersed over the leaf. The acrostichoid condition is found in several groups, representing a condition of sorus elaboration developed independently in those groups. This type of sporangium distribution has been considered a generic character, but it should not be given too great value in taxonomic study.

Indusium. The sori of the leptosporangiate ferns are protected in several ways. Circinate vernation may provide a shelter during the earliest stages. In a few, the sori lie in furrows in the blade or are covered by hairs. The most common types of protection are the *indusium* (Fig. 102*A* to *D,G*) and the reflexed or inrolled margin or lobe of the leaf (*Adiantum*). The

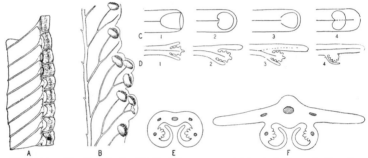

Fig. 104.—The "phyletic slide" of the sorus and false indusia. *A, Saccoloma elegans;* portion of pinna with marginal sori (the sporangia removed) showing fusion of ventral indusial lips to form a marginal flange, along the leaf blade. *B, Microlepia platyphylla;* portion of pinna with superficial sori. The ventral lips of the indusia are fused with the leaf blade. *C, D,* Diagrams showing stages in the phyletic slide of the sorus from marginal to superficial position: *C,* face view; *D,* vertical section. The ventral indusial lip is enlarged and is ultimately supplied with a vein. *C*1, *Davallia; C*2, *Humata; C*3, *Nephrolepis; C*4, *Dryopteris. E, F,* sections of pinnae showing sori protected by false indusia: *E, Lomaria* type, leaf margin inrolled, serving as an indusium; *F, Eublechnum* type, leaf margin as in *E,* flanges developed on 'shoulders' of blade. (*A* to *D, after Goebel; E, F, from Bower, "The Ferns," by permission of the Cambridge University Press, publishers.*)

indusium is a proliferation of the leaf surface, either of an area adjacent to the sorus or of the receptacle. The indusium is of most varied form and position, and doubtless is also of varied origin. It may surround the sorus as an upraised fold or ridge of delicate tissue, forming a cup-shaped (*Cyathea*, Fig. 168) or two-lipped structure (*Hymenophyllum*, Fig. 145*C*). It may cover the sorus as a scale-like structure attached laterally (*Cystopteris*, Fig. 102*A*) or as a radial, umbrella-like projection attached medianly on the placenta (Fig. 102*B*). Morphologically it apparently usually represents an epidermal ridge, but in some cases it seems to have formed by the fusion of a

whorl of hairs or scales.   As a ridge it is usually a minor upgrowth
of blade tissue, though in some cases it seems to be a major one.

The indusium in evolution has undergone remarkable modification in form and position.   Primitively it doubtless was a radial
structure, surrounding the sorus.   Zygomorphy developed,
probably at different times and in different ways.   Where the
change began while the sorus was marginal, the indusium became
first two-lipped (Fig. 102*D*); then, with the change to superficial
position, one lip was lost (being transformed into leaf margin or
merging with the expanding blade, Fig. 104*A* to *D*) and the
indusium became unilateral.   Where the change occurred in

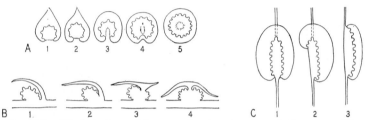

Fig. 105.—The indusium.   Diagrams showing steps in evolutionary modification.   *A, B*, face and vertical section views showing transition from lateral
zygomorphic to median radial indusium—*Cystopteris* type to *Aspidium* type; *C*,
face view showing transition from *Aspidium* type to *Athyrium* and *Asplenium*
type (indusium transparent).   (*After Goebel.*)

superficial sori (*Cyathea* to *Hemitelia*), the indusium was lost
except at one point.   From the zygomorphic form a radial
indusium has apparently again been built up, but of a different
type, with attachment in the center of the sorus.   The point of
attachment has migrated from the margin to the center of the
receptacle, and radial symmetry developed (Fig. 105*A,B*).
The elongate lateral indusium (Fig. 102*G*) has apparently been
derived from the simple zygomorphic type by the extension of
the area of attachment along one side, as the sorus became longer
(Fig. 105*C*).

Where the sorus is *naked* (without an indusium), it may either
be primitively of this type, ancestral forms never having possessed
an indusium, or it may have lost this protective structure.
Gleichenia (Fig. 120), *Plagiogyria* (Fig. 102*H*), and *Todea* (Fig.
113*D*), for example, belong to groups in which apparently no
indusium has ever been present; in some genera of the Polypodia-

ceae, on the other hand, where sori are naked (Fig. 102*E*), the ancestral forms undoubtedly had indusia.

A false indusium is formed when a part of the blade itself is folded back or rolled in and covers the sori (*Adiantum; Onoclea,* Fig. 99*B* to *D*). True indusia may be present under the false, but in such cases the former are usually reduced or vestigial. The line between true and false indusia is in some cases difficult to draw.

Where the sori are marginal the indusia are cup-shaped or two-valved, with one lobe ventral and one dorsal (Fig. 102*D*). This condition is surely related to the phyletic slide of the sorus to the dorsal surface, and the elaboration of such an indusium was probably one basis on which were taken the first steps toward the new position. The ventral part of the indusium was apparently built up into leaf blade and extended (Fig. 104*A* to *D*). Lateral fusion with lobes of adjacent indusia (Fig. 104*A,B*) built up a new leaf margin, which later was increased. Minor parts of the leaf blade in superficial forms may therefore be fundamentally elaborated indusia.

Another type of leaf modification led to a condition superficially similar. In this case (Fig. 104*E,F*) the leaf blade is reduced, becoming a false indusium, and a new blade is built up by the development of lateral projections. The blade then consists chiefly of wings; the apparent indusium is the body of the leaf blade; the sori are without true indusia.

Order of Development within Sorus. There are three types of order of development among the sporangia in a sorus. Where all the sporangia mature at once, the condition is said to be *simple;* where the sporangia mature progressively on an elongate receptacle, the condition is *gradate* (Fig. 106*C* to *E*); where sporangia of all ages occur together in a sorus, the condition is *mixed* (Fig. 106*A,B*). On this basis ferns are often grouped as *Simplices, Gradatae,* and *Mixtae.* The three types of sorus represent progressive stages in specialization, the simple being primitive and the mixed most advanced. In the gradate and mixed types the sporangia mature over a much longer period than in the simple, a condition supposedly of advantage biologically. The three groups are not natural, for they represent, in the character on which they are based, merely the attainment in elaboration of a certain level, and this level is reached in unrelated groups at the same time and in related groups at different times.

The form of the receptacle and the sequence in sporangial development are obviously correlated: in the Simplices the receptacle is merely an area or a low mound on the leaf surface; in the Gradatae the receptacle is elongate, reaching its greatest length in types with a basal meristem; in the Mixtae it is flattened and low—doubtless the first step toward the acrostichoid condition—and in some forms the sporangia arise, as in many Simplices, directly from the unraised leaf surface.

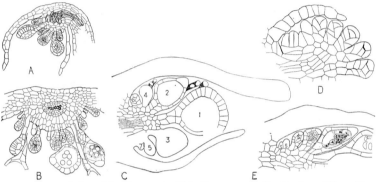

Fig. 106.—Order of development within the sorus: *A*, *B*, mixed condition; *C* to *E*, gradate condition. *A*, *Pteridium aquilinum*; *B*, *Polypodium aureum*; *C*, *Microlepia speluncae* (sporangia numbered in order of development); *D*, *Onoclea sensibilis*; *E*, *Dennstaedtia apiifolia* (*S*, developing sporangia). (*After Bower, B from "The Ferns," by permission of Cambridge University Press, publishers.*)

Sporangium. The sporangia are rounded or flattened structures, sessile or usually with a stalk, which varies from short and stout to long and slender, the latter condition being advanced. The orientation of the sporangia is in nearly all cases constant in the Simplices and Gradatae, but in the Mixtae there is no constancy. The wall is thin, of a single layer of cells with an annulus. The annulus varies greatly in form and in degree of specialization. It is, however, constant for families and provides a taxonomic character of much value. In dehiscence a series exists from longitudinal (over the apex) to transverse, the method of opening being correlated with the elaboration of the annulus. In the simple and gradate groups the annulus is unspecialized, or is transverse or oblique; in the Mixtae it is usually vertical. The function of the annulus at first is merely to open the wall, allowing the spores to sift out; when most specialized, it actively disperses them. Both bilateral and tetrahedral spore types are found. In spore number there is progressive reduction from lower to higher forms.

Development of Sporangium. The method of development of the sporangium sets this group of ferns apart from the others. Here the sporangium is formed from a single initial—the leptosporangiate method—whereas under the eusporangiate method (page 8) a number of initials are concerned. There are further important differences in these two methods of sporangium

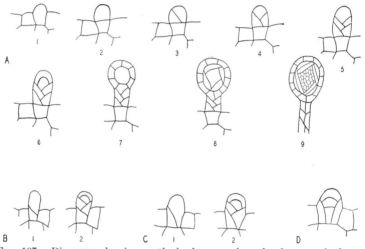

Fɪɢ. 107.—Diagrams showing method of sporangium development in leptosporangiate ferns. *A,* the usual method; *B* to *D,* variations in early stages.

development. In each case superficial cells are concerned, and the first division is periclinal or oblique. Under the eusporangiate method the cells so formed build together the sporangium and its contents, the outer forming the wall, the inner the sporogenous tissue; under the leptosporangiate method the outer cell builds the entire sporangium, its contents, and its stalk, the inner cell taking no part in the process.

The progress of leptosporangiate development is as follows (Fig. 107*A*): Following the first division of the initial, the outer cell becomes a pyramidal apical cell which cuts off basal cells to form a stalk until a distal, arched, periclinal division limits growth in length. There is thus formed a central cell, usually tetrahedral in form, surrounded by a one-layered wall. Anticlinal divisions in the wall divide this layer into many cells. The central cell represents the primary sporogenous tissue. From it are cut off by periclinal divisions one or two layers of thin cells which become the tapetum. The remaining central cell is divided to form, ultimately, the sporocytes, which vary in number in different families.

Vegetative Propagation. Reproduction is secured vegetatively by several methods. The chief method is that of deciduous leaf-borne buds which are formed in many species in different families. These buds are borne on the blade; in the axils of pinnae; at the tip or along the sides of the lengthened rachis; or on bladeless leaf runners.

Apospory. The development of gametophytes directly from sporangial or soral tissue, without the formation of spores, is found in some of the families. The prothallium may develop from cells of an abortive sporangium, or directly from cells of the leaf surface or margin without the beginning of sporangium structure.

GAMETOPHYTE

The prothallia are mostly thalloid, green, and surface-living, cordate in form and thin in texture, with the sex organs on the lower side—archegonia on the thickened central cushion or ridge, and antheridia more broadly distributed. In most forms the prothallia are monoecious, and perhaps in all, with the exception of the heterosporous forms, they are potentially so. Under some conditions of light and moisture supply, dioecious plants develop in forms that are typically monoecious: the crowded and starved individuals are male; those under more favorable growth conditions are female, or bear sex organs of both types. Conditions as to separation of sexes are apparently somewhat similar to those in *Equisetum* (page 102). It is claimed that some species even under favorable conditions are incompletely dioecious— part of the individuals being female, the others bearing both kinds of sex organs; but this condition is probably only a form of the normal monoecious state, since the female individuals may—if fertilization does not occur—develop adventitious branches which bear antheridia. In rare cases prothallia are perhaps normally dioecious.

The antheridia differ greatly from those of the Ophioglossales and Marattiales. They are projecting subspherical structures

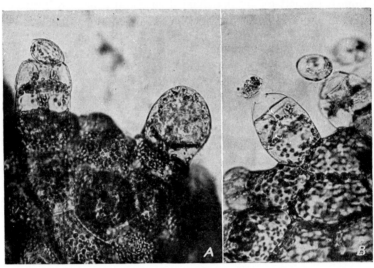

Fig. 108.—*A, Onoclea sensibilis; B, Athyrium Filix-foemina.* Antheridia of advanced type showing dehiscence. (*After Hartman.*)

(Fig. 108), with a sperm number much smaller than that of these other groups. There is considerable variety in structure, with a

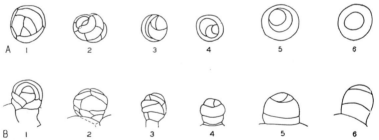

Fig. 109.—Antheridia of leptosporangiate ferns showing progress in simplification. *A*, top view; *B*, side view. 1, *Osmunda* (Osmundaceae); 2, *Gleichenia* (Gleicheniaceae); 3, *Trichomanes* (Hymenophyllaceae); 4, *Hemitelia* (Cyatheaceae); 5, *Woodsia* (Polypodiaceae); 6, *Athyrium* (Polypodiaceae). (1, 2, *after Campbell; 3, after Bower; 4, after Stokey; 5, after Schlumberger; 6, based on Hartman.*)

definitely established progress from fairly complex to simple (Fig. 109). The chief differences are in number and form of the wall cells, the presence or absence of a base or stalk, and the

number of sperms.   The method of development and the form
commonly illustrated in textbooks is the simplest—that of the
highest families.   It is in general as follows (Fig. 110*B*): A

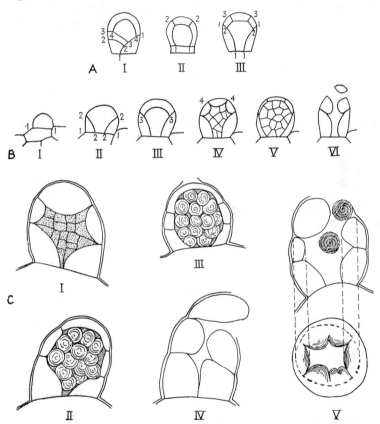

Fig. 110.—Antheridia of leptosporangiate ferns.   *A*, variations in structure
and development (as seen in optical longitudinal sections) showing progress
toward simplification: *A* I, Osmundaceae; *A* II, Schizaeaceae; *A* III, Polypodiaceae (Fig. 109).   *B*, development of simple, high type.   *C*, late stages in
development of the simple type (*Woodsia*): *C* I, spermatogenous cells enclosed
by two collar-like cells and a cap cell; *C* II, sperms mature, wall cells compressed;
C III, mature antheridium, the cuticle ruptured; *C* IV, same antheridium as in
C II, the cap cell raised, the wall cells expanded, the sperms extruded; *C* V,
dehiscing antheridium in optical longitudinal section and top view showing
nature of star-like opening.   (*A, after Goebel; C, after Schlumberger.*)

papillate projection is cut from an epidermal cell by a periclinal
division.   The cell thus cut off enlarges and is divided in an
unusual manner, by a funnel-shaped wall which in most cases

reaches the basal wall of the cell.   A large upper and central cell is thus formed, surrounded by a collar-like, outer, basal cell. In the upper cell an arching periclinal wall cuts off an outer hemispherical cell.   There are now three cells, two outer and an inner.   In the upper outer cell, a circular division next cuts out a central *cap cell*, which forms a lid-like top.   The wall of the antheridium now consists of a single layer of cells, three in number, two ring-like, the third cap-like in form.   The wall cells are at first expanded and compress the central cell.   Divisions of the central cell form sperm mother cells, in most cases 32.   As these cells mature, they enlarge greatly compressing the

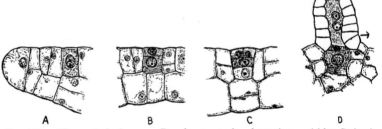

A   B   C   D

Fig. 111.—*Thyrsopteris elegans.*   Development of archegonium.   (*After Stokey.*)

wall cells (Fig. 110*B*, V; *C*, III).   When the sperms are mature, the cap cell is loosened and the cuticle ruptured.   In most cases the cap cell is pushed off, though it may be freed merely at one edge and lifted like a lid (Figs. 108*A*; 110*C*, V).   The opening is instantaneous, and the sperms are forced out by the enlargement of the flattened wall cells.   The sperms are multiciliate and similar to those of other ferns.   The star-like outline of the opening, which is characteristic of empty antheridia of most families, is not the result of disintegration of the cap cell, as has been commonly supposed, but represents the inner limits of the wall cells protruding into the antheridium cavity (Fig. 110*C*, V).

In the development of the more complex types the first divisions may form a base of one to several cells, and the dome-shaped cell may be divided by walls running over the top (Figs. 109*A*, 1–4, *B*, 1–4; 110*A*).   In such forms no cap cell as such is formed, although it may be said that the cap cell is divided several times, the last division cutting out a cell which serves to provide an opening.

The archegonium is similar to that of other ferns in general form. The development is that usually described for the fern archegonium. An epidermal initial, by periclinal division, cuts off a primary neck cell (Fig. 111). The inner cell, then, by a similar division forms a basal cell and a central cell. From the neck cell by anticlinal divisions is built up the neck; from the central cell by periclinal divisions the axial row, which consists of an egg cell, a ventral canal cell, and two or four neck canal cells or nuclei. The basal cell (which in some cases is not formed) takes no important part in the development of the archegonium. One or two divisions, anticlinal or periclinal, may occur in it.

The neck of the archegonium of leptosporangiate ferns is in general longer and projects farther than that of the Marattiales and of most of the Ophioglossales. Within the group there is some variation in length, the more advanced forms having the shorter necks; and in form, the primitive types being straight, the advanced recurved.

Apogamy. Frequently, in the higher families, the young sporophyte develops from the gametophyte without the union of gametes, growing directly from the cushion by a process of budding. Archegonia may be present but if so are nonfunctional.

Embryo

The first division of the zygote is nearly always longitudinal, parallel with the long axis of the archegonium and apparently typically at right angles to the long axis of the prothallium. Definite and mostly uniform quadrants are formed, and these are related to the organs of the embryo. (For further discussion see later chapters.)

CHAPTER IX

OSMUNDACEAE ROYAL FERNS

The Osmundaceae form one of the smallest groups of the leptosporangiate ferns. There are only two genera, *Osmunda* and *Todea*, with about 17 species. The first genus is cosmopolitan, the second confined to Australasia and South Africa. The various species live chiefly in shade in moist woodlands. Though small, the family is of special interest because in some respects it is intermediate between eusporangiate and leptosporangiate types. Some species of *Todea*, especially those with filmy fronds, are grown in greenhouses.

SPOROPHYTE

Habit. All the species are perennials with short, erect or ascending stems and a crown of large leaves. In *Todea* the older plants resemble small tree ferns in habit. The stems of *Osmunda* in temperate zones are subterranean because of the great mass of fibrous roots which covers them and forms a hummock on which the plant seems to be growing. In some species, especially in the drier soils, the rhizomes are semiprostrate.

Stems. The stems are stout and clothed with ragged persistent leaf bases and many hard, dark roots. In temperate regions the stems are usually buried to a greater or less extent in humus. In *Todea* they may form erect 'trunks' 1 or 2 m tall. Growth is in all cases slow, and the leaf bases are closely packed. Branching, which is dichotomous, is infrequent or rare in most species.

Leaves. The leaves are large, reaching in *O. cinnamomea*, the cinnamon fern, and other species a length of 2 or 3 m, and pinnately or bipinnately compound. The stout petioles have stipule-like wings at the base. The blade ranges in texture from leathery to filmy. In some species of *Todea* it approaches in thinness that of the Hymenophyllaceae, being only two or three cell layers thick and lacks stomata and intercellular mesophyll

176

spaces.   The filmy species of the genus are by some taxonomists regarded as constituting a separate genus, *Leptopteris*.   But the filmy character is present in other families and is clearly the result of adaptation to moist and deeply shaded habitats, and is not in itself a basis for generic distinction.   It provides an excellent example of parallel development.   The spreading fronds of *Todea superba* and similar species with shining, translucent blades and finely cut segments place these plants among the most beautiful of ferns.

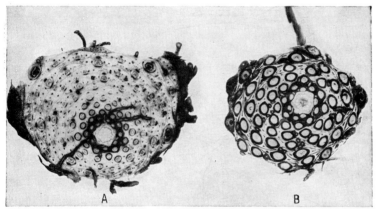

FIG. 112.—Stem structure of the Osmundaceae.   *A, Osmunda cinnamomea; B, O. regalis.*   The stems are clothed with abundant, persistent leaf bases.   The small, light core is the stele.   The dark layer surrounding the stele is the sclerotic cortex.   Roots penetrate the leaf bases.   The leaf traces show the spiral leaf arrangement.   ×3.

Leaf arrangement is spiral (Fig. 112) although the basket-like clusters suggest a whorled position.   The dermal appendages are simple hairs, which are in many cases soft, long, and abundant.

Roots.   The roots, two at the base of each leaf, are coarse and hard, flattened where they project between the appressed leaf bases.   They branch freely and form dense firm masses about the stem.   In wet habitats the upper roots of some species form just below the leaf crown a mat of delicate aerial roots densely covered with brown root hairs.   In old plants of *Todea barbara* large masses of tangled roots bury the branching stem so that the 'trunk' becomes an irregular rounded mound with a diameter of 1 m or more—hence the name "elephant fern."

Anatomy.   The stem has a massive cortex of dark-colored sclerenchyma and a stele which is proportionally very small

(Fig. 112).   The thick stem is in considerable part made up of the armor of persistent leaf bases.   The vascular tissue forms a reticulate cylinder of many strands from which the leaf traces depart obliquely, passing for some distance through the sclerotic cortex.   These traces, crescent-shaped in cross section, are prominent in the dark cortex and conspicuous features of the anatomy.

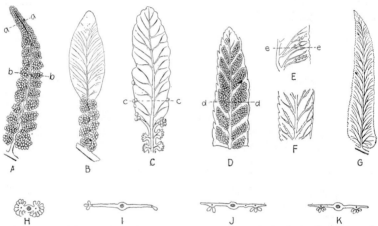

FIG. 113.—Pinnae of the Osmundaceae showing method of transformation of tassels into expanded fertile blade with dorsal sori.   *A* to *C*, *E*, *G* to *I*, *K*, *Osmunda regalis; D, F, J, Todea africana.   A*, fertile pinna with tassels; *B*, pinna with proximal portion fertile, distal portion sterile; *C*, pinna as in *B*, but with transitional median region where sporangia are borne marginally; *D*, pinna with large dorsal sori, the sori representing tassels connected by blade tissue developed from their axes between and ventral to them; *E*, portion of green pinna with abortive sporangia; *F*, portion of *D* with sporangia removed; *G*, sterile pinna; *H*, cross section of *A* at *b-b; I*, cross section of *C* at *c-c; J*, cross section of *D* at *d-d; K*, cross section of *E* at *e-e.   (*B, D, F, after Bauer; C, after Zimmermann; E, H, after Goebel.*)

The stem of the young plant is protostelic, but a pith is formed after the first few leaves develop.   An external endodermis is present, an internal one and internal phloem only rarely.   The leaf gaps are small.   The vascular bundles are horseshoe shape in cross section and form a compact cylinder. The xylem is endarch in most species, mesarch in the others. The tracheids are scalariform-pitted, with abundant, narrow elongate pits.

Reproduction.   In *Todea* sterile and fertile leaves are much alike, with the sporangia on the dorsal surface in clusters along

the lateral veins (Fig. 113*D*). There are no indusia. In
Osmunda the leaf is divided into fertile and sterile parts, the
former bladeless and nongreen. In *O. regalis* the terminal
part is fertile, in *O. Claytoniana* a median part. In *O. cinnamomea* certain leaves, two or three each season, are given over
wholly to sporangium bearing; these are brown, without photosynthetic tissue, and shrivel as soon as the spores are shed.
In this genus the sporangia are borne on slender leaf segments,
covering them densely (Figs. 113*A*, 114*A*) and forming short-
cylindrical clusters, which are commonly called "marginal
tassels" (Fig. 113*A*). Leaflets intermediate between typical

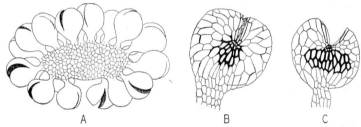

A   B   C

Fig. 114.—*Osmunda regalis.* Cross section of tassel (*a-a* in Fig. 113 *A*)
showing arrangement of sporangia; *B*, *C*, sporangia, showing form, dehiscence,
and annulus. (*A, after Bauer; B, C, after Williams.*)

fertile and sterile forms are frequent. These transitional
leaflets (Fig. 113*B,C*), which have both green blade and sporangia,
show that in this family the dorsal position of the sporangia
(*Todea*) has been derived from the tassel condition (*Osmunda*),
with a marginal position apparently intermediate. The tassels
correspond to sections of the sterile leaflets (Fig. 113*C*). The
intermediate forms (Fig. 113*B,C,E,F*) show the development of
blade tissue between, and ultimately above, the fertile segments,
so that the clusters become dorsal.

The sporangia of this family are large for forms in the
true ferns, pyriform with a stout short stalk and a wall of one
cell layer (Fig. 114). The annulus is a cluster of lateral cells
near the apex or a short, broad, transverse row (Fig. 114*B,C*).
In dehiscence the wall splits over the apex and down the opposite
side and opens widely. The spore output is 128 to 512, which
is large for leptosporangiate forms. All the sporangia of a region
mature together, that is, they are of the Simplices type.

In development the sporangium is inconstant. It may be formed from a single epidermal cell (the method found in leptosporangiate ferns) or from more than one cell (the usual method in eusporangiate types), cells around the initial entering into the formation of the wall and stalk. In each case the segmentation of the initial, usually conical in the first case and cubical in the second (Fig. 115), is variable. The tapetum is massive, with two or three layers.

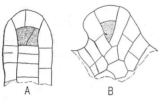

FIG. 115.—Sporangium development in the Osmundaceae. Early stages: *A*, from cubical initial; *B*, from conical initial. (*After Bower,* "*The Ferns*," *by permission of The Cambridge University Press.*)

GAMETOPHYTE

The spherical spores have a prominent triradiate ridge and abundant chloroplasts (Fig. 116*A*) and germinate within 24 hours. The mature gametophytes are elongate, dark-green, fleshy thalli with a projecting midrib on the lower side (Fig. 116*I*).

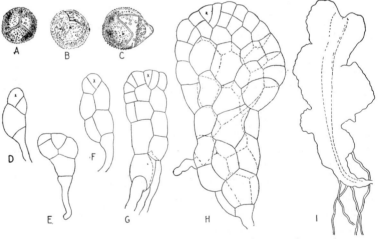

FIG. 116.—*Osmunda Claytoniana.* Development of gametophyte. *A*, spore; *B*, spore with wall breaking open along triradiate ridge; *C*, first division, rhizoidal cell formed; *D* to *H* successive stages in development; *I*, mature gametophyte (midrib indicated by dotted lines). (*After Campbell.*)

They are long-lived, living more than one year, and may reach a length of 5 cm. They resemble those of the Marattiaceae more than those of leptosporangiate ferns.

The early stages are variable. The first division usually cuts off a small rhizoidal cell (Fig. 116*C*); the following divisions may result in the formation of a several-celled filament or a mass of cells (Fig. 116*D* to *H*). In either case growth by an apical cell is soon established, and a thick thallus built up. Growth in later stages is by marginal cells. Adventitious lobes commonly form at the base and break away, establishing new plants.

Sex Organs. The gametophytes are typically monoecious, but the smaller weaker ones are usually male. The antheridia are formed on the margins and lower side of the thinner lateral parts. In small slender types they may be terminal. The archegonia develop on the sides of the midrib region and project

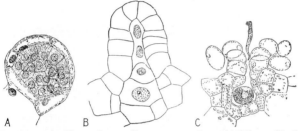

A   B   C

Fig. 117.—*Osmunda Claytoniana.* Sex organs. *A,* antheridium; *B, C,* archegonium; *C,* open, with egg and remains of canal cells. (*After Campbell.*)

horizontally. The antheridia (Fig. 117*A*) are projecting structures as in all leptosporangiate ferns, but are large and complex as compared with those of other families. In a superficial cell a wall is formed which cuts out one basal corner and meets the basal wall. (Thus there is no funnel-shaped basal cell.) Others similarly cut out basal portions successively, the main cell behaving like a three-sided apical cell and in most cases building up a short, stout stalk, on which the antheridium stands (Fig. 109*B* 1). After basal divisions cease, a dome-shaped periclinal wall cuts out a cover cell which is divided into three or four cells, one of which is the cap cell. The cell below forms spermatogenous tissue from which come 100 or more sperms. The development of the archegonium is much as in other ferns. The neck has the usual four rows but is longer than that of the eusporangiate types, having about six tiers, and projects farther (Fig. 117*B*). The axial row is, however, much the same. The neck canal cell is two-nucleate, with at times a wall between the nuclei as in the Marattiaceae.

Embryo

The first division in the fertilized egg is parallel with the archegonium axis (Fig. 118*A*) and usually parallel with the anterior-posterior axis of the gametophyte. The second division is probably in most cases also parallel with the archegonium axis but at right angles to the first, that is, as seen in Fig. 118, in the plane of the page. (This division is reported to be in some cases transverse to the archegonium axis.) In both cases quadrant cells are formed, but the relation of these quadrants to

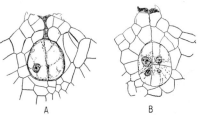

A   B

Fig. 118.—*Osmunda Claytoniana.* Archegonia with young embryos. *A*, 4-cell stage; *B*, 8-cell stage. (*After Campbell.*)

the embryonic organs is apparently not constant. Octants are then formed (Fig. 118*B*), but the divisions which follow are not regular. It is doubtful whether the young organs can be referred to definite quadrants, the condition in most leptosporangiate ferns, as is claimed by some students. The many-celled embryo, which is soon built up, retains its more or less spherical shape for some time—longer than in typical leptosporangiates. Apparently the leaf and stem come from approximately the half next the archegonium neck, the foot from the other half. The root is endogenous in origin, not exogenous as it is when developed directly from a quadrant cell. The young leaf does not develop rapidly and break through the archegonium tissue early, as is usual in leptosporangiate forms. The foot becomes large, extending deeply into the prothallium, with its surface cells sometimes markedly haustorial. The young sporophyte grows out, in most cases, laterally from under the prothallium rather than anteriorly, as usual in leptosporangiate ferns.

Discussion and Summary

The Osmundaceae are in many ways intermediate between the eusporangiate ferns and typical leptosporangiate ferns. In the development of the sporangium more than one cell is involved in many cases.   Among the initials there are both the cubical type (characteristic of eusporangiates) and the conical type (found only in the leptosporangiates), the latter more common. The sporangium is large and bears many spores—fewer, however, than in the eusporangiates—and has a tapetum of two or three layers, but it is thin-walled.   The annulus is of primitive type, a mere cluster or short band of cells, not a specialized ring. It is, further, in many cases indefinite in limit, its thick walls merging into the thinner walls of surrounding cells (Fig. 114). The opening is apical (longitudinal), apparently the primitive position for dehiscence.

The gametophyte is large, fleshy, and long-lived, much resembling that of the Marattiaceae.   Sex organs are, however, borne only on the lower surface.   The antheridia are of the leptosporangiate type—projecting, not sunken—but contain a much larger number of sperms than those of other families. The archegonia, in their longer, projecting necks, are similar to the typical leptosporangiate form.

The first division of the fertilized egg is, as in leptosporangiate forms generally, parallel with the archegonium axis.   It is, however, in a different plane, being parallel with the anterior-posterior axis of the prothallium rather than transverse to this. The second division is also commonly longitudinal, but is in some cases transverse.   The early segmentation of the embryo thus follows the method of neither group.   Quadrants are formed, but it is apparently not possible to trace the organs directly to these. In this and in the fact that the leaf, stem, and root arise from one half of the embryo, the other half forming a foot, there is resemblance to the eusporangiate forms.   There is further similarity to these forms in the endogenous origin of the root and the presence of a large foot.   The embryo is, however, prone, as in leptosporangiates, and not erect, as in eusporangiates, and the leaf and stem of the young sporophyte appear from beneath the gametophyte rather than pierce the thallus.

The winged petiole bases suggest stipules, and a resemblance has been seen in this feature to the stipule-bearing eusporangiate groups.

In anatomy the family is distinct.   Its abundant sclerenchyma is in strong contrast with the soft tissues of the eusporangiate

families.   Its complex stele is of a type altogether different from
the complex stele of the Marattiaceae.

Osmunda is the more primitive genus in method of sporangium
bearing; here, as in other families, the dorsal position is advanced,
and the condition in *Todea* has been derived from that in *Osmunda*.
That the series is to be read in this direction is clear.   Evidence
from fossil types (Chaps. XIV, XVI) indicates that bladeless fertile
leaf segments represent a primitive stage.   This is the condition
in the Ophioglossaceae, a primitive fern group.   (The method of
sporangium bearing, though suggesting that of *Botrychium* and
Helminthostachys, is, however, somewhat unlike that of these
genera.)   In *Osmunda* neither type of leaf segment is to be
considered derived from the other; both exist in earliest land
plants.

The family is a primitive one.   It appears transitional between
the leptosporangiate and the eusporangiate families, but its
characters are as a whole not definitely intermediate, and it
surely does not connect the groups phylogenetically.   Fundamentally its characters are closer to those of the leptosporangiate
group than to those of the eusporangiate forms.   Its relation to
other ferns is further discussed later.

GLEICHENIACEAE

Although only a small family, the Gleicheniaceae show
characters of much morphological interest.   There are only
two genera—*Stromatopteris,* which is monotypic, and *Gleichenia,*
with about 80 species—which inhabit the tropics and the temperate parts of the southern hemisphere.   Many of the species
are xerophytic and are found in dry sunny habitats where they
may form masses of vegetation.

Sporophyte

Habit.   All species are rhizome types, most of them with
large, scrambling leaves of peculiar form.   The stems branch
dichotomously, and in most species the leaves also appear to
fork freely in this manner.   The dichotomy of the leaf is, however, false: terminal growth is arrested by the formation of a
dormant bud (Fig. 119); growth in length is continued by lateral
pinnae, which in turn cease to grow apically.   Thus a conspicuous

pseudodichotomy is built up. With growth of this sort, lateral lobes successively taking up elongation, and with such growth continued for a long time, extensive straggling leaves are formed which become entangled with other similar leaves and often form almost impenetrable thickets. Under special conditions the dormant tips may take up the growth at a later time.

Reproduction. There is no segregation of fertile and sterile leaf parts; the sporangia are borne in sori on the dorsal surface

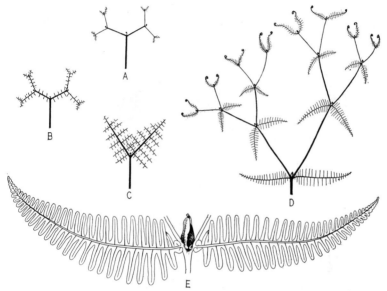

Fig. 119.—Leaf of the Gleicheniaceae. *A* to *D*, diagrams showing variety of leaf form; *E*, portion of leaf at fork, showing dormant terminal leaf-bud. (*A to C, after Diels in Engler and Prantl; E, after Goebel.*)

of green leaves. The sorus is in many species a flat, rounded cluster with a uniseriate ring of a very few large sporangia—in most species two to six—and no indusium (Fig. 120*A* to *D*). In some cases solitary sporangia are frequent. In other species accessory sporangia are borne centrally above and between the members of the usual whorl, forming an upper tier (Fig. 120*B* to *D*). The sporangia are commonly closely appressed to one another and in some species may be fused to some extent. The sporangia are pyriform, subsessile, or with short stalks (Fig. 120*E,F*), and with a sharply defined uniseriate annulus which is oblique-horizontal and complete except at the line of dehiscence, which is longitudinal (Fig. 120*D*).   The spore number varies greatly in different species but is always large: (128), 256, 512, (1024).   There is no indusium, but in a few species protection is secured by a partial sinking in the leaf blade.

Sporangium development follows the leptosporangiate method but is said to be not quite so regular as in higher families.   The tapetum is of two layers, with one massive.   The sporangia of a sorus mature simultaneously.

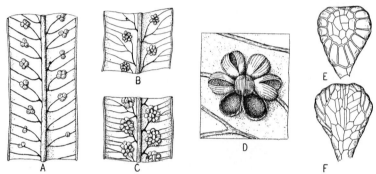

Fig. 120.—Sori and sporangia of the Gleicheniaceae.   *A, Gleichenia pubescens; B, D,   G. linearis; C,   G. pectinata; E, F,   G. dichotoma.   A* to *C*, portions of leaf showing size and position of sori; *D*, a sorus showing number, arrangement, and dehiscence of sporangia; *E, F*, sporangia showing annulus.   (*B* to *D, after Bower; E, F, after Campbell, "Mosses and Ferns," with permission of The Macmillan Company, publishers.*)

Anatomy.   The family is simple anatomically.   Most of the species have protostelic stems with mesarch xylem, and leaves with large, simple traces.

GAMETOPHYTE

The prothallium is of the common thalloid type but usually shows an elongate midrib, resembling that of the Marattiaceae and the Osmundaceae.   This midrib develops early and in some species becomes prominent.   The wings often are fluted and leaf-like, and the prothallium becomes complex in form.   Adventitious lobes are borne freely on the margins and lower surface; these may break away and form normal prothallia.   The archegonia are borne on the sides of the midrib and at its apex. Their necks are long (of about 10 tiers) and straight or bent forward.   In most cases a wall separates the two neck canal cells.   The antheridia are borne on the lower side of the wings and on the sides of the midrib, and, in at least one species, also on the upper side of wings and midrib. They are large—the largest yet reported in leptosporangiate ferns—and may, in some species, contain several hundred sperms. They are borne on a stout stalk and in general much resemble the antheridia of the Osmundaceae (Fig. 109B2). An endophytic fungus is present. (There is apparently considerable variation in size and structure of the antheridium and in the number of sperms in different species.)

EMBRYO

Little is known in detail about the embryo, but it appears to be of the leptosporangiate type.

DISCUSSION AND SUMMARY

The family possesses characters which definitely indicate primitiveness. The stems are dichotomous and in most species protostelic. The leaves have indeterminate growth. The sorus is simple, without an indusium. In many species the sporangia are in a single row, as in the Marattiaceae. The sporangia are large, rounded, with many spores, and all those in a sorus develop together. The gametophytes resemble those of the Osmundaceae and Marattiaceae in form and multiply by fragmentation as do those of primitive families. In the presence of antheridia on both surfaces there is further resemblance to the Marattiaceae, and in the fact that the archegonia are borne on the sides of the midrib to the Osmundaceae. In the large size and many sperms of the antheridia there is resemblance to both these families. The archegonium necks are long and straight or curved forward, and the two neck canal cells are usually separated by a wall. (In advanced families the curve in the neck is backward.)

The sorus shows in the various species an advance in number of sporangia from the flat simple whorl with one to six (Fig. 120A), to the heap with many (Fig. 120C). The additional sporangia are placed in the center and above the original series, forming a soral type which seems to be a step toward the elongate type of more advanced families. In form and position, and in the tendency to synangy, the sorus resembles that of the Marattiaceae.

From this evidence the family is a primitive one among leptosporangiate types. This conclusion is borne out by the fossil record (Chap. XVI).   Though possessing several important primitive characters in common with the Osmundaceae and the

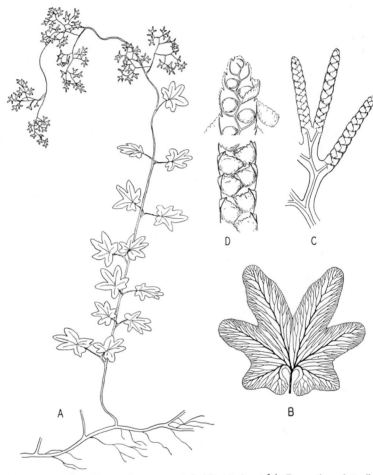

Fig. 121.—*Lygodium palmatum.*   *A*, habit, × about ⅕; *B*, portion of sterile pinna; *C*, portion of fertile pinna; *D*, portion of *C* enlarged showing solitary sporangia covered by lobes of leaf tissue.   (*A, after Lotsy, modified.   B, after Prantl in Engler and Prantl.*)

Marattiaceae, the differences, especially those of anatomy, are so great that there is no obvious relationship with either of these families.

SCHIZAEACEAE

The Schizaeaceae are a small family of wide distribution, with the majority of forms in the tropics and the southern hemisphere. There are four genera—*Schizaea, Lygodium, Anemia,* and *Mohria* —and about 115 species. The family is represented in north-

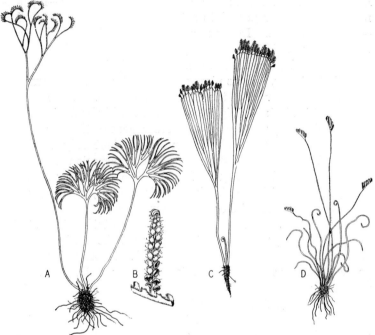

Fig. 122.—*Schizaea. A, B, S. dichotoma,* $\times \frac{1}{5}$; *C, S. flabellum,* $\times \frac{1}{6}$; *D, S. pusilla,* about natural size. *A, C, D,* habit; *B,* portion of fertile frond enlarged showing large, solitary, marginal sporangia. (*A, C, after Lotsy; B, after Bauer.*)

eastern North America by two unusual ferns—the tiny "curly grass," *Schizaea pusilla* (Fig. 122*D*), and the beautiful "climbing fern," *Lygodium palmatum* (Fig. 121), the use of which for decorative purposes has been responsible for its extermination in many regions.

SPOROPHYTE

Habit. The species vary greatly in size and habit; there are large and small, upright and creeping forms, with leaves of many types arranged in various ways.   From habit alone some species of *Schizaea* (Fig. 122) would hardly be recognized as ferns.   The branching of the stem is dichotomous.

Leaves.   In several respects the leaves of this family present important morphological features.   Apical growth is in some forms long-continued, extending even over years in species of *Lygodium*.   Such leaves are almost—perhaps truly—indeterminate; they are reported to attain in some cases great length —30 m and more.   In appearance and behavior, as well as in this unlimited apical growth, they resemble stems.   The climbing fern is a good example: the stem is entirely below ground; the leaf climbs freely, and its pinnae resemble leaves (Fig. 121*A*).

In form the leaves of the family are diverse.   Dichotomy is prominent in *Schizaea* (Fig. 122) and can readily be distinguished in *Lygodium* (Fig. 121); in the other genera the fronds are apparently pinnate, though this condition undoubtedly represents concealed or modified dichotomy.   The venation is chiefly dichotomous and open (Fig. 121*B*).   The dermal appendages (except in *Mohria*) are simple and filamentous, in many cases resembling the soft hairs of the Osmundaceae.

Reproduction.   The leaves are typically divided into sterile and fertile parts, the latter being the tips of the leaf lobes (Figs. 121*A*, 122*C*) or entire pinnae (Fig. 123).   In *Anemia* the two lower pinnae are fertile and raised on long stalks (Fig. 123), resembling in position and appearance the fertile 'spike' of *Botrychium* (Fig. 78).   In species of *Schizaea* some of the leaves are fertile, others sterile (Fig. 122*A,D*), as in *Osmunda cinnamomea*.   The fertile leaf segments in these various types are bladeless or provided with a narrow lamina (Figs. 121*C*, 122*B*). *Mohria* differs from other members of the family in that the sporophylls are leaves with broad blades.

The sporangia are solitary and borne on the margin, or close to the margin on the dorsal surface of the leaf, where they form two rows (Figs. 121*D*, 122*B*, 123*B*).   They are large, spherical, ovoid or ellipsoid, sessile or with short stout stalk.   The apical cap-like annulus (Figs. 122*B*, 123*B*) usually consists of a single complete row of cells, sharply defined, but in some forms it is ill-defined with rather indefinite rows of cells.   The sporangia are usually naked, but in *Lygodium* (Fig. 121*D*) they are covered by folds of leaf tissue.   These protective flaps are not true

Fig. 123.—*Anemia mandioccana.* *A,* frond, $\times\frac{2}{3}$. *B, C,* portion of fertile pinna enlarged. (*After Bauer.*)

indusia but consist of extensions of the leaf margin which run back over the lower surface.

The sporangia arise from strictly marginal cells, but during development they become dorsal in most forms by the growth of the leaf blade above and beyond them (Fig. 124). This change of position of sporangia during development, which is found also in other families, is spoken of as the "ontogenetic slide" and is

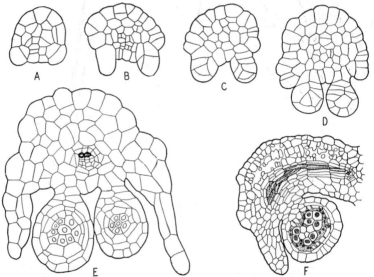

Fig. 124.—Sporangium development and position in the Schizaeceae. *A* to *E*, *Schizaea rupestris*; *F*, *Mohria caffrorum*. *A* to *E*, cross sections of young pinna showing development of marginal sporangia which become apparently dorsal in position, and development of ventral indusial 'shoulders'; *F*, vertical section through tip of pinna showing marginal (apparently dorsal) sporangium. A false leaf margin is formed by indusial outgrowth. (*After Bower.*)

considered a part of the evidence that the superficial position in ferns generally has been derived from the marginal. The method of development is leptosporangiate. The tapetum is massive and in most cases two-layered. The spores are tetrahedral or bilateral, and numerous—usually 128 (256 in some species, and 64 in one hygrophilous species).

Anatomy. The group is simple anatomically. The stems of the four genera show a series from a protostele (*Lygodium*) through simple siphonosteles to dictyosteles. The leaf traces are simple.

GAMETOPHYTE

The prothallia in three genera are of the cordate thalloid type common in ferns, but in *Schizaea* they are filamentous, resembling uniseriate branching algae (Fig. 125). Adventitious lobes develop freely at the base of the thalloid forms. The sex organs are of the type common in leptosporangiate ferns, though the number of sperms is in general larger and the archegonium neck

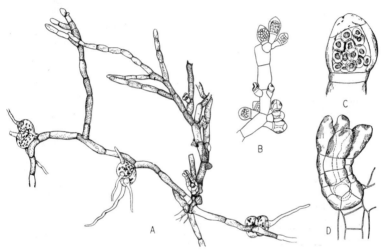

FIG. 125.—*Schizaea pusilla.* Gametophyte. *A*, portion of filament showing archegonium, antheridia, and swollen, mycorrhizal cells; *B*, antheridial branch showing antheridia of various ages; *C*, antheridium; *D*, archegonium. (*After Britten and Taylor.*)

is straighter. In *Schizaea* the sex organs are terminal on short lateral branches (Fig. 125*B* to *D*); the archegonium is entirely exposed (Fig. 125*A,D*), as nowhere else in vascular plants. The filaments have numerous greatly enlarged cells which are mycorrhizal and to which are attached rhizoids.

The development of the embryo is apparently of the type characteristic of leptosporangiate ferns.

DISCUSSION AND SUMMARY

Many characters point to primitiveness in this family. Dichotomy of stem and leaf is outstanding. Leaf venation is of the open dichotomous type. If fern leaves represent branch systems, the frond of *Lygodium* in its almost unlimited apical growth is the most primitive among ferns. The division of the leaf into fertile and sterile parts—an archaic condition—is like that in *Osmunda* and the Ophioglossaceae. As in these other primitive groups the sporangia are not borne in sori but are solitary, or are borne in tassels or rows (which represent linear tassels with sporangia pushed from a marginal to a dorsal position). There are no true indusia. In *Anemia* the two lower pinnae are fertile and borne erect on long stalks; there is a strong resemblance to the condition in *Botrychium* where two lower pinnae are similarly fertile, long-stalked, and erect. In *Botrychium*, however, the two leaf lobes are fused. In those frequent cases in *Botrychium* where the two pinnae are not fused, the resemblance, which is not merely superficial, is close. The existence of this condition in *Anemia*, with similar anatomical structure, is additional proof of the fact that the fertile spike of the Ophioglossaceae represents two basal pinnae.

The position of the sporangium is a primitive one; in all cases it is fundamentally marginal. Arising from marginal initials the sporangia are pushed over into a dorsal position during development. They remain, however, close to the margin. This family demonstrates in this "ontogenetic slide" the change which has clearly taken place in phylogeny.

The sporangia in their large size, rounded form, short stout stalks, two-layered tapetum, and many spores are primitive. In their thin wall and method of development they belong with leptosporangiate types. In number of spores there are far fewer than in eusporangiate types but more than in the advanced leptosporangiate forms. The annulus, though complete and well defined in most cases, is less well developed and specialized than in higher forms.

The gametophytes are in general not different from those of most leptosporangiate ferns. They develop adventitious lobes freely at the base, as do those of more primitive families (Osmundaceae, Marattiaceae). Such lobes are lacking in the advanced families. The sex organs are of the usual type, though the number of sperms is larger than that of advanced families.

The filamentous prothallium of *Schizaea* has aroused much interest. It has been commonly believed to represent a most primitive type because it so closely resembles in form the protonema (gametophyte) of mosses. This resemblance has been emphasized because of the supposed bryophyte ancestry of the ferns. However, other members of this family, and other families recognized as primitive, give no evidence of filamentous gametophytes. Elsewhere this condition occurs only in the Hymenophyllaceae, a specialized family, and there is of a different type. The filamentous gametophyte of *Schizaea* is not simple, but is elaborated in relation to mycorrhizal conditions. The morphological meaning of this condition is not clear, though it apparently does not represent a primitive state but seems more likely to be a specialized one.

Mohria is the advanced genus in the family, in anatomy, sporangial position, leaf form, and dermal appendages. The family is a primitive one among the leptosporangiate types (page 284).

Bibliography

OSMUNDACEAE

CAMPBELL, D. H.: On the prothallium and embryo of *Osmunda Claytoniana* L. and *O. cinnamomea* L., *Ann. Bot.*, **6**: 49–94, 1892.

FAULL, J. H.: The anatomy of the Osmundaceae, *Bot. Gaz.*, **32**: 381–419, 1901.

———: The stele of *Osmunda cinnamomea*, *Trans. Canad. Inst.*, **8**: 515–534, 1909.

CROSS, G. L.: Embryology of *Osmunda cinnamomea*, *Bot. Gaz.*, **92**: 210–217, 1931.

KNY, L.: Beiträge zur Entwickelungsgeschichte der Farnkräuter, I. Entwickelung des Vorkeimes von *Osmunda regalis* L., *Jahrb. wiss. Bot.*, **8**: 1–15, 1872.

MILDE, J.: Die Fructification der Osmunden, *Bot. Ztg.*, **26**: 64–74, 1868.

SEWARD, A. C., and S. O. FORD: The anatomy of *Todea* with notes on the geological history and affinities of the Osmundaceae, *Trans. Linn. Soc. London*, 2d ser., **6**: 237–260, 1903.

SINNOTT, E. W.: Foliar gaps in the Osmundaceae, *Ann. Bot.*, **24**: 107–118, 1910.

WILLIAMS, W.: Sporangial variation in the Osmundaceae, *Trans. Roy. Soc. Edinburgh*, **55**: 795–805, 1927.

GLEICHENIACEAE

BOODLE, L. A.: Comparative anatomy of the Hymenophyllaceae, Schizaeaceae and Gleicheniaceae, III. On the anatomy of the Gleicheniaceae, *Ann. Bot.*, **15**: 703–747, 1901.

BOWER, F. O.: Studies in the morphology of spore-producing members, IV. The leptosporangiate ferns, *Phil. Trans. Roy. Soc. London* **192B**: 29–138, 1899.

CAMPBELL, D. H.: The prothallium of *Kaulfussia* and *Gleichenia, Ann. Jard. Bot. Buitenzorg*, **22**: 69–102, 1908.

RAUWENHOFF, N. W. P.: La génération sexuée des Gleichéniacées, *Arch. Néerl. Sci. nat.*, **24**: 157–231, 1891.

SCHIZAEACEAE

BARTOO, D. R.: Development of the sporangium in *Schizaea rupestris, Bot. Gaz.*, **88**: 322–331, 1929.

BAUKE, H.: Beiträge zur Keimungsgeschichte der Schizaeaceen, *Jahrb. wiss. Bot.*, **11**: 603–650, 1878.

BINFORD, R.: The development of the sporangium of *Lygodium, Bot. Gaz.*, **44**: 214–224, 1907.

BOODLE, L. A.: Comparative anatomy of the Hymenophyllaceae, Schizaeaceae and Gleicheniaceae, II. On the anatomy of the Schizaeaceae, *Ann. Bot.*, **15**: 359–419, 1901.

BRITTON, E. G., and A. TAYLOR: The life history of *Schizaea pusilla, Bull. Torrey Bot. Club*, **28**: 1–19, 1901.

PRANTL. K.: "Untersuchungen zur Morphologie der Gefässkryptogamen," pt. II. "Die Schizaeaceen." W. Engelmann, Leipzig, 1881.

ROGERS, L. M.: Development of the archegone and studies in fertilization in *Lygodium palmatum, La Cellule*, **37**: 325–352, 1927.

CHAPTER X

MARSILEACEAE   WATER FERNS

The Marsileaceae are a small group of ferns which live in the water or in wet habitats and which in general appearance hardly resemble ferns. There are three genera: *Marsilea*,[1] with more than 50 species distributed pretty well over the earth; *Pilularia*, with 6 species in Europe, America, northern Africa, and Australasia; and *Regnellidium*, a monotypic genus described from Brazil in 1904. *Marsilea* is primarily a warm-climate genus; tropical Africa and Australia are most rich in species. The genus varies hardly at all in habit, but markedly in number, shape, orientation, and attachment of the fruiting bodies. The "fruits" of Australian species form an occasional food for the aborigines and are said to have been useful in this way to explorers. The leaves are browsed by cattle when other vegetation is scarce.

Sporophyte

Habit. In habit the plants are adapted to growth in shallow water or in wet places where they become stranded as the water level falls. A few species grow in soil which is dry throughout most of the year. Forms which grow in permanent water creep out upon the shores. All are rhizomatous with stems creeping on or just below the surface. Roots are borne at the nodes and the erect leaves alternate in two rows on the upper side of the rhizome (Figs. 126, 127). Branching is free, the branches being axillary or arising lateral to or below the leaf. The young parts of some species, and especially the fruiting bodies of many, are thickly covered with simple hairs, and a few forms are silky-hairy throughout.

Leaves. The leaf of *Marsilea* has four leaflets in a 'terminal' cluster (Fig. 126); that of *Regnellidium* has a deeply two-lobed blade (Fig. 127*A*); that of *Pilularia* is awl-shaped and simple, without a definite blade (Fig. 127*B*). In all genera the leaf is strongly circinate during development; in the two with blade

[1] The valid, older spelling is *Marsilea*.

the leaflets are folded together upward until nearly mature. The leaflets of *Marsilea* vary little in form in most species; those of *M. macrocarpa*, *M. biloba*, and a few others may be once or

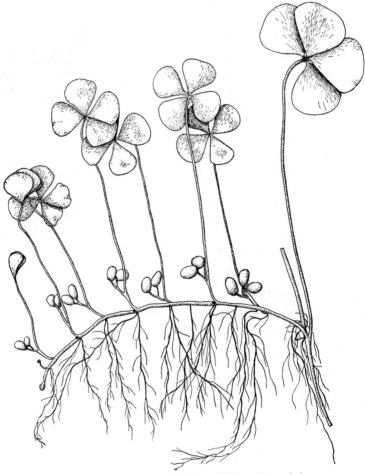

Fig. 126.—*Marsilea quadrifolia.*   Habit.   Natural size.

twice deeply lobed dichotomously; those of *M. angustifolia* are narrowly elliptical. Of the four leaflets two form a distal pair, standing noticeably higher (Fig. 126), even when floating; the other two, though seeming to form a proximal pair, are really alternate, as is shown most clearly by the anatomy (Fig. 128*A*).

Occasionally there are in *Marsilea* six leaflets; in such cases the alternate arrangement of the four proximal leaflets is more clear. The distal pair represents a terminal dichotomy of the

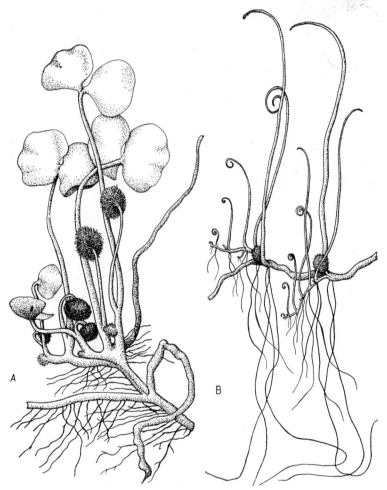

FIG. 127.—*A, Regnellidium diphyllum*, habit; *B, Pilularia globulifera*, habit. Natural size. (*A, after Lindman; B, after Meunier.*)

leaf, a fact borne out by the lack of an apex, by the Y-shaped forking of the vascular bundle, and by the condition in the closely related *Regnellidium*, where the leaf blade is dichotomous with the division incomplete. The cluster of four leaflets

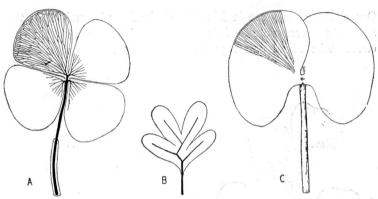

Fig. 128.—Leaf of the Marsileaceae showing arrangement of the leaflets and vascular anatomy. *A, B, Marsilea; B,* diagram showing arrangement of leaflets as a result of three dichotomies; *C, Regnellidium.* (*A, after Williams, modified; B, after Bower; C, after Lindman.*)

Fig. 129.—Leaves and sporocarps of the Marsileaceae showing reduction series. *A,* apex; *D,* dorsal; *V,* ventral.

undoubtedly represents the result of three successive dichotomies of the leaf tip, forming a scorpioid *sympodium* (Fig. 128*B*). The resemblance to leaf segments of species of *Lygodium*, which are built up in the same fashion, is close. When the plant grows in the water the leaflets float on the surface; on land they are smaller and firmer and held in a spreading position. At night the leaflets of the aerial leaves commonly assume a 'sleeping' position, being folded upward (ventrally), as in the bud. In *Regnellidium* there are apparently similar periodic movements in position. The venation of the leaf is dichotomous, in *Regnellidium* without anastomoses (Fig. 128*C*), in *Marsilea* with frequent cross connections (Fig. 128*A*) so that it approaches the netted state. In each case there is a marginal tie-up of veinlets.

In form the three genera represent adaptation to the aquatic habit by reduction. In *Marsilea* and *Regnellidium* the terminal part of the leaf blade persists, floating on the surface when the plant is submerged; in the small and delicate *Pilularia* the leaves are bladeless (Fig. 129). The smallest species, *P. minuta*, has a rhizome only 0.5 to 0.7 mm in diameter and filiform leaves 35 to 40 mm long. The simplification is most prominent in the leaf: in *Regnellidium* the two proximal leaflets have been lost; in *Pilularia* all the leaflets have disappeared and the rachis has become the photosynthetic area. In the latter genus the sporocarp and the number of sori and spores are also much reduced (page 215).

Anatomy. *Marsilea* is a typical leptosporangiate fern in development and in anatomical structure. The stem has an amphiphloic siphonostele with internal and external endodermis and large simple leaf traces and gaps. The xylem and phloem are those of most ferns. In *Pilularia* internal structure is much the same, though the vascular tissue is greatly reduced. In some species there is no internal endodermis. Very little is known of the anatomy of *Regnellidium*.

Reproduction. Borne laterally on the petioles (often apparently adaxially or in their axils) are prominent reproductive structures known as *sporocarps*. These are stalked, nut-like bodies, bean-shaped to subspherical or ovoid (Figs. 126, 127). In *Regnellidium* and *Pilularia* and in many species of *Marsilea* the sporocarps are solitary; in other species of the last genus there are 2 to 20 or more: when very few they are borne on a forked peduncle, as in *M. quadrifolia* (Fig. 130); when several to many, in a row, as in *M. caribaea* and *M. polycarpa* (Fig. 130). Where the stalk is attached at the leaf base, its lateral position is often more clearly seen. The position of the stalk ranges in the different species from erect to horizontal, to reflexed, and in a few species to descending (when the capsule is buried in the ground) (Figs. 127, 130). The point of attachment of the sporocarp stalk ranges from well up to low down on the petiole, to the leaf axil, and to the rhizome near by. The sporocarps of

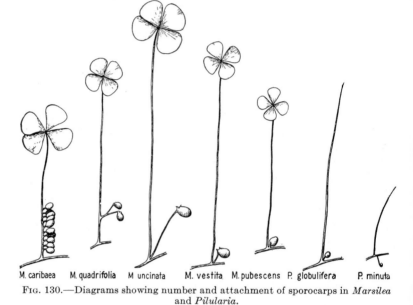

M. caribaea   M. quadrifolia   M uncinata   M. vestita   M. pubescens   P. globulifera   P. minuta

Fɪɢ. 130.—Diagrams showing number and attachment of sporocarps in *Marsilea* and *Pilularia*.

most species of *Marsilea* and those of *Regnellidium* are markedly bilaterally symmetrical; those of some species of *Marsilea* and those of *Pilularia* are commonly said to be radially symmetrical but are in fact like those of the others in symmetry (page 214). Most species show at the back near the point of attachment of the stalk one or more protuberances in the median plane. These consist of teeth (one or two)—sometimes called "tubercles"—and a raphe (Fig. 131). The raphe represents the end of the stalk fused laterally to the back of the sporocarp; it is therefore usually prominent when the stalk meets the sporocarp obliquely (Fig. 131*E,F,I*) and is absent when the fruiting structure is attached directly on the end.   At the distal end of the raphe is the lower tooth, usually the stouter and more prominent of the two.   The upper tooth lies a short distance above the lower and is usually more slender and delicate than the lower.   The teeth vary in form and prominence: in a few species they form conspicuous spiny projections (Fig. 131*F*,*G*), perhaps of importance in the distribution of the fruits; in many species one or both are lacking.   In *Pilularia* the upper tooth is absent and the lower forms a rounded knob at the base of the sporocarp.   In *Regnel-*

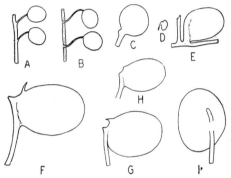

Fig. 131.—Sporocarps of the Marsileaceae.   Diagrams showing attachment of sporocarp to stalk, raphe, and form and number of teeth.   ×2½.   *A, Marsilea caribaea; B, M. polycarpa; C, Pilularia globulifera; D, P. minuta; E, M. pubescens; F, M. uncinata; G, M. vestita; H, M. quadrifolia; I, Regnellidium diphyllum.*   (Based,—*B, on Hooker and Greville; C, D, on Johnson; I, on Lindman.*)

lidium the raphe, which is said to be brightly colored, is the only one of these structures present.

The sporocarps are very hard, with a thick wall strongly resistant to mechanical injury and to drying out.   It is reported that sporocarps on herbarium sheets 50 years old have "germinated"; that specimens kept in alcohol many years will open and extrude spores.   Whether such spores are viable is uncertain. Most species live in marshy places which are dry during part of the year, and the sporocarps protect the spores until the next wet season; doubtless they serve not only this purpose but to carry the plant over longer unfavorable periods.   A resting period, perhaps comparable in some way to the after-ripening period of many seeds is apparently necessary since the spores in ripe sporocarps will not germinate at once.

In structure and development the sporocarps are complex and their morphological nature has long been an uncertain matter. The variety of form, of orientation, and the method of attachment add greatly to the puzzle of fundamental form. Though commonly considered ventral structures—as they indeed may appear to be in such species as *M. quadrifolia*—careful examina-

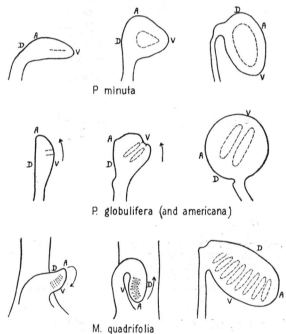

P minuta

P. globulifera (and americana)

M. quadrifolia

Fig. 132.—Development and orientation of the sporocarp of *Pilularia* and *Marsilea*. In *Marsilea* the origin of the sporocarp on the side of the petiole and its migration toward a ventral position is shown. The dotted lines indicate position of sori. *A*, apex; *D*, dorsal surface; *V*, ventral surface. (*Based in part on Johnson.*)

tion shows them to be obviously lateral in most species of *Marsilea*; and ontogeny demonstrates those that are superficially ventral to be lateral in origin (Fig. 132), the adaxial position being assumed by a twisting at the point of attachment. Anatomy makes the lateral relation certain, since the vascular supply to the stalk is cut off from the lateral margin of the petiole bundle. (In some species of *Pilularia* the sporocarp trace is fused to the trace of the axillary bud, but in such cases, as in all others, the sporocarp develops from a marginal leaf cell.)

The sporocarp and its stalk thus clearly represent a lateral segment of the leaf.   What parts of the vegetative segment of the
leaf are represented in the sporocarp can best be considered only
after detailed structure in the three genera has been discussed.

The Sporocarp of Marsilea.   Structure.   Attached to the
inner wall of the sporocarp lie two rows of elongate sori, one
along each side.   The sori extend transversely—"dorsiventrally"
—to the long axis of the sporocarp (Figs. 132, 133).   (The
application of the terms dorsal and ventral to the sporocarp is
a matter of convenience; it is not implied here by such usage
that the areas so designated represent dorsal and ventral surfaces
of the leaf.   The terms are used to indicate respectively the
abaxial and adaxial margins—away from and toward the growing
point.)   Each sorus is surround by a delicate indusium, and the
two rows of sori, close-packed, fill the sporocarp cavity.   The
receptacle of the sorus is ridge-like and bears along its top a
row of megasporangia and around its sides many microsporangia.
Sections in three planes demonstrate the position of the sori and
their sporangia (Fig. 133).

The sporocarp opens only in water, splitting, bivalve-like,
along the ventral side and apex, the margins spreading.   A ring
of gelatinous tissue which extends around the cavity in the
dorsiventral plane (Fig. 133) absorbs water and, expanding
greatly, protrudes along the open margin of the sporocarp (Fig.
134*A*).   As it pushes out, it drags with it the sori, which are
attached to it by their ends (Fig. 134*B* to *D*).   Each sorus is
now an elongate sac-like structure (Fig. 134*D*), having been
freed from the wall of the sporocarp by abscission below the
receptacle (Fig. 133*B,C*).   The abscission line extends along the
base of the receptacle across the vascular bundle (Fig. 133*B,C*).
The indusium and, on one side, the receptacle form the wall of
the sac.   As the ring continues to expand, the soral sacs become
free at their ventral ends, and soon the ring itself is broken on
the ventral side distal to the sori (Fig. 134*C*).   The slender
ventral segment shows a row of "mammiform projections"
which are commonly said to represent the areas of attachment
of the ventral ends of the soral sac and are so illustrated in
published figures.   In *M. quadrifolia*, at least, these projections
probably represent not such connections but the thicker areas
on the ring between the pairs of sori; the ventral ends of the

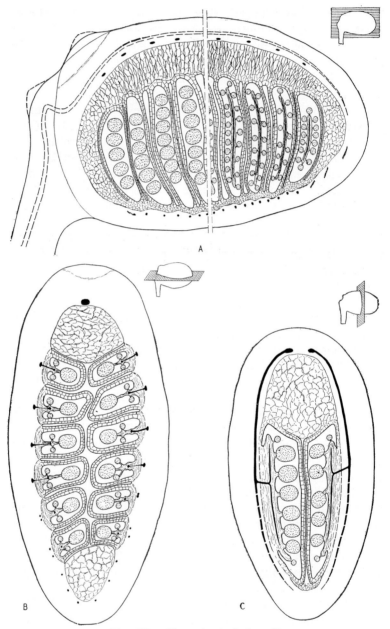

FIG. 133.— (See next page for legend.)

sacs then lie between the projections. The dorsal segment elongates greatly, completing the withdrawal of the sori, and the ring becomes a worm-like structure, attached by one end to the sporocarp, with two rows of soral sacs extending from one side (Fig. 134*E*). The ventral segment is weak and soon

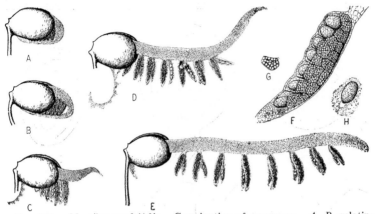

Fig. 134.—*Marsilea quadrifolia*. Germination of sporocarp. *A, B*, gelatinous ring expanding from apex and ventral side, pulling with it the sori; *C*, the ring broken on the ventral side near the distal end of the sporocarp; *D*, dorsal portion of ring continuing to expand, pulling out the proximal sori; *E*, ring completely expanded, the ventral segment disintegrating; *F*, sorus, containing microsporangia and megasporangia, open at ventral end; *G*, microsporangium with microspores; *H*, megaspore with gelatinous coat.

disintegrates. The ventral ends of the sori are torn open when freed from the ring, and part of the spores of each sorus (in some cases enclosed in sporangia) at once escape from the open end (Fig. 134*F,G*). The ring and the soral sacs persist for several days and other spores may be discharged later. The delicate sporangium walls break open or decay rapidly and the spores germinate at once. (The above description applies to *M. quadrifolia*. The behavior of the gelatinous ring is perhaps different in detail in other species.)

Fig. 132.—Diagrams illustrating the structure of the sporocarp of *Marsilea*. *A*, section in the dorsiventral plane somewhat to one side of the median line, one portion slightly farther away than the other; *B*, longitudinal section at right angles to *A;* *C*, transverse section at right angles to *A*. The vascular strands are indicated by heavy black. The gelatinous ring is shown with irregular, cell-like structure. The central clear areas containing the rounded stippled spores are the sori. Limiting the sori are the indusia, with rectangular cell-like markings. The receptacles are shaded with light, straight lines, the lines of abscission indicated by thin dotted lines. (*Based on diagrams by L. W. Sharp.*)

The sporocarp of *Marsilea* is complex also in anatomy (Fig.
135*A*,*B*). The simple vascular strand of the stalk bends at a
marked angle at the level of the lower tooth, then passes along
the dorsal side, soon forking dichotomously. Rib-like bundles
extend laterally down the sides, also forking dichotomously.
Near the point of this last division a small bundle extends inward

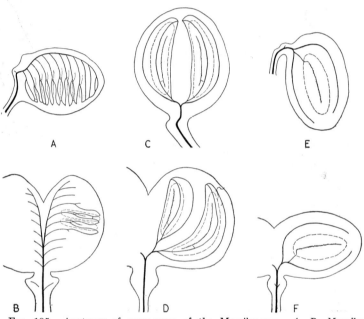

Fig. 135.—Anatomy of sporocarps of the Marsileaceae. *A*, *B*, *Marsilea*
quadrifolia; C, D, Pilularia globulifera; E, F, P. minuta. *A, C, E,* lateral view;
B, D, F, valves of sporocarp spread apart.   Dotted lines indicate soral limits.
(*A, B, based on Johnson, on Williams, and on original studies; C, D, based on*
Meunier and on Johnson; E, F, based on Johnson.)

to the receptacle, where it forks, the branches running dorsally
and ventrally respectively in the receptacular ridges.   The ends
of the 'rib' branches anastomose with each other low down
toward the ventral margin of the sporocarp.

Development of the Sporocarp.   The sporocarp arises as a lateral
projection (Fig. 132) and soon becomes elongate and terete.
Growth by marginal cells is established very early (Fig. 136*C*,*D*);
development is thus at this stage similar to that of a normal fern
pinna (Figs. 124, 136*A*).   As the distal part enlarges to form the
sporocarp, two rows of soral mother cells appear on the ventral

side (Fig. 136*B*), arising directly from the marginal cells of the
earlier stage (Fig. 136*D*). The sori are therefore definitely
external and marginal in origin. The marginal cells and their
derivatives are, by unequal growth in the young organ, pushed

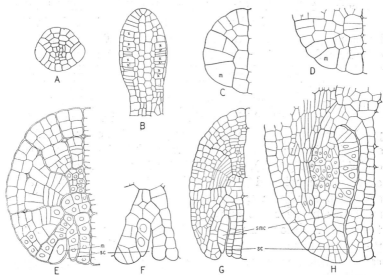

FIG. 136.—Development of the sporocarp of *Marsilea*. *A, Pteris serrulata;*
B, Marsilea polycarpa; C to *H, M. quadrifolia. A,* cross section of tip of pinna;
B, ventral view of young sporocarp, showing the two rows of marginal soral
mother cells (*x, x'*) already pushed from the margin toward the median line;
C to *H,* portions of cross sections showing successive stages in development of
sorus, soral canal, and enclosing shoulders (sporocarp wall); *C, D,* early stages
showing (*m*) the marginal cell and the beginning of its migration to the ventral
side of the sporocarp; *E,* the marginal cell has become a soral mother cell and
the soral canal is beginning to develop beside it; *F* to *H,* the sorus developing
(in *H* the sporangium mother cells appearing), the soral canal deepening; *E* to
H, the downward development of the shoulders encloses the sori which are
open to the outside only by the soral canals—at a stage slightly older than *H* the
canals are closed by the growth of the shoulders (Fig. 137 *C*). *m,* marginal
cell; *sc,* soral canal; *smc,* sporangium mother cell; *x, x',* sorus initials. (*A, B,*
after Goebel; C to *H, after Johnson.*)

downward to the lower surface and to some extent toward
the median line; the margins are therefore now two parallel lines
along the ventral surface between the median line and the sides.
As increase in diameter continues, growth of the cells lateral to
the soral mother cells surpasses that of the developing sorus so
that the sporangial mother cells, as they form, are buried.
Beside each sorus, toward the median line, a small crescent-
shaped depression appears which deepens rapidly as the tissues

grow about the sorus (Fig. 136*E* to *H*). These depressions become spaces above and around the sori, opening to the outside by small pores; they are known as *soral canals* and appear linear in longitudinal section (Fig. 136*E* to *H*). In cross section they are crescent-shaped. Along the median line superficial cells develop four rows of cells; these enclose the sori on the inside but are separated from them by the canals. The four rows of cells form the indusia of the sori; later they split, separating into two-layered strips and become the walls of the individual sacs (the indusia of separate sori). Lateral to the sori the 'shoulders' of the sporocarps develop strongly (Fig. 136*E* to *H*), building the massive outer wall which crowds over toward the median line pinching off the soral canals and completing the enclosure of the sori. If this development is compared with that of the sporangia of *Schizaea* (Fig. 124), close similarity is seen. (The presence of the soral canals and their extension to the surface of the young sporocarp supply an explanation of the probable position of the soral tips between the mammiform projections. The ends of the soral sacs are then not opened by a tearing away from the projections but are the originally open ends—the mouths of the canals—which were closed by overgrowth of the sporocarp shoulder.)

Nature of the Sporocarp. Morphologically the sori are obviously marginal structures borne in the same manner as are marginal sori in other fern families. The development of a protecting fruit body has greatly distorted the normal structure. The margins, with their sori, are pushed downward and laterally toward the median line (Fig. 136*C* to *H*); that is, the blade edges are curled downward and inward (as are the fertile edges of many fern fronds). Indusia develop on the side toward the midrib and grow over the sori longitudinally (parallel to the vein on which the sorus is borne, as in many ferns). The soral canals are the chambers within the indusia. The formation of the lower part of the sporocarp wall on the shoulders of the young leaf—as in many ferns the outer indusium develops beyond the margin—is apparently an exaggerated development of the tissue of that region; the ventral section of the sporocarp wall is not therefore the margin of the blade but merely a wing or flange upon its surface, morphologically comparable to the "indusial flaps" of *Schizaea* (Fig. 124) and to the prominent wings of the

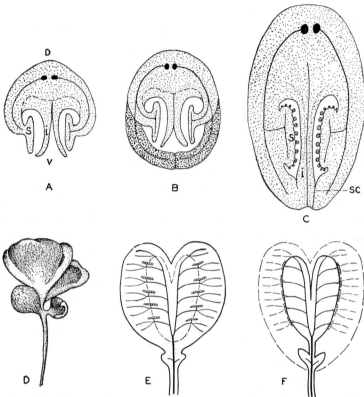

FIG. 137.—Nature of the sporocarp of *Marsilea*. *A*, *B*, diagrammatic cross sections illustrating theory of sporocarp structure and formation. *A*, the margins curled downward and inward, their sori (*s*), partly enclosed by indusia (*i*), facing inward; *B*, winglike shoulders (heavily stippled) developed, which likewise are curled downward and inward until they meet, enclosing the sori. The vascular strands terminate in the sori, but accessory branches are developed in the wings (Fig. 104, *E*, *F*); *C*, diagrammatic cross section of mature sporocarp showing position of sori, indusia, and wings, and the closure of the soral canals; *D*, abnormal leaf of *M. hirsuta* showing condition transitional to sporocarp—the leaflets are thick, brownish, with incurved margins, the proximal ones greatly reduced; *E*, diagram of sporocarp with valves spread showing relation of vascular supply to sori, and, by broken lines, the limits of the two distal leaflets, which are fused along one margin; *F*, diagram of opened sporocarp showing morphological structure: unbroken lines show the four leaflets and the basic vascular supply; broken lines show the wing-like shoulders and the accessory vascular supply. (*C*, *based on Johnson; D, after Büsgen.*)

pinna of *Blechnum* (Fig. 104*E*,*F*). On the basis of such an interpretation the nature of the sporocarp is as shown in Fig. 137*A* to *C*.

The relation of the sporocarp to the leaf, as shown by ontogeny and anatomy, is that of a lateral segment. That the sporocarp is morphologically comparable to the tip of the leaf with its four leaflets and that the body of the capsule represents the two distal leaflets is apparently well substantiated. Anatomy provides the strongest evidence for this theory in the course of the chief vascular bundles; the similarity to that of the four vegetative leaflets is close. At the base of the sporocarp (in some species) two weak or vestigial strands pass into the lower tooth (Fig. 135*A*,*B*); this suggests that this hump represents the remains of the proximal leaflets. (The protuberance below the capsule in *Pilularia* also has vascular tissue.) A short distance beyond, the main bundle divides dichotomously, the two branches supplying the two valves of the capsule. Evidence from abnormal leaves (Fig. 137*D*) also supports this view. Such leaves are in form, texture, and color intermediate between normal leaves and sporocarps, and the proximal leaflets are in most cases very small, the distal ones large and valve-like.

The body of the sporocarp is made up, therefore, of the two distal leaflets and the two proximal leaflets (greatly reduced). In some species a small portion of the rachis also enters into the sporocarp (Fig. 131*E*,*F*,*I*). The upper tooth is an emergence. The two distal leaflets are fused along one edge for nearly their full length (Fig. 137*E*,*F*).

That the sori are marginal has long been certain. The chief puzzle of the nature of the sporocarp has been the question whether these two leaflets are brought together upward or downward. It has been stated (1) that they must be folded ventrally because that is their position in development and in the 'sleep' condition; (2) that they must be folded dorsally since sori are enclosed, and sori among ferns are never on the ventral surface. Because the sori are marginal and because they face each other in two rows, enclosed in a cavity, it is obvious that there is no placing of the leaflets definitely back to back or face to face; that there is, rather, a recurvature of the leaflet margins toward the rachis. Whether this curvature is toward the ventral or the dorsal side is not certain; it seems probable, however, that the folding is ventral since the leaflets assume this position while developing and periodically after maturity. A detailed study of the structure and orientation of the vascular bundles of the leaf and the sporocarp should aid greatly in determining this matter.

Development of the Sorus.   Sporangium initials form along the top and sides of the receptacular ridge (Fig. 138).   Those along the top appear first, those on the sides later; there is therefore a gradate sequence.   It is reported that additional sporangia are developed later among the early-formed ones; the sequence in such a case is thus not strictly gradate but approaches the

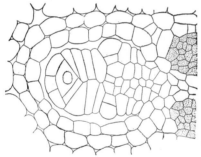

Fig. 138.—*Marsilea quadrifolia.*   Cross section of sorus, with surrounding tissues as sporangium mother cells are developing.   The receptacle bears (in this plane) a terminal mother cell and two lateral mother cells (Fig. 133).   The shaded cells are procambial.   (*After Johnson.*)

mixed.   All sporangia are derived from the marginal cells of the young leaf and are therefore definitely marginal in position. In development the usual leptosporangiate method is closely followed.   The sporangium walls form thin, delicate sacs.   The tapetum has two (sometimes three) layers.   In each sporangium there are 8 or 16 sporocytes.   In the sporangia along the top of the receptacle, which are to become megasporangia, all but one of the 32 or 64 spores which are formed abort; the one surviving spore becomes large and ivory white.   In the microsporangia all spores mature so that there are 32 or 64.   The spores are tetra-hedral but become rounded; the microspores are globose showing the triradiate ridge faintly; the megaspores are ellipsoid, with a hemispherical dark-colored protuberance at the apex.   This papilla may show triradiate markings.   The spore walls have several layers; the outer layer in the megaspore is thick and gelatinous and expands greatly when the spore is freed in the water.

The Sporocarp of Pilularia. *Structure.* In *Pilularia* sporocarp structure is more simple: there are only four (in one species two) sori, the vascular supply has but few branches (Fig. 135*C* to *F*), and there is no gelatinous ring. The sori are similar to those of *Marsilea* in form and lie in the capsule in the same way. The sporocarp is the morphological equivalent of that of *Marsilea*, with the sori greatly reduced in number. It is often said that

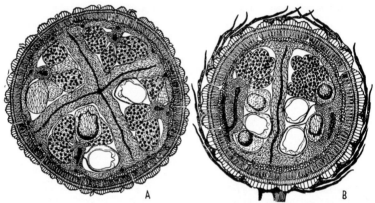

Fig. 139.—*Pilularia globulifera.* Sections of the sporocarp at right angles to one another showing the four sori with their receptacles, microsporangia, megasporangia, and indusia. *A*, longitudinal section (incorrectly called "cross section") (Fig. 132); *B*, transverse section (incorrectly called "longitudinal section"). (*After Luerssen in Rabenhorst.*)

structurally the fruiting bodies of the two genera are not alike because a cross section of the capsule in *Marsilea* gives a longitudinal section of the sorus (Fig. 133*C*), whereas a "cross section" of the sporocarp of *Pilularia* shows cross sections of all the sori (Fig. 139*A*); that therefore the sori are placed differently in the two genera. The ontogeny of the capsule shows clearly, however, that the difference is only apparent, not real, and results from changes in orientation during development. In both genera changes in position in the growing sporocarp are marked, and the final position of the capsule varies greatly in its relation to its stalk and to the leaf which bears it (Fig. 132). In *Pilularia* the growth of the sporocarp is largely on the ventral side, and this crowds the apex over close to the base on the dorsal side and raises the ventral margin to a pseudoterminal position (Fig. 132). The sori come to occupy an apparent distal position with their long axes at right angles to their original position. It is thus evident that sections of the sporocarp of *Pilularia* which show cross and longitudinal sections of the sori are actually longitudinal and transverse sections respectively. The term "transverse" as commonly applied to those sections of the sporocarp of *Pilularia* made in a plane approximately at right angles to the axis of the stalk (Fig. 139) is therefore inaccurate; such sections are really *longitudinal*. Similarly, sections called *"longitudinal"* cut nearly in the plane of the stalk and which show sori cut lengthwise are *transverse* sections of the sporocarp. With an understanding of orientation the sporocarps of *Marsilea* and *Pilularia* have closely similar structure. The sporocarp of the latter genus is smaller, with fewer sori; it does not possess the upper tooth.

Within the sorus megasporangia are borne chiefly toward the dorsal ("basal") end, microsporangia at the ventral ("distal") end (Fig. 139*B*); the two types may, however, be intermingled to some extent. The number of sporangia in a sorus is less than in *Marsilea*, and in *P. minuta* there is but one megasporangium and two microsporangia in each sorus. The megaspores differ from those of *Marsilea* in form, being somewhat pear-shaped with a more elaborate gelatinous layer of greater thickness.

The sporangia are similar to those of *Marsilea*. The megasporangium appears to show, however, a vestigial annulus of the complete ring type at the apical end. This is believed to be of much importance in connection with the phylogeny of the family. The other genera show no annulus on the delicate sporangial wall.

The tissues about the sori are gelatinous and at germination time swell as a mass and carry the sporangia out through the opening sporocarp, which splits into four or more valves.

Development. In details of development the sporocarp, sori, and sporangia are closely similar to those of *Marsilea*. Attention has sometimes been called to four "prominences" on the "apex" of the young sporocarp, and these have been considered to be the tips of four fused leaflets which are considered to make up the fruiting structure. The splitting of the capsule into four valves has been believed to be supporting evidence for this theory of the nature of the sporocarp. The prominences are not, however, related to the fundamental nature of the sporocarp but to the presence of the soral pits; the sinking of the soral initials, that is, the incurving of fertile areas of leaf margin, brings about the formation of humps lateral to the pits. That these projections are related to the sori and not to the leaflets entering into the make-up of the capsule is evident in the fact that in *P. minuta*, where there are two sori, there are two prominences (not four, as should be the case if the teeth represent valves). Further, the prominences are not at the apex but on the ventral margin (Figs. 129, 132). The tubercle at the base of the sporocarp in this genus is the equivalent morphologically of the lower tooth in *Marsilea*. This is clear from ontogeny, and from the course of the vascular tissue, since in both genera the vascular supply of the sporocarp makes an angle and is abruptly reduced in size at that point. The presence of tracheids in this region in both genera is further evidence of homology.

The Sporocarp of Regnellidium. Details of structure and dehiscence of the sporocarp in the third genus of the family are still insufficiently known. The capsule is bean-shaped (Figs. 127*A*, 129) as is that of many species of *Marsilea;* the attachment of the stalk is, however, near the middle of the long side, and the sori lie at right angles to the stalk. A cross section (at right angles to the stalk) gives therefore a longitudinal view of the sori; and a longitudinal, that is, vertical, section cuts across all the sori and shows their number and position in the capsule. The number and arrangement of sori are similar to those in *Marsilea.* The position of the sori is, however, markedly different from that in the other two genera: here the attachment of the sporangia is along the radial wall of the soral chambers; in the other genera it is on the wall of the capsule. Nothing is known of development in this genus, and the vascular anatomy of the capsule has been described only in part. (Further, the published figures are inconsistent with regard to the course of the bundles which apparently supply the receptacles.) The nature of the chambers and an explanation of the apparently remarkable position of the sori await detailed study, especially of developmental stages and vascular supply. It seems probable, however, from what little is apparent in figures of the course of the vascular supply to the sorus (Fig. 140) that the receptacle is 'stalked,' raised well above the sporocarp wall, on a delicate base and that what seem to be indusial sacs are in part thin receptacular ridges.   If this is the case, the indusium is attached laterally or medianly on the receptacle (as it is in many ferns) and not on the wall as in the other genera.   The sporocarp is two-valved and the spores are extruded as in *Pilularia*.

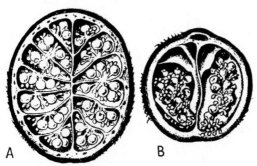

Fɪɢ. 140.—Sporocarp of *Regnellidium.   A*, longitudinal section; *B*, cross section. (*After Lindman.*)

GAMETOPHYTE

The spores germinate at once when set free, and development of the gametophytes is rapid.   At room temperature the microspore germinates in about one hour and sperms are set free in 10 to 12 hours.   Fertilization apparently occurs at once.   The male gametophyte is in general similar to that of the heterosporous groups already described (Fig. 141).   There is first cut off a small prothallial cell (Fig. 141*I*, wall 1-1); the next wall (2-2) divides the large cell equatorially, and each of the cells so formed is apparently an antheridium initial.   In each initial there is cut off on one side by a periclinal wall (3) a large wall cell. A small cell is then cut off (wall 4) internal to this along the median wall.   Another periclinal division (wall 5) completes a jacket of external cells about two inner cells.   These two inner cells are the spermatogenous cells, and by successive divisions each forms 16 sperms.   The jacket and prothallial cells break down and the spermatocytes float within the spore wall.   The sperms when set free by the bursting of the spore wall have a large vesicle with closely wound spiral band (Fig. 141*J,K*).

In *Pilularia* and probably in some species of *Marsilea* there is a minor departure from the above course of gametophyte develop-

ment (which is that of *M. quadrifolia*). The prothallial cell
divides, forming a small "basal cell." There are then two
vegetative cells below the antheridial cells.

The megaspore, like the microspore, germinates very soon
after it is set free in the water. The nucleus lies at the apex,
and the first wall cuts off a small cell, which lies largely or

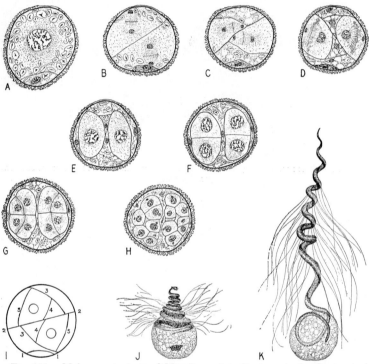

Fig. 141.—Male gametophyte of *Marsilea*. *A* to *H*, stages in development of
gametophyte; *I*, diagram showing position and order of wall formation; *J*, *K*,
sperm: *J* at time of escape from microspore wall; *K*, when entangled in gelatinous
material about megaspore. (*After Sharp.*)

wholly within the apical papilla, from a large basal cell which
contains abundant food material including many large starch
grains (Fig. 142*B*). From the small cell develops the gametophyte proper, a small cluster of cells which form hardly more
than a small and simple archegonium (Fig. 142*C*). The wall
of the papilla splits, as the archegonium grows, into three segments which are pushed outward (Fig. 142*A*). The archegonium

protrudes becoming broad but low, with a short neck of two
tiers of cells only (Fig. 142*D,E*).   It has but one neck canal cell.
The basal cell does not divide; in one species of *Marsilea* its
nucleus is said to enlarge and fragment.

In the gelatinous layer of the megaspore coat there is a cone-
shaped opening above the apex (Fig. 134*H*).   The sperms,

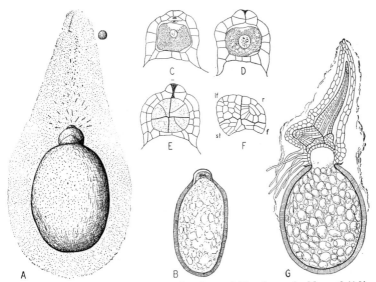

FIG. 142.—Female gametophyte and embryo of *Marsilea. A, M. quadrifolia;
B* to *F, M. vestita; G, M. salvatrix. A,* megaspore, surrounded by gelatinous
sheath, with mature gametophyte: the apical papilla split into lobes which are
thrust back by the protruding gametophyte; the archegonium neck projects at
the apex of the gametophyte and stretched-out sperms are entangled nearby in
the gelatinous sheath; a microspore lies beside the sheath. *B,* the 2-celled
gametophyte; *C,* mature archegonium; *D,* archegonium with zygote; *E,* young
embryo in archegonium; *F,* somewhat older embryo; *G,* mature gametophyte
with developing embryo surrounded by sheath of gametophytic tissue. (*B to F,
after Campbell; G, after Sachs.*)

attracted to this region, pass downward to the archegonium
below.   Many become trapped in the gelatinous material near by
as the wall expands and closes the opening, and their spiral bodies
are greatly stretched out as they die (Fig. 142*A*).

EMBRYO

In *Marsilea*, development of the embryo, like that of the
gametophytes, is rapid; sporophytes reach a stage with the first

leaf several millimeters long in from two to four days after fertilization.

The first division of the zygote is parallel to the long axis of the archegonium. Quadrant segments are formed (Fig. 142*E*), and these bear definite relation to the first organs; the two outer segments form leaf and root, the two inner, stem and foot (Fig. 142*F*). With the development of the embryo the cells of the archegonium venter divide and form a growing sheath which surrounds the young sporophyte (Fig. 142*G*) for some time before leaf and root tip break through. A few rhizoids develop from some of the lowest cells, and the upper tissues become green. If fertilization does not occur, the gametophyte may grow for some time, but no more archegonia are formed. The gelatinous ring and the soral sacs do not readily decay (in *M. quadrifolia* at least), and spores retained within the sacs may germinate there, gametophytes mature, fertilization occur, and the leaves and roots of the young sporophytes burst through the sacs. The earliest leaves of *Marsilea* are subulate, like those of *Pilularia;* then follow, in turn, spatulate; two-lobed, as in *Regnellidium;* four-lobed; and finally the four-leaflet type.

Discussion and Summary

These unfern-like plants represent a group of ferns which have diverged far from their immediate relatives in habitat, habit, and method of reproduction. They are typical leptosporangiate ferns in many characters, standing in respect to order of sporangial development at the gradate level, or perhaps slightly higher since there is evidence of transition to the mixed condition. The adoption of heterospory is the outstanding advance in the family. The development of special structures is surely related to the aquatic habit; the fertile pinnae are modified in a highly complex manner to form a protective structure adapted to habitats where there is a seasonal change from wet to dry; where long periods of drought may alternate with brief wet periods. The extraordinary rapidity of gametophyte and embryo development is perhaps also correlated with possible brevity of the wet period.

The three genera are much alike in technical characters and obviously are rather closely related. In respect to the leaves they seem to form a series in reduction of the leaf blade. The lower submerged pinnae were lost or, if fertile, transformed into purely reproductive structures; in *Marsilea* the four distal lobes persisted, in *Regnellidium* two; in *Pilularia* all were lost. In the sporocarp, also, the last genus shows greatest reduction; the sori are reduced to four—to two in *P. minuta* where the sporangia are but three in number, with a solitary megaspore.

The leaf of the family is fundamentally dichotomous, that of *Marsilea* sympodial, built up by successive dichotomies. This type of branching is evident in the sporocarps also. The venation of leaf and sporocarp follows the same plan.

The sporocarp is the equivalent of the tip of a pinna or pinnule, four leaflets and the end of the rachis going into its make-up. The two distal leaflets make up the body of the capsule, the proximal two forming the lower tooth. The sori are borne on the incurved margins of the thickened leaflets, and heavy shoulders of tissue develop beside the sori enclosing them completely. The incurving is probably adaxial. The sporocarps are all bilaterally symmetrical and, though that of *Regnellidium* is insufficiently known, are apparently homologous.

With this interpretation of the sporocarp the fundamental form of the frond is brought in question. The distal parts of the blade have been retained in a reduction due to life in water, those of the leaf apex being vegetative, those of the pinnae fertile. The modification of a typical pinnate frond would produce the leaf type of species with a solitary sporocarp if all pinnae were lost but the lowest on one side; a similar asymmetrical reduction leaving several pinnae, all on one side, would produce the *polycarpa* condition. But in species, such as *M. quadrifolia*, with two or three (rarely four) sporocarps on one stalk (Fig. 143*C*), the interpretation is not ready. Sporocarp 2 arises from the stalk of number 1, number 3 similarly on the stalk of number 2. A one-sided pinna is thus built up. Among architecture types in fern fronds there are occasionally seen such unilateral pinnae; for example, in *Hymenophyllum secundum* (Fig. 143*A*) and in *Pteris semipinnata*. The leaf of *Marsilea* may possibly have been derived from such a frond (Fig. 143).

The method of freeing the spores from the sporocarp is simple in two genera but remarkably elaborate in *Marsilea*. In respect to this feature, *Marsilea* has advanced beyond its sister genera.

Under heterospory many structural features are found to be similar to those of other groups, but in certain important features there are outstanding differences. The megaspores are borne singly in the sporangia and are large and contain much food

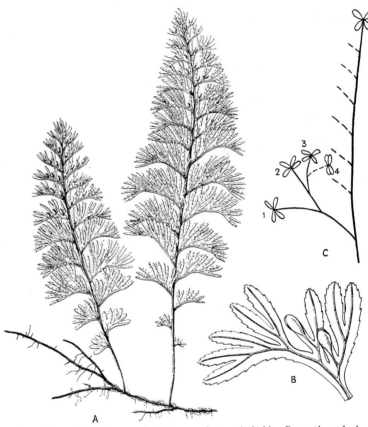

Fig. 143.—*A, B, Hymenophyllum secundum*. *A*, habit; *B*, portion of pinna enlarged; *C*, diagram showing possible origin of the reduced leaf of *Marsilea* (type of *M. quadrifolia*). (*A, B, after Hooker and Greville.*)

material. In their development, however, there is abortion of spores not of sporocytes as in *Selaginella* and *Isoetes*. Reduction in number of megaspores formed goes far in that the number of megasporangia per sorus is small, and in *P. minuta* reaches one— an entire sorus with but one spore, a sporocarp with but two. The development of the gametophytes is in general like that of other heterosporous types.   The female prothallium goes further in reduction in that but one archegonium is ever formed.   The number of cells of the gametophyte is very small; the basal food-containing cell does not divide.

The embryo in development follows the leptosporangiate method, and the restriction of function to definite quadrants is unlike that of other gradate ferns and is like that of the Polypodiaceae, the highest family among leptosporangiate ferns.

The family in many respects—leaf form and structure, type of hair, anatomy, position, and form of sorus and of sporangium, type of annulus—resembles the Schizaeaceae, and it appears to be generally granted that the Marsileaceae represent a side branch from ancestral schizaeaceous stock.   Such a branch—though still with characters of its rather primitive relatives—has progressed far in such features as heterospory and its accompanying reductions, definiteness of quadrant relations, and rapidity of embryo development.

The family, with the Salviniaceae, is commonly considered to form a group of ferns sharply set off from all others—the Hydropteridineae.   It is evident, however, that heterospory marks merely the expression of one tendency for advance—that it does not set off the forms which possess it from those similar in other ways.   It is also clear that the sporocarp is not a peculiar reproductive structure, morphologically unlike anything outside the heterosporous type.   (It is indeed most unlike in the two families of the group.)   The group Hydropteridineae is an unnatural group; its members should be placed among their relatives, the leptosporangiate ferns.

Bibliography

ALLISON, H. E.: Note on the vascular connections of the sporocarp in *Marsilea polycarpa* Hook. & Grev., *New Phyt.*, **10**: 204–206, 1911.

BELAJEFF, W.: Über die männlichen Prothallien der Wasserfarne, *Bot. Ztg.*, **56**: 141–194, 1898.

BOWER, F. O.: On leaf architecture as illuminated by a study of Pteridophyta, *Phil. Trans. Roy. Soc. Edinburgh*, **51**: 657–708, 1917.

BÜSGEN, M.: Untersuchungen über normale und abnormale Marsilienfrüchte, *Flora*, **73**: 169–182, 1890.

CAMPBELL, D. H.: On the prothallium and embryo of *Marsilia vestita*, *Proc. Calif. Acad. Sci.*, 2d ser., **3**: 183–205, 1892.

———: The development of the sporocarp of *Pilularia americana*, A. Br., *Bull. Torrey Bot. Club*, **20**: 141–148, 1893.

————: Affinities of the Marsiliaceae and Ophioglossaceae, *Amer. Naturalist,* **38**: 761–775, 1904.

COKER, W. C.: The nucleus of the spore cavity in prothallia of *Marsilia,* *Bot. Gaz.*, **35**: 137–138, 1903.

DRACINSCHI, M.: Über das reife Spermium der Filicales und von *Pilularia globulifera, Ber. Deutsch. Bot. Gesells.* **48**: 295–311, 1930.

GLÜCK, H.: Die Sporophyllmetamorphose Marsiliaceae, *Flora,* **80**: 303–387, 1895.

GOEBEL, K.: Ueber die "Frucht" von *Pilularia globulifera, Bot. Ztg.,* **40**: 771–778, 1882.

HANSTEIN, J.: Erläuterung des Nardoo genannten Nahrungsmittels der Urbewohner Australiens, einer *Marsilea*-Frucht, nebst Bemerkungen zur Entwicklung dieser Gattung, *Monatsber. Kgl. Preuss. Akad. Wiss.,* Berlin, **1862** (**1863**): (100) 103–119.

JOHNSON, D. S.: On the leaf and sporocarp of *Marsilia quadrifolia, Ann. Bot.,* **12**: 119–145, 1898.

————: On the leaf and sporocarp of *Pilularia, Bot. Gaz.,* **26**: 1–24, 1898.

————: Structure and development of *Pilularia minuta, Bot. Gaz.,* **95**: 104–127, 1933.

————: The curvature, symmetry and homologies of the sporocarps of *Marsilea* and *Pilularia, Bull. Torrey Bot. Club.,* **60**: 555–564, 1933.

LINDMAN, C. A. M.: *Regnellidium* novum genus Marsiliacearum. Ark. för Bot., **3** (6): 1–14, 1904.

LUERSSEN, C.: Die Farnpflanzen oder Gefässbündelkryptogamen, *in* Rabenhorst, "Kryptogamenflora," Leipzig, 1889.

MEUNIER, A.: La Pilularia. Étude anatomico-génétique du sporocarpe chez la *Pilularia globulifera, La Cellule,* **4**: 319–400, 1888.

SCHNEIDER, F.: Beiträge zur Entwicklungsgeschichte der Marsiliaceen, *Flora,* **105**: 347–369, 1913.

SHARP, L. W.: Spermatogenesis in *Marsilia, Bot. Gaz.,* **58**: 419–431, 1914.

SHATTUCK, C. H.: The origin of heterospory in *Marsilia, Bot. Gaz.,* **49**: 19–40, 1910.

STRASBURGER, E.: Apogamie bei *Marsilia, Flora,* **97**: 123–191, 1907.

WILLIAMS, R. G.: The anatomy and morphology of *Marsilea,* Thesis, Cornell University, 1921.

CHAPTER XI

HYMENOPHYLLACEAE   FILMY FERNS

The Hymenophyllaceae are small ferns of humid, tropical and warm-temperate regions. Because of the delicacy and translucent character of the leaves they are objects of beauty and interest wherever seen. They are characteristic of rain forests of the tropics and the southern hemisphere and are especially abundant in New Zealand. As a whole they are hygrophytes, but some species have an extraordinary endurance of xerophytic conditions. The family is small in genera—only two, *Hymenophyllum* and *Trichomanes*—but large in species—about 460, nearly equally divided between the genera.

Sporophyte

Habit. All species are rhizome types (Fig. 144) and a large part of them are epiphytes, which may clothe tree trunks, branches, and rocks as do mosses and lichens. The fronds stand erect or are pendulous. Dwarf species are common— some of them with leaves only 3 to 10 mm long and a rhizome 1 mm in diameter; reduction in size, like the filmy character of the leaf, is clearly the result of adaptation to the moist habitat.

Stems. The rhizomes are slender and often extensive, climbing freely in many epiphytic species. Branching is in most cases axillary. Roots are lacking in many of the smaller forms and are replaced functionally by root hairs along the rhizome and in some cases also on the petiole and even the leaf blade.

Leaves. The filmy nature of the blade is an outstanding character of the family. In the majority of species the lamina, except in the vein regions, consists of a single layer of cells. In this respect it resembles the leaf of mosses. The blades of a few species are three or four cell layers thick, but lack stomata and intercellular spaces. In the delicate forms lateral veins are lacking or are represented by a few nonvascular cells, which are obviously vestiges of normal veins. In spite of this delicate

225

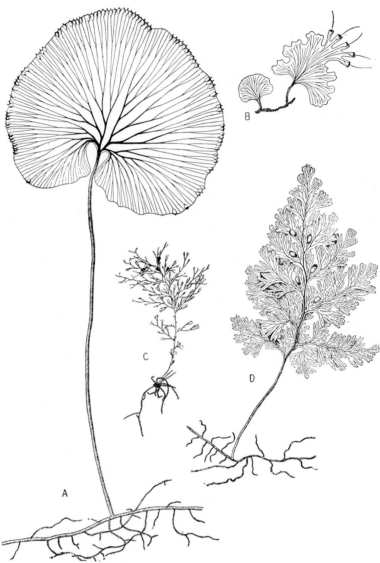

Fig. 144.—Habit of the Hymenophyllaceae. *A, Trichomanes reniforme;* *B, T. cuspidatum; C, T. capillaceum; D, Hymenophyllum multifidum.* About natural size. (*B, after Christ.*)

structure the leaves of some species may dry to brittleness and still recover rapidly with the return of humid conditions. In an occasional species photosynthetic lobes rise from the upper leaf surface. In these respects the filmy ferns further resemble mosses. The blades are glabrous or covered, often densely, with hairs, which apparently serve not for protection against drying but to hold a film of water. Finely cut leaf segments also serve this purpose.

In form the leaves are commonly lobed or divided pinnately or dichotomously (Figs. 143, 144), but there are many simple types. The leaves of some species are divided into hair-like lobes, the segments being $\frac{1}{3}$ mm or less broad and consisting of hardly more than the vein (Fig. 144C). Such segments are in some forms terete, as in submersed aquatic angiosperm leaves. In some species the blades closely resemble the thalli of liverworts in form and lobing. Light shining through the thin blades makes the leaves of most species a brilliant, glistening green, and this, with lace-like structure in some forms, makes the fronds of filmy ferns the most beautiful of leaves. In general color the leaves range, however, from pale to deep green and to brown.

Anatomy. The vascular system is simple. The rhizome is protostelic, with xylem sometimes exarch but typically mesarch. Throughout the family there is strong evidence of reduction in water-conducting tissues as an adaptation to moist habitats. So far has the process gone in some species that there is in the entire plant hardly any xylem, in many cases none in the stem and vegetative leaves, and only vestiges in the fertile leaves. Sclerenchyma in many cases makes up the bulk of the tissues of the stem.

Reproduction. The sporangia are borne in marginal sori which have a prominent cup-shaped, tubular, or two-lipped indusium (Figs. 143B; 144; 145A to C). They are usually numerous, and uniform in orientation and attachment on an elongate receptacle. They are sessile, or subsessile with broad stalk, or sunken in the leaf blade, and range in form from subspherical to strongly flattened. The annulus is oblique-vertical or transverse, and complete (Fig. 145D,E). The spore number varies greatly; from 32 to 421 have been counted. Each sorus is situated at the tip of a vein which extends into the receptacle and ranges in form from linear to subspherical. In *Trichomanes* the slender receptacles, naked after the sporangia are shed, project well beyond the leaf margin (Fig. 144*B*), forming prominent features of fertile leaf structure (whence comes the generic name). In the development of the sorus the receptacle elongates by basal intercalary growth. The sorus is therefore gradate, with the order of sporangium formation basipetal, the older sporangia distal. In mature sori the receptacles, naked of sporangia distally, project as filaments. The sporangia develop in the

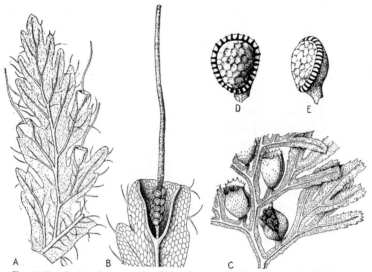

Fig. 145.—Sori and sporangia of the Hymenophyllaceae.   *A, B, Trichomanes alatum;* *C* to *E, Hymenophyllum tunbridgense.*   *A*, portion of fertile frond; *B*, sorus with one side of the vase-shaped indusium removed; *C*, portion of fertile frond with sori with 2-lipped indusia; *D, E*, two views of sporangia. *(After Bauer.)*

usual leptosporangiate manner. The tapetum is two-layered and massive in at least some species.

In most forms fertile and sterile leaves are much alike; in others they are markedly different in form and structure—in some cases the lamina of the fertile leaf is almost lacking.

Both apogamy and apospory have been reported in the family.

Gametophyte

The prothallia, always monoecious, are filamentous or thalloid in *Trichomanes*, and thalloid—with narrow, lobed or branched, ribbon-like body—in *Hymenophyllum* (Fig. 146). Species of the former genus show transition types with irregular, delicate thallus lobes among the filamentous branches. The gametophytes develop slowly, in some species requiring more than three years to reach sexual maturity, and apparently are long-lived. The sex organs are borne, in filamentous forms, on short specialized branches (the antheridia sometimes terminal on the filaments) (Fig. 146*C*); in thalloid forms, on thickened marginal areas or lobes (Fig. 146*A*). The antheridia are complex, with a one-celled stalk and a wall of several cells (Fig. 109), much resembling those of the Gleicheniaceae and Osmundaceae.

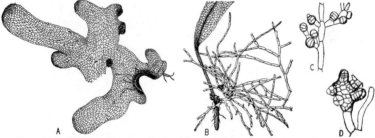

FIG. 146.—Gametophytes of the Hymenophyllaceae. *A, Hymenophyllum axillare; B, C, Trichomanes rigidum; D, T. sinuosum. A,* thalloid prothallium, with sex organs on thickened marginal areas; *B,* filamentous prothallium with young sporophyte; *C,* antheridial branch; *D,* archegonial branch. (*After Goebel.*)

There is probably no funnel-shaped basal cell and no definite cap cell is formed. There are apparently more than 32 sperms. The archegonia are borne in clusters on the specialized thickened reproductive branches (Fig. 146*D*). Though borne on a filamentous gametophyte, they are not naked like those of *Schizaea* but are enclosed in a sheath. They are of the usual fern type, but the necks are straight. The structure of the neck canal cells seems to be unknown. A fungus is often present in the filamentous forms, as it is in similar types in the Schizaeaceae, though in this family there is no accompanying morphological modification.

Multiplication by gemmae and by fragmentation is frequent.

EMBRYO

Little is known of the embryogeny, but the young sporophyte seems to develop as in other leptosporangiate ferns.

DISCUSSION AND SUMMARY

The family has often been considered a most primitive one among ferns because of the small size of its members and their moss-like leaf texture, lack of roots, and protonema-like gametophytes. In some of the older systems of classification the filmy ferns formed the group "Bryopterides," a connecting link between bryophytes and ferns. There is, however, little doubt but that most if not all of the characters, both of sporophyte and gametophyte, that suggest extreme primitiveness are the result of reduction due to adaptation to moist habitats. Surely small size and filmy leaf blades are the result of such modification; the lack of roots (an advanced character generally in vascular plants), the vestigial vascular supply throughout the plant, and the presence in other nonfilmy families of occasional filmy species are sufficient evidence of strong simplification. The filamentous state of the gametophyte also is to be looked upon as derived and not primitive. Certainly in families more primitive in many respects the gametophytes are thalloid; and bryophytes with filamentous prothallia are no longer to be looked upon as ancestors of vascular plants. Filamentous prothallia develop in many ferns with abundant moisture and lack of light. Within the genus *Trichomanes* the more primitive species have thalloid gametophytes, and it is clear that the filamentous habit has arisen within the genus. The gametophyte, like the sporophyte, has been reduced in adaptation to shade and abundant moisture. Parallel development may be seen in the two generations; in each a small and delicate type has developed from a coarser form.

The family is surely not a remarkably primitive one, showing relationship to bryophytes. Certain characters, however— protostelic stem and dichotomous venation; gradate sori; short-stalked or sessile sporangia; a fairly large spore output; a massive tapetum; a straight archegonium neck—indicate a fairly low position among fern families. But, since the family is definitely leptosporangiate and does not, in sporangium development, suggest transition to the eusporangiate method and since the sori are gradate, it must be ranked higher than the families so far considered.

SALVINIACEAE   WATER FERNS

The Salviniaceae are a small group of water-inhabiting ferns of markedly unfern-like habit and appearance. There are two genera, *Salvinia* and *Azolla*, the former with 13, the latter with 5 species. Like the Marsileaceae, this family differs from most ferns in the possession of heterospory and of a special type of reproductive structure, the sporocarp. All forms are small and floating. The various species inhabit the tropical and warm temperate regions of both hemispheres, but none is native in Europe. *Salvinia* is chiefly an African genus. *S. natans* and *A. caroliniana* are considered annual species; all other members of the family are apparently perennial.

The two genera differ so much in many ways that it is necessary to consider them separately.

SALVINIA

SPOROPHYTE

Habit. The stem is a delicate floating rhizome—in length up to 10 cm—branched, and closely covered with oblong, ovate, or hemispherical leaves (Fig. 147*A*). There are no roots. The sessile or short-stalked leaves are arranged in whorls of three, two lateral and floating, the third submersed. The submersed leaf is dissected into 8 to 12 filiform segments which are thickly covered with hairs. Such leaves much resemble roots but probably do not function as such. The hairs are not root-hair-like, being multicellular and rigid and often spongy-tipped. It has been suggested that they protect the sporocarps, and also that the submersed leaf acts as a stabilizer and as a drag against drifting. The members of the leaf whorls alternate at successive nodes; there are therefore six rows of leaves, though the arrangement suggests two dorsal floating rows and one ventral submersed row. The floating leaves are greatly modified as floating organs: in most species they are more or less boat-shaped, and in all they are covered with stiff hairs and papillose projections so that they are not readily wet. A branch initial forms at every node between the submersed leaf and a floating leaf, but only part of these buds develop. The stems are fragile and readily break apart; vegetative multiplication is secured in this manner, and the plants, when flourishing, quickly cover closely the surface of small bodies of quiet water.

Anatomy. Comparatively little seems to be known of the vascular structure. The rhizome is siphonostelic with a delicate, broken cylinder of xylem. The vascular tissue is that of aquatic plants generally and shows strong reduction, especially of water-

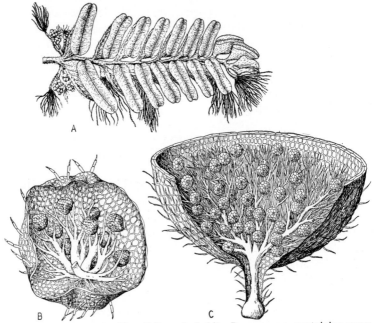

Fig. 147.—*Salvinia oblongifolia.* *A*, habit; *B*, sporocarp containing megasporangia, one side removed; *C*, sporocarp containing microsporangia, the distal end and one side removed. (*After Martius.*)

conducting cells. The xylem is more reduced than that of the smaller stem of *Azolla*.

Reproduction. Only in *S. natans* does reproduction appear to have been studied in detail; the following account is based, therefore, as to details, chiefly upon this species. It is unfortunate that other species have not been studied more completely, since *S. oblongifolia* shows markedly different and most important characters, especially the branched megasporangium stalks.

The sporocarps, 4 to 20, are borne in clusters or rows upon some of the inner segments of the submersed leaves (Fig. 147*A*). Each sporocarp is terminal upon a branch of a segment, and the clusters are therefore sympodial in nature.   In shape the sporo-

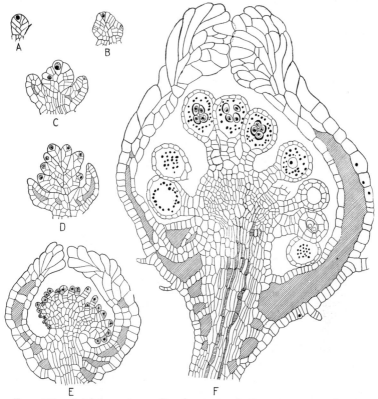

Fig. 148.—*Salvinia natans*. Development of the sporocarp. *A*, sorus primordium with apical cell; *B*, indusium formation beginning on sides; *C*, *D*, later stages, the indusium developing and (in *D*) the sporangium stalks forming; *E*, sporangium initials formed, the indusium enclosing the sorus; *F*, sporocarp well grown, a single spore tetrad surviving in each sporangium.   (*After Zawidski.*)

carps are globose or ovoid, in some species more or less flattened, with ridged or smoothly rounded sides.   The sporocarp wall is delicate, of but two cell layers, with large longitudinal chambers, and is clothed with hairs when young.

All sporocarps are alike in size and external structure, but the first one or two formed in each cluster bear megasporangia, the others microsporangia. As the base of the sporocarp is a stout columnar receptacle into which passes the vascular strand of the leaf segment. In the sporocarps bearing megasporangia there are several (up to 25) ellipsoid or ovoid sporangia borne in small groups on branched stalks (Fig. 147*B*) or solitary on short stalks (Fig. 148*F*); in the other type there are numerous spherical microsporangia borne on slender, branched stalks, whose ultimate divisions consist of a single row of cells.

The clusters of sporangia represent sori; the sporocarp wall is a basal indusium which arises as a ring of tissue and grows up

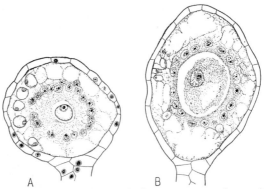

Fig. 149.—*Salvinia natans*. Developing megasporangium. *A*, surviving megaspore surrounded by tapetal nuclei—the degenerating spores in peripheral position; *B*, older stage. (*After Kundt*.)

about the young sorus enclosing it (Fig. 148).   The sporangia develop in the usual leptosporangiate manner (Fig. 148*D,E*). The wall is delicate, of one cell layer, and there is a prominent tapetum of a single layer of cells. (Two layers have been reported, apparently inaccurately.)   There is no evidence of an annulus.   In the developing megasporangium there are eight sporocytes from which 32 spores are formed; of these all but one abort.   About the surviving spore the cytoplasm derived from the tapetum and from the degeneration of the sister spores (Fig. 149) forms a hardened vacuolate layer, the perispore (often called the "epispore") (Fig. 150).   This additional coat is thicker at the apex of the spore and complex in structure there, with a three-angled, pollen-chamber-like cavity with a central mound containing a median cavity, and three projecting ridges

(Figs. 150, 152*A* to *C*).   The median cavity is also three-angled, and the central mound consists of three flaps, which are separated at germination (Fig. 152*A* to *C*).   The projecting folds apparently lie over the three flat sides of the tetrahedral spore.

In the microsporangia there are 16 sporocytes and therefore 64 spores, all of which mature. These spores, showing prominent triradiate markings, become scattered through the abundant tapetal cytoplasm (Fig. 151*C*), which like that of the megasporangium, becomes frothy with vacuoles (Fig. 151*D*).   As the spores mature, the cytoplasm becomes hardened forming a rounded alveolate mass, called a *massula*.

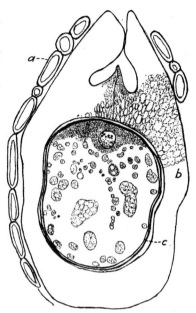

Fig. 150.—*Salvinia natans.*   Vertical section of megaspore showing megasporangium wall (*a*), perispore (*b*), and spore wall (*c*).   (*After Arnoldi.*)

The mature sporocarps sink to the bottom.   In annual forms this occurs when the plants go to pieces in the fall.

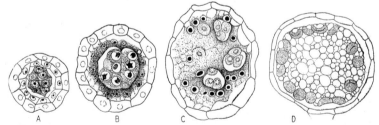

Fig. 151.—*Salvinia natans.*   Development of the microsporangium.   *A, B,* young sporangium with 16 sporocytes—in *B*, the tapetal cells degenerating; *C,* microspore tetrads floating in tapetal cytoplasm; *D,* mature microsporangium showing microspores in peripheral position.   (*After Yasui.*)

When the sporocarps open by decay, the spores, surrounded in nearly all cases by the sporangium walls, rise to the surface.

GAMETOPHYTE

The megaspores float on the surface of the water in a horizontal position.   Since they maintain there a definite orientation they appear to be stabilized in some way.   At the first division there

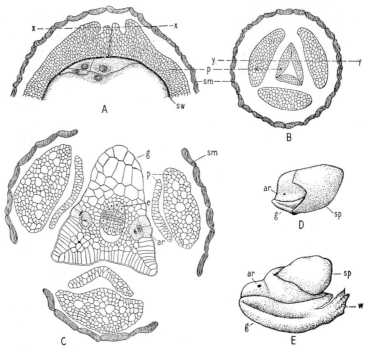

Fig. 152.—*Salvinia natans.* Development of female gametophyte. *A*, median section through apex of spore cut in plane *y-y* in *B* showing sporangium wall, perispore, and the cushion of cells formed from the cell cut off at the apex of the spore (below lies the large basal cell); *B*, transverse section of spore apex cut in plane of line *x-x* in *A*; *C*, transverse (vertical) section of apex of spore showing the sporangium wall, the six lobes of the perispore, the gametophyte with archegonia, and an embryo; *D*, floating megaspore (with sporangium wall removed) bearing gametophyte; *E*, later stage, the gametophyte greatly enlarged. *ar*, archegonium; *e*, embryo; *g*, gametophyte; *p*, perispore; *sm*, sporangium wall; *sp*, spore; *sw*, spore wall; *w*, wing of gametophyte.   (*A, C* to *E, after Lasser.*)

is formed a small apical lens-shaped cell, from which is built up (Fig. 152*A*) a cellular gametophyte, and a large basal cell filling the spore wall (Fig. 153*D*).   The nucleus of the basal cell divides later by free-nuclear division and many nuclei become scattered through the rich cytoplasm, but no walls are formed and the cell remains a food reservoir.   The apical cell forms a cushion of cells on which appears a central archegonium initial.   Above and behind the archegonium (the spore lies horizontally) a small mound of tissue develops; this perhaps serves to aid in opening the spore as do similar mounds in *Selaginella* (page 41). The spore wall and perispore are broken open and the lobes of the epispore spread apart by the protruding gametophyte (Fig. 152*C*). The first division in the apical cell is anticlinal (Fig. 152*A*) and the two unequal cells formed at this time develop upper and lower segments of the gametophyte which remain distinct superficially (Fig. 152*D,E*).   The upper segment is the larger and bears the central apical archegonium.   Two (in some cases four) other archegonia soon appear, one on each side of the first.   The three archegonia form a horizontal row across the 'nose' of the upper segment (Fig. 152*D*), their long axes parallel with the water surface.   At this stage the cushion is a thick, lobed cap over the spore apex, triangular in cross (vertical) section (Fig. 152*C*). On the upper side is the opening mound, which develops no further; across the lower side is a meristematic layer from whose two margins develop narrow horizontal wings which extend backward along the sides of the spore (Figs. 152*E*, 157).   These wings are delicate horizontal strips of tissue which serve apparently as stabilizing organs.   Growth of the tissue below the archegonia is such that these organs are soon turned through 90 deg., their necks no longer facing forward, but upward.   The developing gametophyte becomes green and much larger than the spore. It is commonly invested with the remains of the sporangium wall. If none of the first archegonia is fertilized others may form, even in large numbers, lateral to the first ones on the 'shoulders' of the gametophyte which seem to develop excessively under this condition.   Where fertilization does not occur, the wings do not develop or are vestigial; this appears to be evidence that the wings serve to maintain gametophyte and embryo in a position favorable to the development of the latter.

The archegonia are deeply sunken, their short necks barely projecting (Figs. 152*C*; 153*A,C*).   There is one neck canal cell with two nuclei.

The microsporangium does not open, and the microspores germinate in the massula within the sporangium.   As the spore enlarges, its contents are divided transversely into three cells

(Fig. 154*A*).   The lowest cell cuts off a small basal cell, which in position and size resembles the prothallial cell of male gametophytes in other heterosporous groups (Fig. 154*C*).   In the two upper cells there are formed by successive divisions (Fig. 154*C, D*)

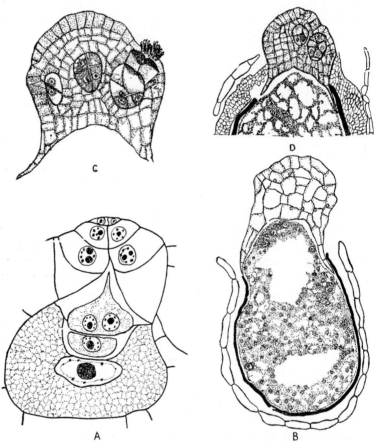

Fig. 153.—*Salvinia natans.   A*, archegonium; *B*, young female gametophyte attached to spore wall, with enclosing sporangium wall; *C*, tip of young gametophyte with three young embryos; *D*, tip of spore with young gametophyte bearing embryos (surrounding the gametophyte are spore wall, perispore, and sporangium wall).   (*A, after Yasui; B to D, after Arnoldi.*)

two spermatogenous cells and four sterile cells.   In each of the spermatogenous cells four spermatocytes develop (Fig. 154*E,F*). The spermatocytes are in two clusters of four each, separated by a large sterile cell and partly surrounded by smaller sterile cells (Fig. 154*E,F*). They lie on one side of the gametophyte and are not completely shut off from the spore wall as are the spermatocytes in other included gametophytes. Each cluster

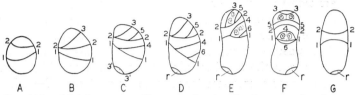

Fig. 154.—*Salvinia natans*. Diagrams showing development of male gametophyte. *A* to *E*, "side" view; *F*, "front" view; *G*, "back" view. The walls are numbered in order of formation. *A*, after first two divisions; *B*, the upper cell divided; *C, D*, prothallial cell formed, and, by consecutive divisions in the upper and middle cells, two spermatogenous cells (lying between walls 2, 3, and 5 and 1, 4, and 6) partly surrounded by sterile cells; *E, F*, four spermatocytes formed (only two in plane of section) in each spermatogenous cell, and the basal cell enlarged and elongated; *r*, prothallial cell. (*Based on Belajeff.*)

is believed to represent an antheridium. Because the antheridia lie along one side, it is often stated that the gametophyte is dorsiventral. The basal cell, after the cutting off of the prothallial cell, enlarges and elongates (Fig. 154*E,F*), pushing

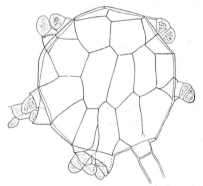

Fig. 155.—*Salvinia natans*. Male gametophytes breaking through sporangium wall. (*After Pringsheim.*)

the upper cells (before or as they divide) to the surface of the massula and through the sporangium wall (Fig. 155). The length of the elongating cell depends upon its position in the massula.

Embryo

The archegonium neck spreads open at maturity and the ventral canal and neck canal cells go to pieces. Sperms in large numbers crowd about the neck, as in *Marsilea*, and fertilization occurs. The first division of the zygote is longitudinal or nearly so ("tangential to the neck") and not quite median so that somewhat unequal parts are formed (Fig. 156*A*). Division then proceeds in the usual manner to the formation of octants. From the center a cross-sectional 'slice' is next set off—either

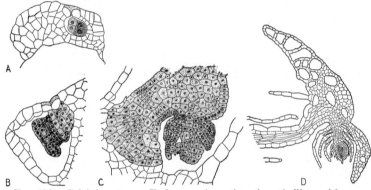

Fig. 156.—*Salvinia natans.* Embryo. *A*, section of prothallium with young embryo in archegonium (the first wall lies between the lighter and the darker cells); *B*, the developing embryo, still within the archegonium, a foot forming from the lightly shaded cells, a leaf and stem tip and a column from the darker cells; *C*, the rapidly enlarging embryo—the foot not extensive, the column well developed, the stem tip elongating (only base of first leaf shown); *D*, the elongated column, with first and second leaves and stem tip. (*After Lasser.*)

from the octants on one side, or from those on both sides of the first division wall—by divisions parallel to this wall. The four octants (or the outer parts of them) that lie on one side of the first wall—those below the archegonium neck and toward the spore— form a foot which, though markedly haustorial in nature, does not enlarge greatly (Fig. 156*B,C*). The two outer octants of the other half become the first leaf. Of the two inner octants on this side, one becomes the stem apex, the other is apparently functionless. The central layer develops rapidly into a columnar structure connecting the foot with the leaf and the stem tip (Fig. 156*C,D*), which it raises out of gametophytic tissues. Interpretation of the embryo in the stages immediately following

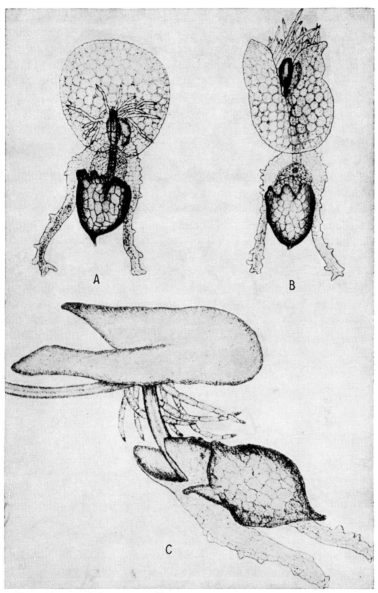

FIG. 157.—*Salvinia natans.* Gametophyte with young sporophyte. *A, B,* dorsal view; *C,* side view. *A,* megaspore, covered by sporangium wall, with attached prothallium, whose lateral wings extend backward, and young sporophyte showing long column and shield-shaped, first leaf before inversion; *B,* as in *A,* after inversion of first leaf, the plumule now pointed upward and the rhizoids below; *C,* as in *A,* but older, the stem developed. (*After Lasser.*)

the formation of octants is difficult, and opinions as to morphological relationships of the segments differ greatly. The foot plus the "column" is called the "foot" by some investigators. Others see a division into quadrants which form leaf, stem, root, and foot, the root segment early ceasing to grow and becoming indistinguishable from the foot tissues. Such an abortive root is called vestigial. Since the results of apparently thorough studies differ so much, it is evident that other species must be studied to determine the rather important matter of whether in this rootless plant there is an embryonic root.

The leaf segment develops pseudoterminally on the column a prominent cordate or sagittate leaf (Figs. 156*D*, 157). The stem apex is inverted, pointed backward toward the gametophyte. As the embryo grows, the strongly arched tip of the column is straightened and the leaf, which is at first shield-like and convex above, is inverted and flattened (Fig. 157).

In the center of the column is a delicate, xylemless vascular strand which extends from the foot to the first leaf where it "branches dichotomously," one branch entering the leaf, the other the stem tip. As the stem tip elongates, there are formed two alternate leaves which, like the first, are floating, then a three-membered whorl as in the mature plant, with the submersed leaf an unbranched filament.

AZOLLA

Sporophyte

Habit. The species of *Azolla* are small, delicate, moss-like plants with fragile rhizomes covered by crowded overlapping leaves. Branching is free, and dense, fern-frond-like plants are formed (Fig. 158). On the lower side simple roots, solitary or in clusters, extend a short distance downward in the water. The leaves are alternate and stand on the dorsal surface of the rhizomes in two rows. Each leaf is divided into an upper aerial and a lower submersed lobe (Fig. 158*C*). The upper lobe, which stands oblique and touches the water only on one edge, is several cells thick in the central region and is photosynthetic, with palisade tissue below and stomata on both surfaces. In its lower surface are large cavities where mucilage is secreted and where live colonies of the alga *Anabaena*. This lobe is said to be inverted, its dorsal surface being uppermost. The submersed lobe is one cell layer thick through most of its extent; its

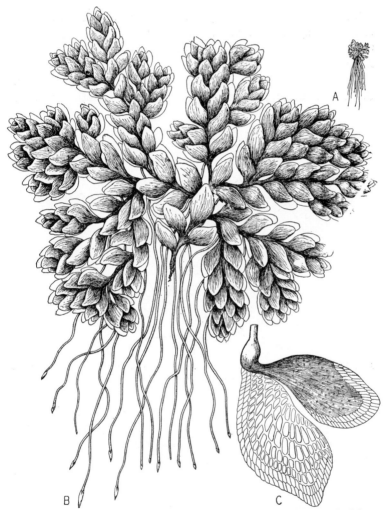

FIG. 158.—*Azolla microphylla.*   *A, B,* habit; *A,* natural size; *B,* enlarged; *C,* leaf.
(*After Martius.*)

function appears to be, in part, water absorption. Plants of *Azolla,* like those of *Salvinia,* retain their floating position because they are not readily wet. The prevention of wetting is secured in *Azolla* by papillae on the exposed leaf surfaces and by the abundant small spaces between the many close-packed leaf lobes.

The plants fragment easily, and therefore vegetative multiplication is rapid. The surface of stagnant pools may become closely covered with *Azolla* as it often is with the duckweed *Lemna*.

Anatomy. Plants of this genus, although of small size and delicate structure, resemble closely those of other ferns in

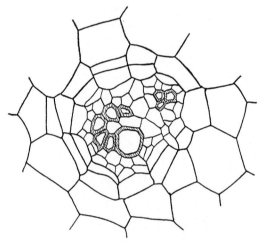

Fig. 159.—*Azolla filiculoides.* Cross section of stele of rhizome showing leaf trace and gap. (*After Queva.*)

anatomy. The rhizome has a slender, apparently siphonostelic central cylinder with typical leaf and branch traces and gaps (Fig. 159). The xylem is in most places only one layer of tracheids thick; the phloem is especially well developed on the lower side of the stele. The leaf trace forks dichotomously before entering the leaf. The branches arise above every third leaf, and hence alternately on the rhizome. They are not, however, axillary, the attachment of their traces being to the ventral side of the stele.

The roots are attached on the lower side close to the points of origin of the branches; when the roots are clustered, one is above and one below the point of attachment of the branch and one on the base of the branch itself.   Their traces are attached to the lower side of the stele.

Reproduction.   Sporocarps are borne on the first leaf of a lateral branch.   In these fertile leaves the submersed lobe is reduced to two (rarely four) divisions on each of which a sporocarp is borne terminally (Fig. 160*B*), and the upper lobe has a marginal flap, one cell layer thick, which covers the sporocarps

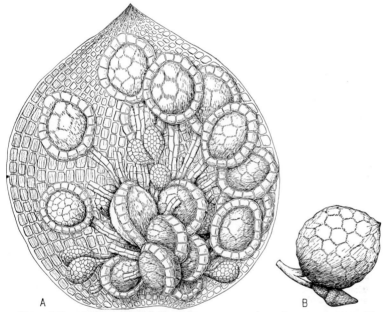

Fig.   160.—*Azolla   microphylla*.   Sporocarps.   *A*,   microsporocarp with indusium opened vertically showing microsporangia; *B*, sporocarps on leaf segment, microsporocarp above, megasporocarp below.   (*After Martius.*)

like a hood.   The sporocarps contain either microsporangia or megasporangia and are unlike in size and shape: those bearing microsporangia are large—almost as large as the upper leaf lobe— and spherical; those with megasporangia are much smaller and ellipsoid or flask-shaped.   The wall, like that of *Salvinia*, is two-layered and is delicate, except at the tip of the megasporocarp where it is firmer and "woody."   The microsporangia are numerous and borne on long simple stalks radiating from a columella; the megasporangium is solitary in the base of the sporocarp.

The sporangia develop in the usual leptosporangiate manner. As they begin to form, a ring of meristematic tissue appears around the receptacle and forms the sporocarp wall. This wall and the sporangia grow together (Fig. 161), the wall finally surpassing the sporangia and nearly or quite enclosing them. Filaments of *Anabaena*, which are commonly present about the growing points of the stem, are in many cases enclosed in

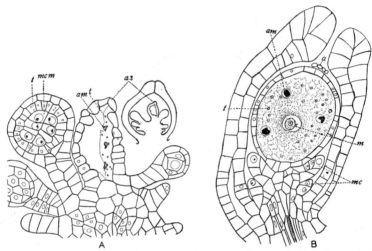

Fig. 161.—*Azolla caroliniana.* Development of sporocarps. *A,* central portion of partly grown microsporocarp (outline of entire sporocarp above on the right) showing abortive megasporangium and megaspore, and microsporangia in various stages of development; *B,* developing megasporangium with surviving megaspore and three abortive megaspores—the microsporangia have ceased to develop. *a,* cells of *Anaboena; am,* abortive megaspore; *as,* abortive megasporangium; *m,* persisting megaspore; *mc,* microsporangia which cease to develop; *mcm,* microspore mother cells; *t,* tapetum or tapetal nuclei. (*After Pfeiffer.*)

the top of the sporocarp cavity as they are in the leaf chambers. There is no definite annulus, but some species show (Fig. 160*A*) a ring of cells, annulus-like in form and position, which probably represents a vestigial annulus. The ring is oblique and complete.

In the formation of a sporocarp a megasporangium develops terminally on a short stout receptacle (Fig. 161*B*). In this sporangium at an early stage are eight sporocytes surrounded by a prominent one-layered tapetum and a wall also of a single layer. The walls of the tapetal cells break down, and the protoplasts fuse forming a multinucleate mass, a periplasmodium

(Fig. 161*B*). This cytoplasmic mass surrounds the sporocytes and soon pushes between them so that as tetrads are formed the spores are scattered through the sporangium. Meanwhile the receptacle (apparently the stalk of the sporangium) has become massive, and on its sides have arisen several young microsporangia (Fig. 161*B*).

After this stage either the megasporangium or the microsporangia develop, the other kind of sporangium aborting. Where the megasporangium persists, it enlarges greatly, closely filling the sporocarp and crowding the shrunken remnants of partly developed microsporangia down against the receptacle. Where the microsporangia persist, the megasporangium collapses and shrivels (Fig. 161*A*), and the microsporangia develop rapidly on long stalks, the sporocarp enlarging greatly to accommodate them. The receptacle elongates by a basal meristem and new microsporangia appear below the first ones so that there is a definite basipetal sequence in the sorus from the megasporangium to the later formed microsporangia.

In the maturing microsporangium there are formed 16 sporocytes and 64 spores. The periplasmodium is abundant, and increases greatly with the extensive increase in size of the sporangium (which may be as great in volume as 600 times). The nuclei of the mass increase in number, the new nuclei being smaller than the original ones. The spores at first are scattered through the cytoplasm (Fig. 162*A*,*B*) but soon move to a peripheral position where they are rather uniformly distributed (Fig. 163*B*2).

Each spore lies in a vacuole slightly larger than itself (Figs. 162*A*,*B*; 163*B*2); but after the change of position a clear, homogeneous fluid collects about the spores and the vacuoles enlarge until they are separated only by thin plates of plasmodial substance (Fig. 163*A*3,*B*3). The partitions break down and the vacuoles fuse—at first in twos and threes (Fig. 163*A*4)—until there are five to eight large vacuoles which occupy most of the plasmodial sphere (Fig. 163*A*5). Each vacuole has a delicate, firm, limiting membrane and contains 8 to 12 spores. Nuclei and starch grains float in the clear fluid which is rich in dissolved food substances. In the center of the vacuole appear slender threads and granules which build up a cobweb-like framework (Fig. 163*A*6,*B*4); from this is formed a honeycomb-like structure which matures first at the center, then develops centrifugally until the vacuole is filled and the network is attached to the outer membrane. The spores lie in the outer region. Around the outside is a remnant layer of plasmodial substance (Fig. 162C).

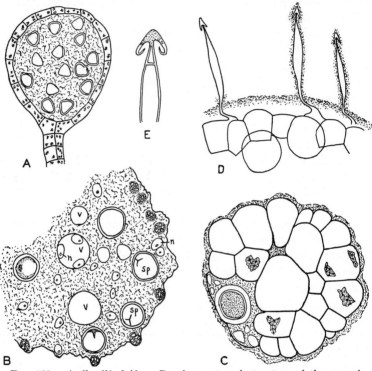

Fig. 162.—*Azolla filiculoides*. Development and structure of the massula. *A*, microsporangium with microspores lying in vacuoles slightly larger than themselves in periplasmodium; *B*, periplasmodium with spores, vacuoles, and nuclei; *C*, cross section of mature massula, with sheath of periplasmodium, showing microspore and the meshwork which has filled the vacuole (within the meshes "plasmatic remains"); *D*, cross section of peripheral region of massula showing part of meshwork with developing glochidia and the periplasmodial sheath; *E*, tip of a mature glochidium. *n*, nucleus; *sp*, spore; *v*, vacuole. (*After Hannig*.)

From each of the vacuoles has developed a rounded massula. It is clear that the massula in this genus is not merely a segment of the periplasmodium, as commonly stated, but a body developed within the periplasmodium.

The development of a massula is extraordinary. It and its cell-like chambers and walls increase in size; its nuclei multiply.

On its surface in some species appear tubular outgrowths with anchor-shaped tips, called *glochidia* (Fig. 162*D,E*). These appendages develop early—before the meshwork appears—as glove-finger-like processes of the massula membrane. They soon become flask-shaped and the remarkable heads are formed;

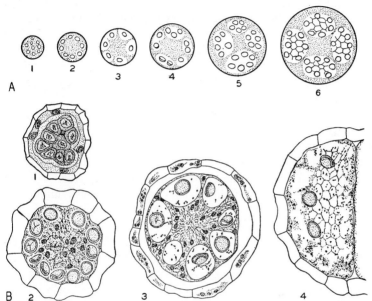

FIG. 163.—*Azolla filiculoides*. Development of massulae. *A*, diagrams showing origin and fusion of vacuoles and beginning of mesh formation; *B*, sporangium from early stage to beginning of mesh formation within the massulae. *A* 1, the spores scattered through the periplasmodium; *A* 2, the spores in peripheral position; *A* 3, vacuoles about the individual spores increasing in size; *A* 4, vacuoles fusing; *A* 5, vacuoles further fused so that only a small number are present, each containing several spores; *A* 6, meshwork forming in the central part of each vacuole and surrounding the spores. *B* 1, young sporangium with sporogenous cells and a tapetum already beginning to break down; *B* 2, the spores formed and in peripheral position in the periplasmodium; *B* 3, vacuoles about the spores greatly increased in size; *B* 4, the meshwork forming in the center of a vacuole, embedding the spores, and extending peripherally. (*After Hannig.*)

they then elongate and transverse septa may appear. The base is thin and strap-like, and the glochidia therefore vibrate with the slightest movement of the fluid in which they lie. Because the massulae fill the sporangium the glochidia are more or less appressed to the surface of the massula until the massulae are set free. At first the glochidia are mere lobes of the limiting membrane of the massula, but as the meshwork within reaches the surface at maturity they are tied into the net (Fig. 162*D*).

The periplasmodium is not completely used up in the formation of the massulae, and a thin layer, with nuclei, starch grains, and chloroplasts, surrounds the massulae (Fig. 162*C,D*). This remnant disintegrates with the sporangium wall at maturity. Definite glochidia seem to be present in only one section of the genus, *Euazolla;* in the other section the massulae are naked or have irregular, finger-like projections on only one side. (Details of massula form, however, as well as of gametophyte structure and embryogeny are probably well known only in *A. filiculoides* and *A. caroliniana.*)

In the megasporangium early stages are closely like those in the microsporangium, but there are only 8 sporocytes and 32 spores. The spores are separated by the periplasmodium, as are the microspores, and all but one abort. The surviving spore takes a basal position and enlarges until it nearly fills the lower half of the sporangium. The sporangium enlarges filling the sporocarp closely and its wall becomes thin and greatly compressed, perhaps in some cases degenerating. The single spore lies within a vacuole, as does each microspore. The periplasmodium makes a thin layer about this vacuole but fills the top of the sporangium above the spore. In this upper mass, where lie the spores that are degenerating, three other large vacuoles appear. These vacuoles are pear-shaped, and lie, mutually compressed, above the three flat faces of the spore apex. Within them are held the abortive megaspores, about equally divided. The development of these vacuoles is similar to that of a massula in a microsporangium, and it is apparent that each of the three apical vacuoles and the vacuole in which the megaspore lies are homologous with a massula of the microsporangium.

The megaspore and the vacuole in which it lies grow together. The clear fluid between the vacuole membrane and the spore wall becomes granulate and its distribution irregular. Pits appear in the surface of the membrane, and on the top of the spore a central mound is built up. This mound in some cases becomes extensive, forming a cushion-like columella below the three upper vacuoles (Fig. 164*A,B*). Within the irregular sheath of cytoplasm about the spore a foamy meshwork appears as in the other

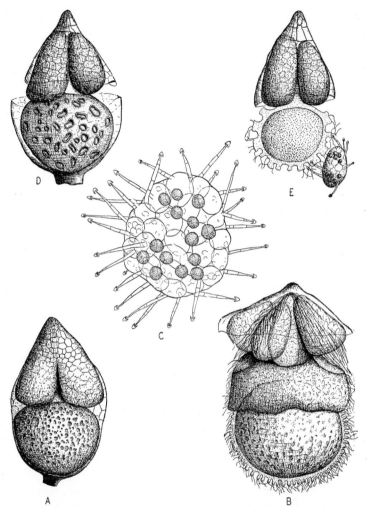

Fɪɢ. 164.—*A to C, Azolla caroliniana; D, E, A. filiculoides.   A*, megasporocarp
(its walls transparent) containing the large basal spore covered by the pitted
perispore, and the apical massulae ("floats") which surround a central columella;
B, megaspore with an apical cap of sporocarp tissue, a cushion-like columella,
four "floats," and numerous whip-like appendages (the perispore is seen in
optical section); *C*, massula with microspores and many glochidia; *D*, dehiscing
megasporocarp with basal spore, covered by large-pitted perispore, and apical
massulae; *E*, megaspore, seen in optical section, showing pits and appendages and
an attached massula with microspores and glochidia (sporocarp cap and "floaters"
as in *D*).   (*After Bernard.*)

vacuoles, and a perispore is formed.   The internal structure of the perispore is similar to that of its sister massulae, though the meshes are finer.   Minute whip-like appendages appear scattered over the surface of this perispore layer and a tuft of them is borne at the top (Fig. 164*B,E*).   The origin of these appendages has not been determined, but they are hollow and therefore are probably projections of the vacuole membrane and homologous with glochidia.

The three upper massulae are lightly attached to one another and to the spore and because of their spongy structure have been believed to serve as "floats" or "swimming apparatus" for the spore.   The fourth massula forms the perispore about the megaspore.

GAMETOPHYTE

The mature sporocarps sink to the bottom and their walls decay, setting free the massulae and spores.   The megasporocarp in many cases dehisces by a median transverse split (Fig. 164*D*), brought about, it is said, by the "floats."   That these apical massulae are not a "swimming apparatus" is evident because the spores do not float until the embryonic leaf raises them to the surface.   Further, the massulae from the microsporangia, which have the same light structure, do not float on the surface.   The spores therefore, in contrast with those of *Salvinia*, germinate under water.

The very light massulae from the microsporangia move freely in the water and come by chance to be attached to the megaspore or its accompanying structures (Fig. 164*E*).   The attachment is secured by the entangling of the hooked tips of the glochidia with the whip-like appendages of the perispore, which move freely with water currents.   The glochidia are commonly said to become attached to the irregularities of the perispore (and this may be in part the case), but the much smaller projections have not usually been seen.   The attachment of the massulae to the megaspore wall increases greatly the chances of fertilization, and the function of the appendages of the massulae appears to be to hold male and female gametophytes together.

Male Gametophyte.   The microspore germinates within the massula.   The spore wall opens along the triradiate ridge, and a papilla protrudes.   This papilla is cut off by a transverse wall near its base (Fig. 165*A*).   The large cell filling the spore cavity cuts off a small lenticular basal cell (Fig. 165*B*).   The external cell is divided into three by transverse walls.   Of these the outer and inner divide no further, becoming, respectively, the cap and basal cells of an antheridium.   In the other cell two periclinal walls separate a central cell from two jacket cells.   One of these outer cells divides later, and the central cell is then surrounded by a jacket of five cells.   From the central cell there develop eight spermatocytes.   The gametophyte remains embedded in the outer part of the massula, and the sperms are probably freed by the decay or softening of its substance.

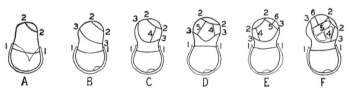

FIG. 165.—*Azolla.*   Diagrams showing development of male gametophyte.   *A* to *D*, *F*, side view; *E*, side view at right angles to *A* to *D*.   *A*, first two divisions form a basal cell, a central cell, and a cap cell; *B*, basal cell has formed a small prothallial cell and the central cell has divided transversely (wall 3-3); *C*, *D*, two periclinal walls (4, 5) separate an internal cell from two jacket cells; *E*, one of the jacket cells is divided anticlinally (wall 6); *F*, the central cell has divided to form spermatocytes (only four showing).   (*After Belajeff.*)

Female Gametophyte.   Germination takes place within the spore and the early stages of the gametophyte closely resemble those of *Salvinia.*   An apical lenticular cell is cut off.   This cell divides anticlinally into two unequal cells, from which a hemispherical cushion is formed.   In or near the center of the upper surface an archegonium initial is formed.   All the cells then expand, the spore is split open, and the gametophyte protrudes as a bulging cushion with a concave lower surface (Fig. 166*B*).   In the large cell within the spore free-nuclear division has meanwhile occurred, and the many nuclei so formed lie close below the cellular gametophyte.

The archegonium closely resembles that of *Salvinia* in form and in its axial row.   The neck is perhaps somewhat more prominent, with three or four tiers of four cells each.

The developing gametophyte becomes more or less triangular in cross section, pushing aside as it grows the upper parts of the perispore and the three massulae (Fig. 166*A*).   The latter structures and the cap of sporangium wall and sporocarp tip (indusium) remain attached (Fig. 166*A*), however, until pushed off by growth of an embryo below.   If the first archegonium is fertilized, others usually do not appear, but in most cases one or two others form near by.   If these are not fertilized several more—up to 10—may develop.   The gametophyte remains

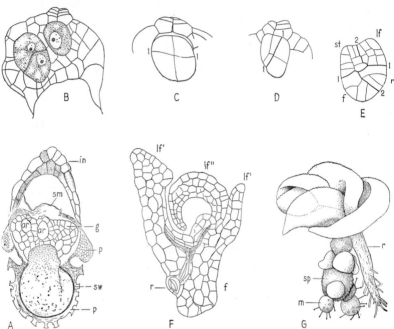

FIG. 166.—*Azolla filiculoides.*   Female gametophyte and embryo.   *A*, the gametophyte with spore wall and cap of indusium and sporangium in longitudinal section, the large basal (food-reservoir) cell filling the spore wall, the cushion bearing archegonia; *B*, cushion of the gametophyte with archegonia, one with zygote (?), the other with 2-celled embryo; *C*, 8-celled embryo with first wall transverse; *D*, older embryo with first wall oblique-vertical; *E*, longitudinal section of embryo showing segmentation; *F*, longitudinal section of young plant; *G*, young plant still attached to megaspore.   *ar*, archegonium; *f*, foot; *g*, cushion of the gametophyte; *in*, sporocarp wall (indusium); *lf′*, *lf″*, first and second leaves; *m*, massula; *p*, perispore; *r*, first root; *sm*, sporangium wall; *st*, stem; *sp*, spore; *sw*, spore wall.   (*After Campbell.*)

always small, however, not developing vegetative tissue as does that of *Salvinia*, and has very little or no chlorophyll.

EMBRYO

The zygote elongates before division and the first wall is transverse or oblique-longitudinal (Fig. 166*C,D*).   Definite quadrants are formed from which develop the four primary organs, leaf, stem, root, and foot, as in typical leptosporangiate ferns (Fig. 166*E*): the two outer quadrants form leaf and stem; the two inner, root and foot. The foot is a short cylindrical structure. The first leaf is funnel-like, slit on one side, and surrounds the stem apex; it resembles the first leaf of *Salvinia*. As the embryo grows, the cap of sporocarp, sporangium, and massulae is pushed upward and off. With the development of air chambers within the first leaf the embryo rises to the surface of the water, usually carrying with it the gametophyte and spore (Fig. 166*G*), and the leaf becomes a floating organ.

Discussion and Summary

The two genera show many similarities, even in minute details, and some marked differences. Adaptation to a floating habit has resulted in similar body modifications: the leaves have become floating organs, the submersed ones or the submersed lobes transformed into absorbing and reproductive structures. Roots have been lost in one genus and the vascular tissue greatly reduced in both. The small size and delicate structure, with vegetative reproduction by fragmentation, are doubtless adaptations to water surface as a habitat and are paralleled in such angiosperms as the Lemnaceae. The genera are in strong contrast with the Marsileaceae where adaptation is to life in soil in wet places and only reproduction is necessarily in the water.

In reproduction similarities of detail are remarkable. The sporocarp is a terminal or marginal sorus with a cup-shaped indusium enclosing the sporangia. Such a structure morphologically differs greatly from the sporocarp of the Marsileaceae, and it is obvious that the possession of sporocarps cannot be used to hold the two families together. Within the Salviniaceae an important difference seems to be the fact that in *Salvinia* the sporocarps contain but one kind of sporangia, whereas those of *Azolla* are potentially bisporangiate. Ontogeny shows that in the latter genus both kinds of sporangia are alike up to a late stage—the formation of the spores—and it is apparent that heterospory has in the history of the group developed from homospory, and that originally a sporocarp probably bore both micro- and megasporangia. In *Salvinia* segregation of spore type among the sporocarps is complete; in *Azolla* the bisporangiate condition is passed through in ontogeny, but the monosporangiate condition is established. Heterospory has attained the same level of advancement in both genera in that a single megaspore persists in the megasporangium, but in *Azolla* the megasporangia of a sporocarp have been reduced to one. The megasporocarp of *Azolla* is a highly reduced and specialized reproductive body—a sorus with only one sporangium which bears only one spore, this spore closely surrounded by the sporocarp wall, with the sporangium wall crowded between, or degenerate. (A closely analogous condition may be seen in angiosperm fruits where in achene types the embryo and endosperm fill the ovary, the ovule integuments being lost.) The stalks of the sporangia are in their branching unlike those of other groups. *S. natans* in the possession of unbranched megasporangium stalks is apparently not typical of the genus. Since the number of megasporangia is small and the species is an annual, this species, *S. natans*, is probably a highly specialized species; it is unfortunate that it is the only one known in detail.

In sporangium development the family is like other leptosporangiate ferns. In soral development it is at the gradate level.

In both genera the function of the tapetal cytoplasm has been greatly elaborated, and massulae are formed. In *Azolla* the massulae attain an extraordinary degree of complexity of structure and function. It has been suggested that the periplasmodium—a group of fused protoplasts—is an active protoplast, capable of growth and of the initiation of form and structure; indeed the results of the activities of the periplasmodium are amazing in their form and adaptation to reproductive processes.

The massulae of the two genera and of the two kinds of sporangia are clearly homologous. The perispore of the megaspore of *Salvinia* represents a massula equivalent to that of the microsporangium. The perispore of *Azolla* is a sister massula of the apical "floats," and each is homologous with one of the massulae containing microspores. The three lobes of the apex of the perispore of *Salvinia* are perhaps homologous with the three "floats" of *Azolla*. The origin of structure in all the massulae is the same; the degenerating megaspores are included, as are the microspores, except that in one massula there is but one huge spore which nearly fills it; the limiting membrane has projections, hook-like in one type, lash-like in the other, which seem to be alike morphologically.

The massulae arise as vacuoles within the periplasmodium and are not divisions of this cytoplasmic mass, as usually stated. The massulae and the "floats" are not "swimming bodies"; the spores are not borne to the surface by them, although their spongy character doubtless makes spore distribution under water more ready. The glochidia serve to hold near together the two kinds of spores; attachment is apparently to the homologous whip-like appendages rather than to the irregularities of the perispore. The megaspore of *Azolla*, with its elaborate cap of sporocarp, sporangium, and massulae and its cloak (another massula) with the lash-like appendages, is one of the most remarkable of plant reproductive structures.

The megaspores of *Salvinia* germinate on the surface, those of *Azolla* under water. In details of early gametophyte development the genera are exactly alike. Later they differ in that the prothallium of *Azolla* does not become extensive, is hardly green, and apparently is wholly dependent upon the stored food of the spore; that of *Salvinia* becomes a prominent green structure adapted to horizontal growth on or near the surface of the water.

In embryogeny both genera depart somewhat from the leptosporangiate type. In *Salvinia* early segmentation is typical, but a definite association of quadrants with first organs is lacking. This is perhaps in part the result of the rootless condition of the mature plant, the embryo possibly showing a vestigial root whose poor development distorts the usual symmetry. Even the vestiges of an embryonic root may, however, be absent, a condition which also would distort the young embryo. The early development of the prominent column—which is probably the stem—adds further to the unusual form of the embryo.

The embryo of *Azolla* is typical of leptosporangiate ferns in the formation and function of the quadrants, but the first division is in many cases transverse or oblique rather than longitudinal. The divergences from the usual in embryogeny of both these genera are doubtless related to the development of the embryos in water, for the position of the family among leptosporangiate ferns cannot be doubted.

The relationships of the Salviniaceae are obscure: that they are closely related to the homosporous leptosporangiate ferns is clear; that they have nothing in common with the Marsileaceae is equally evident. The possession of sporocarps and of heterospory has made the two families a "biological group" but not a natural one. The sporocarp method of protecting spores during development and through possible following dry periods is probably an adaptation to aquatic life; heterospory occurs as the expression of the tendency found in many groups of vascular plants.

The gradate sorus, marginal or terminal on leaf lobes, with an elongate receptacle and a probable vestigial oblique-complete annulus strongly suggest the Hymenophyllaceae. The presence in the receptacle of a basal meristem and of a vascular bundle and the dichotomous leaf, leaf trace, and venation strengthen this suggestion. The Salviniaceae appear to represent a highly specialized offshoot from some fairly primitive leptosporangiate group. The Marsileaceae seem from such evidence to have been derived from schizaeaceous stock; so definite an assignment cannot at present be made for the Salviniaceae. The filmy fern line provides, however, a probable point of derivation, since important structural features are the same, and the Hymenophyllaceae are greatly reduced in size and structure in adaptation to moist habitats.

The placing of the two genera in separate families, chiefly on the basis that the sporocarp in one is mono-, in the other bisporangiate, which is in some cases the taxonomic treatment, is not justified because of the close similarity in minute details, especially those of reproduction and embryogeny.

Bibliography

HYMENOPHYLLACEAE

BOODLE, L. A.: Comparative anatomy of the Hymenophyllaceae, Schizaeaceae, and Gleicheniaceae. I. On the anatomy of the Hymenophyllaceae, *Ann. Bot.*, **14**: 455–496, 1900.

BOWER, F. O.: On some normal and abnormal developments of the oöphyte in *Trichomanes*, *Ann. Bot.*, **1**: 269–305, 1888.

GIESENHAGEN, C.: Die Hymenophyllaceen, *Flora*, **73**: 411–464, 1890.

GOEBEL, K.: Archegoniaten Studien. Weitere Untersuchungen. Ueber die Geschlechtsgeneration der Hymenophyllaceen, Flora, **76**: 104–116, 1892.

————: Zur Keimungsgeschichte einiger Farne, *Ann. Jard. Bot. Buitenzorg*, **7**: 74–119, 1888.

HOLLOWAY, J. E.: The experimental cultivation of the gametophytes of *Hymenophyllum pulcherrimum*, Col., and of *Trichomanes reniforme*, Forst. f., *Ann. Bot.*, **44**: 269–284, 1930.

————: Studies in the New Zealand Hymenophyllaceae, Pt. I., *Trans. N. Z. Inst.*, **56**: 577–618, 1923.

KARSTEN, G.: Morphologische und biologische Untersuchungen über einige Epiphytenformen der Molukken, *Ann. Jard. Bot. Buitenzorg*, **12**: 117–195, 1895.

SHREVE, F.: Studies on Jamaican Hymenophyllaceae, *Bot. Gaz.*, **51**: 184–209, 1911.

SALVINIACEAE

ARNOLDI, W.: Beiträge zur Morphologie der Keimung von *Salvinia natans*, *Flora*, **100**: 121–139, 1910.

BAKER, J. G.: Synopsis of Rhizocarpeae. 1. Salvinieae, *Jour. Bot.*, **24**: 97–101, 1886.

BELAJEFF, W.: Über die männlichen Prothallien der Wasserfarne (Hydropterides), *Bot. Ztg.*, **56**: 141–194, 1898.

BERNARD, C.: A propos d'*Azolla, Rec. Trav. Bot. Néerl.*, **1**: 1–13, 1904.

CAMPBELL, D. H.: On the development of *Azolla filiculoides*, Lam., *Ann. Bot.*, **7**: 155–187, 1893.

GLÜCK, H.: Die Sporophyllmetamorphose, *Flora*, **80**: 303–387, 1895.

HANNIG, E.: Über die Bedeutung der Periplasmodien. II. Die Bildung der Massulae von *Azolla, Flora*, **102**: 243–278, 1911.

KUNDT, A.: Die Entwicklung der Micro- und Macrosporangien von *Salvinia natans, Beih. bot. Centralbl.*, **27**: 26–51, 1910.

LASSER, H.: Zur Entwicklungsgeschichte des Prothalliums und des Embryos bei *Salvinia natans, Flora*, **117**: 173–220, 1924.

PFEIFFER, W. M.: Differentiation of sporocarps in *Azolla, Bot. Gaz.*, **44**: 445–454, 1907.

PRINGSHEIM, N.: Zur Morphologie der *Salvinia natans, Jahrb. wiss. Bot.*, **3**: 484–541, 1863.

QUEVA, C.: L'*Azolla filiculoides* Lam. Étude anatomique, *Bull. Soc. Hist. Nat. d'Autun*, **23**: 233–256, 1910.

STRASBURGER, E.: "Über *Azolla*," Jena, 1873.

YASUI, K.: On the life-history of *Salvinia natans, Ann. Bot.*, **25**: 469–483, 1911.

ZAWIDSKI, S.: Beiträge zur Entwicklungsgeschichte von *Salvinia natans, Beih. bot. Centralbl.*, **28**: 17–65, 1912.

CHAPTER XII

CYATHEACEAE

Though arborescent types occur in several fern families, the Cyatheaceae are outstandingly a tree-fern group. Like the Hymenophyllaceae the family is small in genera—only three, *Alsophila, Hemitelia,* and *Cyathea*—but large in species—about 425. Most of the best known and conspicuous tree ferns belong here, and the term "tree ferns" is often used as a common name for this family (especially if there is included in the family the Dicksoniaceae). The Cyatheaceae are largely confined to the tropics and subtropics, with some forms in temperate regions, especially in the southern hemisphere. They live chiefly in humid forests, but some are xerophytic and flourish in open sunny habitats. A few species may be gregarious, but most of them grow scattered among other plants, forming either undergrowth or part of the dominant forest. A number of species are in cultivation in greenhouses, and the more xerophytic species are frequent in gardens in warm regions. Tree-fern trunks, because of their imperishable nature, are often used for timber in the tropics.

Sporophyte

Habit. Though most species have erect stout trunks (Fig. 167), which often reach a height of 15, and at times perhaps 25 m, with a palm-like crown of leaves, some few have more slender trunks and branch rather freely, developing a shrub-like habit. Runner-like stems are formed at the base in some species, and at the tips of these new trunks arise. Branching of the trunk in the dendroid types is apparently frequent in some species. This branching, though stated to be the result of dichotomy, results in most cases probably from adventitious buds or from branches developed from the leaf bases. Comparative study of the habit of many species in the family seems to show that the tree form has been derived from the rhizome type, the stem

FIG. 167.—A tree fern.   The Cervantes Otaguidin Trail, Mountain Province,
Luzon, Philippine Islands.   (*Photograph by Charles Martin.   Courtesy of the
National Geographic Society.*)

becoming erect and simple. In those tree species in which the branching is frequent, simplification of the stem has not as yet been completed. The arborescent habit provides a good example of homoplastic development, for in other families—Osmundaceae, Dicksoniaceae, Polypodiaceae—where this type occurs, it appears likewise to be derived.

Stems. The trunks of the tree types range from slender to stout—from a few to 25 or 50 cm in diameter. The stem itself, however, usually makes up only a small part of the trunk, for the outer part consists of a thick layer of matted adventitious roots. In the lower growing forms branches may develop freely from the bases of the leaves.

Leaves. The leaves are in most species large—sometimes several meters long—and wide-spreading, usually twice pinnately compound. The venation is mostly open, with a few vein fusions; a definite reticulum is not formed. In some species there are at the base of the leaves small, frond-like structures, known as *aphlebiae*, which differ from the rest of the leaf in form and appearance. These are perhaps basal pinnae which have been 'left behind' in the ontogeny of the leaf by intercalary growth above them. Chaffy scales are the characteristic dermal appendages and in many species thickly cover the leaves and stem when young. Though in some species the leaves are deciduous (Fig. 167), the trunks of others are clothed with persistent, decaying leaf bases.

Anatomy. The stem ranges in anatomy from the simple siphonostele to complex dictyosteles with medullary and sometimes also with cortical strands; the more complex types are most common. The leaf traces also are in most cases complex, being broken up into many bundles. No cambium is present.

Reproduction. The sporangia are borne in superficial sori on leaves which usually are not different from the sterile leaves. The sorus is gradate (in some species with transitions to mixed) with, in *Cyathea*, an indusium which is radially symmetrical and surrounds the sorus (Fig. 168*A,B*) and, in *Hemitelia*, an asymmetrical indusium, attached at one side of the sorus and covering it like a scale (Fig. 169*C*). The indusia of *Cyathea* provide an excellent example of specific variation in form, ranging from saucer-like (Fig. 169*B*) through cup shape to globose. In the last type the indusium completely encloses the sorus and is ruptured by the maturing sporangia. The sori of *Alsophila* (Fig. 169*D*) are naked (a few species have a minute vestigial indusium), and the sporangia are protected by hairs. The sporangia (Fig. 168*C,D*) are smaller than those of families thus far discussed and are borne typically on a short slender stalk of about four rows of cells. The annulus is complete and oblique (nearly vertical) with a poorly defined stomium. The spore number is small, 64 in most species.

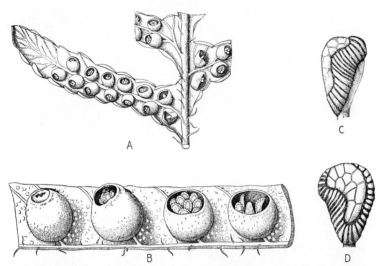

Fig. 168.—Sori and sporangia of the Cyatheaceae. *A, B, Cyathea elegans; C, D, Alsophila australis.* *A*, portion of fertile frond, dorsal view; *B*, sori showing stages in development; *C, D*, views of a sporangium. (*A, B, after Bauer; C, D, after Goebel.*)

GAMETOPHYTE

The prothallia are of the cordate thallus type, but when full-grown become longer and more massive than the "common type" (polypodiaceous), with often a heavy rib (Fig. 170), and a longer time is required for development. Forking is frequent and may be continued (Fig. 170*E*). The sex organs are borne in the usual manner. The antheridia are complex, though much less so than those of the Osmundaceae and Gleicheniaceae. They have a stalk of one cell, a funnel cell, a ring cell, and a cap cell which is divided once, or in some cases twice. In this five-cell form they approach the polypodiaceous type. The archegonia

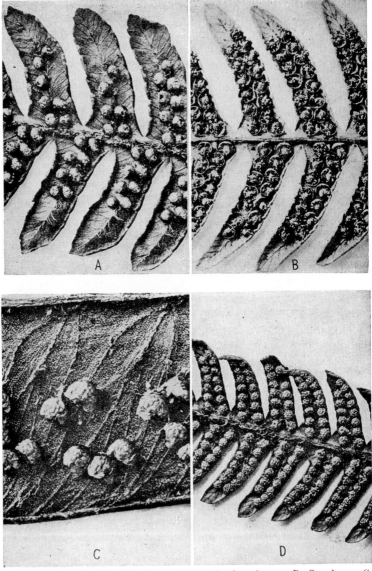

FIG. 169.—Sori of the Cyatheaceae. *A, Cyathea elegans; B, C. arborea; C, Hemitelia horrida; D, Alsophila myosuroides. (After Maxon; courtesy of the Smithsonian Institution.)*

are of the usual type (Fig. 171). Their necks are long, with mostly six or seven tiers of cells, straight or slightly curved. There are normally two neck canal nuclei (sometimes four); only rarely are two neck canal cells formed. Apogamy is occasional.

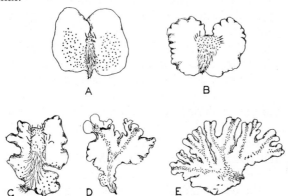

Fig. 170.—Prothallia of the Cyatheaceae. *A, Alsophila Cooperi; B, E, Hemitelia Smithii; C, A. excelsa; D, A. armata.* (*After Stokey.*)

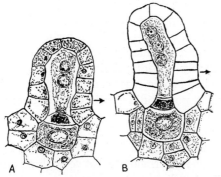

Fig. 171.—Archegonia of the Cyatheaceae. *A, Hemitelia horrida; B, Cyathea dealbata.* (*After Stokey.*)

EMBRYO

Very little appears to be known about the embryo.

DISCUSSION AND SUMMARY

The Cyatheaceae occupy an intermediate position among fern families. As gradate forms they stand definitely between the simplices and the mixtae; in other respects also they form a transition group between the more primitive and the more advanced families.   In details of structure of both gametophyte and sporophyte they suggest relationship to the Gleicheniaceae. The soral type of the Cyatheaceae with its elongate receptacle can readily be derived from the gleicheniaceous type with the heaped sporangia.

The open leaf venation, with the first steps toward a netted condition, indicates a fairly primitive stage with respect to this character.   The presence of chaffy appendages suggests a higher position.

The three genera show remarkably varied conditions as to the protection of the sorus.   It is probable that they present a series in the reduction of the indusium.   In *Cyathea* the indusium is cup-like and radially symmetrical; in *Hemitelia* it is scale-like, with attachment only on the side away from the leaf margin; in *Alsophila* there is no indusium.   In other families also progress in indusium form is seen from symmetry to zygomorphy and to the loss of the indusium.

The sporangia are definitely smaller than in the less advanced families, and the spore output is reduced to 64 and in some species to 32 or 16.   The stalk, though still as in lower groups, is more slender, with commonly four rows of cells.   The annulus has become nearly vertical; it lies, therefore, close to the stalk and is said to be in some cases continuous across it.   A stomium is present but is poorly differentiated.   Dehiscence has become definitely transverse.

The prothallia in form and slowness of growth—though in general of the type characteristic of the highest leptosporangiate ferns—tend to be intermediate between these and those of the more primitive families.

The sex organs are intermediate in form between those of the more primitive and those of the higher types.   The antheridia are less complex than those of the Osmundaceae and Gleicheniaceae but more complex than the simple polypodiaceous form in that they possess a stalk cell, and that the cap cell is divided once or twice.   The neck of the archegonium is intermediate in length and in extent of curvature between that of the highest and that of the lowest families.   Wall formation between the neck canal nuclei has not entirely disappeared.

The Cyatheaceae hold among fern families an intermediate position in evolutionary advance; they form, in a general way at least, a group transitional from the simplices to the mixtae type. They bear many resemblances to the Gleicheniaceae to which they seem to be undoubtedly related. Other relationships are discussed later (page 286).

DICKSONIACEAE

The Dicksoniaceae contain both low-growing rhizomatous and tall arborescent forms. There are nine genera, of which *Cibotium*, *Dicksonia*, and *Dennstaedtia* are best known, and about 155 species. Though the majority of species are tropical, a number are found in temperate regions. The arborescent species are largely confined to the tropics, but several (species of *Dicksonia*) are prominent ferns of the warm-temperate southern hemisphere. There are species, even among the tree types, which are somewhat xerophytic. Some of the creeping species have rhizomes as large as the trunks of the erect forms; for example, *Cibotium Barometz*, the "Scythian" or "Tartarian lamb." A number of species are in cultivation in greenhouses and in gardens in warm regions. The natives of the Hawaiian Islands once obtained starch for food from the stems of *C. Chamissoi*, and in recent years starch has been obtained in commercial quantities from the trunks of these tree ferns and placed upon the market.

Sporophyte

Habit. The Cyatheaceae are commonly considered to be "the tree-fern family" because of the many arborescent species; the Dicksoniaceae are second only to this family in number of tree-forming species. Frequently the two families are united taxonomically, largely, however, upon sporangium characters and not because of the tree habit. The leaves are of the repeatedly pinnate type, reaching large size in the dendroid forms. The dermal appendages of stem and leaf are hairs, which are often long and soft. These hairs may clothe the trunk heavily, as in species of *Cibotium*. Their resemblance to wool was in large part responsible for the tale of the mythical, rooted "Tartarian lamb." In the Hawaiian Islands the abundant soft hairs of this genus have been gathered as stuffing materials for cushions.

Anatomy.   In anatomy the stems range from simple siphonosteles to complex dictyosteles, with leaf traces also ranging from simple to complex.

Reproduction.   Sterile and fertile leaves are much alike.   The sori are marginal and gradate, with a cup-shaded indusium, which is two-lipped.   The receptacle, standing at a vein ending, is in many cases a flattened structure, bearing the sporangia on its margin in two series.   The sori in part of the family seem to be superficial rather than marginal; in some cases the sori, though

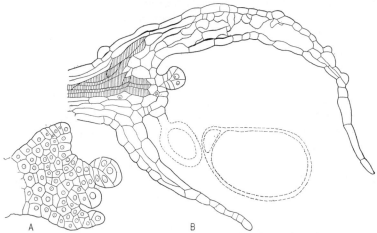

Fig. 172.—*Dennstaedtia punctilobula.*   Sorus in longitudinal section, showing marginal origin, gradate arrangement of sporangia, and development of the ventral indusial lip as leaf blade.   *A*, very young sorus; *B*, mature sorus.   (*After Conard.*)

strictly marginal, are bent downward—as in the hay-scented fern, *Dennstaedtia punctilobula*—and so appear dorsal; in others the fusion of the ventral indusial lips prolongs the blade beyond the sori, which then appear superficial.   That these sori are really marginal, however, as in the rest of the family, is evident from ontogeny (Fig. 172).   In *Dennstaedtia* and in related forms the sorus is not strictly gradate but shows a few sporangia formed late and out of the normal sequence of development.   In this there is clearly an approach to the mixtae condition.

The sporangia, varying in shape, have long or fairly long stalks of four to seven rows of cells and typically 64 spores, with sometimes fewer.   The annulus ranges from strongly oblique to nearly vertical, and there is in many cases a definite stomium; the annulus is usually complete but is sometimes interrupted at the stalk. The tapetum, in some cases at least, is two-layered. Dehiscence is transverse.

Gametophyte

The prothallia are similar to those of the Cyatheaceae, but with their generally broader wings are perhaps more closely like those of the Polypodiaceae. They are slow in maturing (as compared with those of the Polypodiaceae), with sex organs borne somewhat late. The antheridia are similar to those of the Cyatheaceae, though somewhat larger, and contain a high

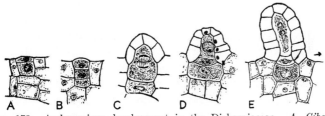

Fig. 173.—Archegonium development in the Dicksoniaceae. *A, Cibotium Barometz,* initial divided periclinally; *B, C. regale* neck initial, central cell, and basal cell; *C, Dicksonia antarctica,* neck partly formed, central cell dividing; *D, D. squarrosa,* neck developing, axial row nearly complete, basal cell divided anticlinally; *E, Culcita macrocarpa,* mature archegonium. (Arrow points toward apex of prothallium.) (*After Stokey.*)

number of sperms. The archegonia have the usual form, with a long neck, in most cases curved away from the notch. There are two (sometimes four) neck canal nuclei without separating walls.

Embryo

From the insufficient information available, development of the embryo is apparently of the leptosporangiate type.

Discussion and Summary

The Dicksoniaceae have in many characters reached a fairly high level of advancement. The sorus is gradate but shows in some forms transition stages to the mixtae type. The sporangia have stalks much longer than those of the primitive families but not so slender as those of the most advanced types. The annulus approaches the vertical type and is in some cases incomplete, as in the highest forms. Spore number reduction has progressed to 64 and in some cases further. The sori, however, remain marginal in position; they have not advanced to the superficial stage, though they show steps by which such advance may be made. In gametophyte characters also the family is fairly well advanced: the prothallus is cordate in form; the antheridia are much less complex than those of the primitive families; the archegonia show no walls between the neck canal cells, and the necks, though still long, are recurved nearly as strongly as those of the highest family.

This family has often been united with the Cyatheaceae, in large part because of annulus characters. These two families contain most of the arborescent species, and it is often assumed that the dendroid habit is evidence of relationship, the two groups forming a "tree-fern family." But it is clear that the tree habit is an example of homoplastic development, having appeared several times among ferns of low-growing type. Similarity in annulus specialization is merely an indication that the two groups have advanced in respect to this character to approximately the same level. Though both families are gradate, the Dicksoniaceae have marginal, the Cyatheaceae superficial sori. This difference, though not sharp, keeps them apart, with the former more primitive in respect to this one feature. The fact that the dermal appendages are hairs in one group and scales in the other is further evidence of their distinctness.

The Dicksoniaceae seem from many characters to be allied more closely to other gradate families whose sori are marginal than to those with superficial sori. The resemblance of their sori to the clusters or groups of sporangia at the leaf tips or vein endings of the Schizaeaceae is strong: the receptacle (in some forms) is flattened, extending along the leaf margin, and the sporangia are borne in two rows along its sides; if an indusium were present about the sporangial groups of the Schizaeaceae, the two structures would be closely alike. The fact that the appendages are hairs—often long and abundant—further suggests the Schizaeaceae.

The Dicksoniaceae are well advanced among fern families. The ancestral relations of the family seem to be with stock having characters similar to those of the Schizaeaceae (page 286).

POLYPODIACEAE[1]

Among the living ferns a large majority are members of the Polypodiaceae, a family often known as "common ferns," doubtless because among those of north temperate regions nearly all belong in this family. As compared with other families the group is very large—with more than 115 genera and perhaps 3000 species—and its members are most diverse in form, size, and habit. Such well known genera as *Adiantum, Pteris, Pteridium, Polypodium, Asplenium, Blechnum, Acrostichum, Aspidium, Davallia,* and *Dryopteris* will serve as examples. The many genera fall into several natural groups which are not closely related (page 274). The family is broadly distributed throughout the world wherever ferns are found, and is abundant in the tropics. The majority of ornamental and commonly cultivated species belong here. There are some xerophytic species and many epiphytes.

Sporophyte

Habit. The numerous species show the greatest variety in size and habit. There are, however, few dendroid types, and these are not large. As a whole the members of the family are smaller than those of the other leptosporangiate groups with the exception of the Hymenophyllaceae and water ferns.. True annuals among ferns are very rare and are found chiefly in this family, for example *Anogramme leptophylla* and *A. chaerophylla.* Some other forms reproduce seasonally by fragmentation or by leaf-borne buds, and are sometimes called annual.

Leaves. In leaves, as in habit, there is much variety in size and form. The typical leaf is repeatedly pinnately compound, but simple types of the most varied shapes are common. The blade ranges from the hard leathery type of the salt-marsh fern, *Acrostichum aureum,* to that of occasional filmy types. The venation ranges from open dichotomous to various types of reticulate. The dermal appendages are in most cases scales.

Anatomy. Stelar structure ranges from simple siphonosteles to the most complex dictyosteles; the leaf traces show progress from large simple strands to types of dissected and com-

[1] Illustrations are not included for this family except in Chap. VIII because it is so fully illustrated in elementary texts.

plex bundle groups. Vessels occur rarely (*Pteridium* and *Dryopteris*).

Reproduction. In many genera fertile and sterile leaves are closely alike; in others various degrees of dimorphism are found. In soral size and shape there is, as in many other characters in the family, the greatest variety. Very large, elongate sori are common in some genera. These are in many cases undoubtedly coenosori. In different groups the acrostichoid condition is present—an example of homoplastic modification. Indusia of all morphological kinds, and of all sizes and shapes are to be found; some sori are naked, in most cases because of the loss of the indusium, but in some perhaps primitively, and some of these naked sori are covered by lobes of the leaf blade, as in *Adiantum*. All sori are, however, of the mixtae type; all sporangia are small, flattened, with long, slender stalks, and are leptosporangiate in development. The stalks are usually three- or four-rowed, but in a few species are one-rowed. The annulus is vertical and incomplete (meeting the stalk), and the stomium is highly developed. Dehiscence is transverse. The number of spores is small, ranging from 64 to 8, with 32 most common. Both bilateral and tetrahedral spores occur.

Vegetative Propagation. Multiplication of the sporophyte by vegetative means occurs in many species as in *Camptosorus rhizophyllus*, the walking fern, *Cystopteris bulbifera*, the bladder fern, and in some species of *Adiantum* and *Asplenium*. In forms with branching rhizomes the dying of the older parts of the rhizome breaks up the plant.

GAMETOPHYTE

Though the prothallia of only comparatively few of the species are known, the cordate thallus type is apparently characteristic. These prothallia differ somewhat from those of similar type in other families; they are more delicate, with generally broader wings and a cushion less massive and less sharply defined than the rib of other forms. There are exceptions to the usual form, as in *Vittaria* where the prothallium is ribbon-like and branched, without a definite cushion, but only rarely do branching and elongate types occur. The gametophytes develop rapidly, bear sex organs early, and are in most cases apparently short-lived. The form of the full-grown prothallium is perhaps rarely seen since the development of an embryo—which normally occurs early—prevents the completion of growth. Probably all forms are fundamentally monoecious; some, however, seem to be partly dioecious—part of the individuals being male, the others sometimes female, but usually bearing both antheridia and archegonia. Under crowded conditions or weak light there develop elongate, more or less filamentous, weak individuals which are in most cases male. Such a condition seems to be closely parallel to that in *Equisetum*.

The antheridia are formed early and are scattered over the lower surface, most abundantly on the older part. They are small, projecting, subspherical, with a simple wall of three cells, (two ring-shaped cells one above the other, and a cap cell at the apex filling the central space in the upper ring cell). The sperm number is small, usually 32. The archegonia are borne in a cluster on the lower side on the younger part, just back of the notch. Their necks are short and usually strongly bent away from the notch. There are two neck canal nuclei.

Embryo

The first division wall in the zygote is parallel with the long axis of the archegonium and probably typically transverse to the anterior-posterior plane of the prothallium. The second is transverse to the long archegonium axis. The quadrants so formed bear uniform and definite relation to the organs of the young embryo: the anterior two become leaf and stem, the lower being leaf; the posterior two develop root and foot, the latter coming from the upper quadrant. Early stages are remarkably uniform. The foot does not become extensive. The leaf and the stem apex develop rapidly, extending beneath the prothallium toward the notch, through which the leaf grows upward.

Discussion and Summary

The Polypodiaceae show a high degree of advancement in many characters. In habit, annual and dendroid forms have appeared. Chaffy scales are the appendages in the majority of species. Simple leaves are frequent and have developed independently in the various groups. Venation, although various, is often of the reticulate type. Dimorphism—of the advanced type—between fertile and sterile leaves is common. The sori are mixed, and the more primitive genera show transitions to this condition from the gradate. The sori are of many advanced types: fused sori (coenosori and the acrostichoid condition) are common; zygomorphic and naked (by loss of indusium) sori are frequent. The sporangia are of the highest type—small, long-stalked, thin-walled, with vertical, incomplete annulus and few spores.

The gametophytes, although thalloid, are not massive, and the midribs are represented by cushions. They are delicate, grow rapidly, reach sexual maturity early, and are short-lived. (The shortness of life is perhaps related to the early development of an embryo which seems to limit growth and length of life.) Only rarely is more than one embryo formed. The antheridia are simple, with walls of three cells only, and the number of sperms is small. The archegonia do not differ markedly from those of other leptosporangiate ferns, but the neck is shorter and strongly recurved. There is no evidence of wall formation between the two neck canal nuclei. The embryo develops rapidly and its quadrants are definite in morphological relation to organs. The Polypodiaceae are in many characters most advanced ferns.

As a family these ferns are extraordinarily diverse, even at first glance; in no respect do they give the impression of a uniform or natural group, as do other fern families. As a group they stand together in the mixed condition of the sorus and in the possession of similar highly specialized sporangia—small, flattened, with a vertical incomplete annulus, a long slender stalk, and a small number of spores. But these characters are approached or reached in other groups, especially in the Dicksoniaceae, so that the line of separation from such other families is indistinct. Many characters which are inconstant in the family are those which are believed to be of much importance in indicating natural relationships: position of the sori—marginal or superficial; type of dermal appendages—hairs or scales; type and form of sorus. The family seems clearly to be an unnatural one, even from superficial study; intensive study has shown it to be polyphyletic. It is made up of several groups which have been derived along separate lines from unrelated or distantly related ancestral stock; each group has independently attained the highest type of soral make-up and of sporangium structure,

In a family based upon these characters homoplasy has brought together unrelated forms. Within this artificial family the various groups that seem on morphological study to be natural correspond in large measure to the tribes and subtribes of taxonomic treatments. The most prominent of these groups need to be discussed briefly in order that the phylogeny of the family may be understood.

Although the sori in most of the groups are superficial, there are two—the davallioid ferns, illustrated by *Davallia*, and the pteroid ferns, illustrated by *Pteridium* and *Pteris*—in which the sori are marginal or show transitions from the marginal to the superficial. These groups have hairs as dermal appendages in those genera with marginal sori, and show the addition of scales and finally the replacement of hairs by scales in the series advancing to superficial forms. The stalks of the sporangia show progressive stages from several-rowed to one-rowed, and in most of the genera the sorus though mixed when mature is gradate in its early stages. These two groups bear many close resemblances to the Dicksoniaceae and clearly are related to this family (Fig. 174). *Dennstaedtia* in the Dicksoniaceae and *Davallia* in the Polypodiaceae are close together morphologically; no sharp line exists, therefore, between these two families. In the characters of gradate-mixed sorus, several-rowed stalk, complete annulus, and hair appendages the davallioid and pteroid ferns form transitional groups to the higher, more nearly "typical" polypodiaceous forms. These groups, it should be noted, are, in the marginal position of their sori, also less advanced than the other groups which have superficial sori.

Among the superficial groups—as among the marginal—there are two in which the sori are gradate, or gradate with transitions to mixed: the woodsioids—*Woodsia* and related genera; and the onocleoids—*Onoclea* and *Pteretis* (*Matteuccia*). Both these groups show undoubted relationship to the Cyatheaceae, *Woodsia* being especially close, and seem to be independent of one another. The woodsioids and the onocleoids form two more of the group of diverse and unrelated polypodiaceous stocks (Fig. 174).

The extensive group of the dryopteroids (more than 1000 species), which contains the large and well-known genera *Dryopteris*, *Aspidium*, and *Polystichum*, also shows in some of its forms evidence of gradate development. This and close resemblances in other features make it evident that the relation of the dryopteroids is with the woodsioids (Fig. 174). Related probably to the dryopteroids are the asplenioids (illustrated by *Asplenium* and *Athyrium*); and to the onocleoids, the blechnoids (illustrated by *Blechnum, Woodwardia, Phyllitis (Scolopendrium)*, and *Camptosorus*) (Fig. 174). The basis for these apparent relationships cannot well be taken up here, since long, detailed character analyses are involved.

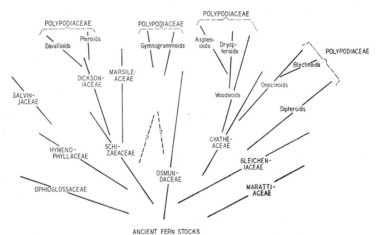

FIG. 174.—Diagram showing interrelationships of ferns.   (*Modified from diagram by Bower.*)

There are thus seen to be even among only a part of the Polypodiaceae two distinct derivative lines from the more primitive families—one from the Dicksoniaceae or closely related types, and one from the Cyatheaceae—and each of these is itself complex. Consideration of other groups within the family make evident a still more complex origin for the family. The only other large group, the gymnogrammoid ferns (illustrated by the genera *Cryptogramma, Adiantum, Pellaea,* and *Cheilanthes*), has apparently been derived along lines altogether independent of the two already discussed. This group, rather varied and perhaps itself polyphyletic, is held together in part by soral characters, especially by the lack of a true indusium. This and other characters associate it probably with osmundaceous and schizaeaceous stock (Fig. 174).

Another independent group among the Polypodiaceae is the dipteroids (represented by *Platycerium*, the staghorn fern). The characters and affinities of this group cannot well, however, be considered in so brief a discussion of the Polypodiaceae as is here included, beyond the fact that they belong with the superficial types, are not related to the Cyatheaceae, and seem to be derived indirectly from the more primitive gleicheniaceous stock (Fig. 174).

The Polypodiaceae are thus a heterogeneous assemblage of greatly specialized members of several distinct stocks and are therefore a highly unnatural family. They serve as an excellent example of a polyphyletic group—a group which is tied together by the attainment of certain advanced characters which have been selected as a taxonomic basis. They stand definitely at the top among leptosporangiate ferns—an aggregation of the highest members of the several lines of this stock; they are the modern, the young ferns. The fossil record bears out this conclusion, which has been drawn from the evidence of comparative study, for no members of the family are known before the Mesozoic.

Bibliography

Cyatheaceae

Bauke, H.: Entwickelungsgeschichte des Prothalliums bei den Cyatheaceae, vergleichen mit derselben bei anderen Farrenkräutern, *Jahrb. wiss. Bot.*, **10**: 49–116, 1876.

Bower, F. O.: Studies in the morphology of spore-producing members. IV. The leptosporangiate ferns, *Phil. Trans. Roy. Soc. London*, **192B**: 29–138, 1899.

Dobbie, H. B.: A forest of forked tree ferns, *Amer. Fern Jour.*, **19**: 41–44, 1929.

Maxon, W. R.: The tree ferns of North America, *Ann. Rpt. Smithsonian Inst.*, **1911**: 463–491, 1912 (publication 2120).

Ogura, Y.: Comparative anatomy of Japanese Cyatheaceae, *Jour. Fac. Sci. Imp. Univ. Tokyo*, Sec. III, Bot. **1**: 141–350, 1927.

Schoute, J. C.: "Ueber verästelte Baumfarne," Groningen, 1914.

Stephenson, B. G.: Young stages of *Dicksonia* and *Cyathea*, *Trans. N. Z. Inst.*, **40**: 1–16, 1907.

Stokey, A. G.: Prothallia of the Cyatheaceae, *Bot. Gaz.*, **90**: 1–45, 1930.

Dicksoniaceae

Conard, H. S.: The hay-scented fern, *Carnegie Inst. publ.* 94, 1908.

Maxon, W. R.: The tree ferns of North America, *Ann. Rpt. Smithsonian Inst.*, **1911**: 463–491, 1912.

————: The genus *Culcita*, *Jour. Washington Acad. Sci.*, **12**: 454–460, 1922.

STOKEY, A. G.: Prothallia of the Cyatheaceae, *Bot. Gaz.*, **90**: 1–45, 1930.

WILLIAMS, S.: Some points in the anatomy of *Dicksonia*, *Proc. Roy. Soc. Edinburgh* **45**: 286–296, 1925.

POLYPODIACEAE

For bibliography see Chap. XIII.

CHAPTER XIII

GENERAL DISCUSSION AND SUMMARY FOR FERNS

FILICALES

Among eusporangiate ferns the differences are so great that it is obvious that there is no close relationship between the two groups; the leptosporangiate ferns, however, form a group held well together by close similarities, and, although among themselves most diverse, they undoubtedly form a closely related, natural group. The characters possessed by them in common and those in contrast with the characters of eusporangiate ferns are shown in Table 3 (page 302) and are discussed later (page 287). The important characters which vary within the leptosporangiate forms are presented in Table 2 (page 280). Some of these are described in detail in the general discussion of the characters of these ferns (Chap. VIII).

It is apparent that the leptosporangiate ferns are a large group with structural features most complex in their relation; that they show steps in evolutionary advance in many features; and that, in a majority of these, change is in progress at the present time. The advances are in many cases along parallel or convergent lines, a feature which adds greatly to the difficulty of determining phylogenetic relationships. As will be more clear after fossil forms have been discussed, these ferns are a modern group, advancing rapidly in diversity and (in the larger families) in number of forms today.

Comparative study of all features of form and life history indicate that three families—Osmundaceae, Schizaeaceae, and Gleicheniaceae—are the most primitive. (This conclusion is strongly supported by the fossil record.) Among the three, relationships are not close, and no one of them can be derived from another. As interrelationships of ferns in a general way are understood today, these three families stand as discrete basic groups among leptosporangiate types (Fig. 174); that is, so far as these advancing ferns are known and understood today they

TABLE 2.—CHARACTERS OF THE LEPTOSPORANGIATE FERNS

	Osmundaceae	Gleicheniaceae	Schizaeaceae	Marsileaceae
Representative genera.	Osmunda Todea	Gleichenia	Schizaea Lygodium Anemia	Marsilea Pilularia Regnellidium
Number of genera and species.	2 genera 17 species	2 genera 80 ± species	4 genera 115 ± species	3 genera 60 ± species
Habit...............	Stout rhizome types to small dendroid forms; leaves large, pinnate	Rhizome types; leaf usually large, falsely dichoto-mous, developing over long period	Upright and rhi-zome types; leaf fundamentally dichotomous, sometimes very long and (?) in-determinate	Marsh or water plants
Distribution..........	Chiefly north and south temperate zones	Tropics and south temperate zone	Widely distributed but chiefly tropical	Broadly distributed
Sori.................	Nonsoral; sporangia on slender leaf seg-ments; or su-perficial	Superficial	Nonsoral; sporangia solitary, on slender leaf segments or marginal	Marginal; indusium equals soral sac
Order of development	Simple	Simple	Simple	Gradate
Sporangia Development.......	Intermediate be-tween eu- and lep-tosporangiate	Somewhat interme-diate but chiefly leptosporangiate	Somewhat interme-diate but chiefly leptosporangiate	Leptosporangiate; heterosporous
Form..............	Large, subglobose with short thick stalks	Large pyriform, subsessile or short-stalked	Sessile or short-stalked	....
Orientation.........	(Nonsoral)	Stalked (nonsoral or solitary)	Uniform	....
Annulus	Rudimentary; clus-ter of subapical cells	Row of cells; ob-lique-transverse, complete	Apical ring or ill-defined row; trans-verse, complete	Vestigial (apical cluster), or absent
Dehiscence.........	Longitudinal	Longitudinal	Longitudinal	....
Spores..............	512—256 (128)	(1024) 512—256 (128)	256—128 (64)	64 microspores 1 megaspore
Gametophyte........	Elongate, massive, fleshy, dark green; with adventitious lobes	Elongate, massive; complex, with ad-ventitious lobes	Cordate (or fila-mentous) thallus; with adventitious lobes	Dioecious; greatly reduced
Antheridia...........	Large, stalked, com-plex; 'cap cell' divided	Large, stalked, com-plex; 'cap cell' divided; in some cases on both sur-faces	(Insufficiently known; probably simple, but with basal cell)	1 (or 2?) within spore wall
Sperms.............	100 ±	Several hundred	(More than 32)	....
Archegonia..........	Many	Many	Many	One
Neck...............	Long, (6 to 9 tiers); straight	Long, (6 to 9 tiers); straight or bent forward	Straight or bent for-ward	Short (2 to 3 tiers)
Neck canal cells.....	2 neck canal nuclei, often with wall between	2 neck canal nuclei, usually with wall between	....	2 neck canal nuclei
Embryo: relation of quadrants to organs.	Obscure or lacking; outer half (?) forms leaf, stem, root Slow in differentiat-ing organs	(Insufficiently known; probably typical leptospo-rangiate)	(Insufficiently known; apparently typical leptospo-rangiate)	Typical leptospo-rangiate

TABLE 2.—CHARACTERS OF THE LEPTOSPORANGIATE FERNS.—(*Continued*)

Hymenophyllaceae	Salviniaceae	Cyatheaceae	Dicksoniaceae	Polypodiaceae
Hymenophyllum Trichomanes	Salvinia Azolla	Cyathea Alsophila Hemitelia	Dicksonia Cibotium Dennstaedtia	Polypodium Adiantum Asplenium
2 genera 460 ± species	2 genera 18 species	3 genera 425 ± species	9 genera 155 ± species	115 genera 7500–8000 species
Small forms; erect and rhizome types; leaf filmy; some rootless by reduction	Small floating aquatics	Chiefly dendroid types	Rhizome and dendroid types	All types
Tropics and south temperate zone chiefly	Tropics and warm-temperate zone	Tropics and south temperate zone	Tropics and temperate zones	Broadly distributed
Marginal; indusium present	Marginal; indusium forms sporocarp wall	Superficial; indusium present or absent	Marginal; indusium present	Superficial; indusium present, or absent by reduction
Gradate	Gradate	Gradate, with transitions to mixed	Gradate, with transitions to mixed	Mixed
Leptosporangiate	Leptosporangiate; heterosporous	Leptosporangiate	Leptosporangiate	Leptosporangiate
Small, subspherical or flattened, short-stalked or sessile	. . . .	Small, flattened, short-stalked	Small, flattened, long-stalked	Small, flattened, long-stalked
Uniform	. . . .	Uniform	Uniform or various	Various
Transverse or oblique-vertical, complete	Vestigial (oblique-vertical, complete), or absent	Oblique-vertical, complete	Oblique-vertical, complete or incomplete	Vertical, incomplete
Longitudinal	. . . .	Transverse	. . . .	Transverse
(512) 421—32	64 microspores 1 megaspore	64—16 (8)	64—16	64—32 (16)
Filamentous or strap-shaped; adventitious buds	Dioecious; greatly reduced	Cordate thallus, usually without adventitious lobes	Cordate thallus, usually without adventitious lobes	Cordate thallus, usually without adventitious lobes
(Large?), complex; stalk cell; 'cap cell' divided	1 or 2, within spore wall	Somewhat complex; stalk cell; cap cell divided	Somewhat complex; stalk cell; cap cell divided	Small, simple; no stalk cell; cap cell undivided
More than 32	. . . .	64—256?	64—256?	Typically 32
Many Short, straight	3 to several Short (3 to 4 tiers)	Many Long, 5 (6 to 7) to 8 tiers; straight or slightly curved	Many Long, (6) 7 to 9 (10) tiers; straight or curved	Many Short, 4 to 5 (6) tiers; strongly curved
. . . .	2 neck canal nuclei	2 neck canal nuclei, rarely 2 cells	2 neck canal nuclei	2 neck canal nuclei
(Insufficiently known; probably typical leptosporangiate type)	Indefinite or typical leptosporangiate	(Insufficiently known)	(Insufficiently known)	Organs definitely determined in quadrant stage

are polyphyletic. They may well represent a single stock, but there is as yet no evidence of such an origin.

The three most primitive families appear to be transitional in several features to the eusporangiate orders: sporangial development is to a greater or less extent intermediate in type between that of eusporangiate and leptosporangiate forms; the sporangium is large and crude in form with simple dehiscence, with a high spore number, but it has a thin wall; the antheridium is large and complex, with many sperms, but it is projecting; in the embryo early delimitation of segments for organ formation is obscure or lacking, but the embryo is prone.

Though among the three families there is little evidence of relationship, the connections of the higher families seem in most cases to be determinable, at least in a general way. From these basic groups progress can be seen along several lines. That these lines of progress represent in many cases the expression of similar tendencies in distantly related stocks is clear.

An outstanding morphological character—and one surely of fundamental importance in the history of the group—is the position of the sorus on the leaf. This and correlated characters separate the three primitive families. Sori of the Gleicheniaceae are superficial; nonsoral sporangia of the Schizaeaceae are marginal and in the Osmundaceae are borne on leaf segments. Probably from all these three families, though chiefly from the first two, have been derived higher groups—groups in which are expressed the soral type of the ancestral group. (Since, however, evolutionary modification of the sorus is from marginal to superficial, it is to be expected that there will be found, among the descendants of the marginal type, forms with superficial sori.) Leptosporangiate ferns fall, apparently, into three main groups which seem to be natural, representing three main lines of progress in this stock (Fig. 174)—a "marginal series" (on the left); a "superficial series" (on the right); and a fundamentally "nonsoral series" (in the center). In the first and third series there are forms which have progressed to the superficial state, a condition which had already been reached by members of the second group in its ancestral forms. (It is to be remembered that these groups are separated not merely on this one character of soral position but on the sum of a group of characters—see family descriptions.)

Osmundaceae. The Osmundaceae resemble the eusporangiate types in perhaps more features than do the other primitive families. In sporangium development some sporangia follow the eusporangiate method. In some recent classifications the Osmundaceae are considered a group intermediate between the "Eusporangiatae" and the "Leptosporangiatae." The sporangia are large, and are crude in form and in method of dehiscence, with a very large number of spores; the tapetum is massive. They are borne on slender naked leaf divisions. The antheridia are large and complex and contain many (about 100) sperms. There is a wall between the two neck canal cells. The embryo in early stages lacks, or shows only obscurely, a limitation of segments to the first organs. The prothallium is elongate, massive, and long-lived. On the other hand, many —probably the majority—of the sporangia develop by the leptosporangiate method; the tapetum is definitely limited; the sporangium wall is thin; the number of spores, though large for leptosporangiate ferns, is much smaller than that of the eusporangiate families; the antheridia are superficial, and, though the number of sperms, like that of the spores, is large for the leptosporangiate ferns, it is far less than that of the eusporangiate orders, and is probably fairly constant; the first division of the zygote is vertical; the embryo is prone. The Osmundaceae seem definitely to be leptosporangiate ferns, although a primitive type. Though many of their characters are intermediate, the group is not to be thought of as forming a connecting link between eusporangiate and typical leptosporangiate forms. The characters are, rather, archaic for ferns and hence resemble those of the more ancient groups. The osmundaceous stock has given rise to few higher forms (Fig. 174); they are survivors of an ancient conservative group.

Gleicheniaceae. The Gleicheniaceae, like the Osmundaceae, show an intermediate method of sporangium development. Their sporangia are large and the spore number high. The gametophytes are elongate and massive, suggesting those of the Osmundaceae and the Marattiaceae. The antheridia are large and complex, and the number of sperms is even greater than that of the Osmundaceae. The sorus is superficial, and the sporangia are arranged like those of the Marattiaceae. Further resemblance to the Marattiaceae is seen in the presence of sex

organs on both sides of the prothallium.   The Gleicheniaceae
are surely a primitive group of leptosporangiate ferns.   This
line, however, unlike that of the Osmundaceae has given rise to
several higher groups among which are the Cyatheaceae (the
others are not discussed here).

Schizaeaceae.   The Schizaeaceae, the third of the three basic
groups, likewise show features suggestive of the eusporangiates,
that is, archaic fern characters.   The sporangia, large, with a
high spore number, are borne on naked leaf segments and are
intermediate in method of development.   The annulus, though
in some forms a definite ring, is still in general unspecialized, and
the dehiscence is longitudinal as in the other two groups.   The
gametophyte is of the higher types, a cordate thallus (or a
specialized filamentous form), but has the adventitious lobes of
other primitive groups.   The antheridium, though less complex
than that of the other primitive families, is still not simple, and
the sperm number is high.   The leaf shows, in the several genera,
stages through which the fertile segments have probably passed
to the monomorphic state.   Further evidence of the primitive
nature of the leaf is shown in its slow and long-continued development.   The Schizaeaceae form a third primitive family, whose
ancestral stock, like that of the Gleicheniaceae, has probably
given rise directly or indirectly to several higher groups.   Among
these groups are the Dicksoniaceae and the Marsileaceae and also
the Hymenophyllaceae.   Among the characters which indicate
these relationships are the elongate marginal sorus (compare
the tassels of the Schizaeaceae and the sori of these families)
and the transverse or oblique complete annulus.

Marsileaceae.   The Marsileaceae show in many characters—
such as dichotomy of leaf, ontogeny, and position of sori, form
of annulus—strong evidence of relationship to the Schizaeaceae.
They represent apparently without question a group derived
from schizaeaceous stock, retaining some of the more important
primitive characters but showing advance in others.   In soral
advance they have reached the gradate stage, the sporangia
remaining marginal, however, in position.   The attainment of
heterospory, with its accompanying great modifications in spore
development, spore type, and gametophytes, represents a further,
and great, advance.   The development of a special fruiting structure is probably related not to heterospory but to the conditions

under which reproduction must take place in amphibious plants. The presence of heterospory and of the sporocarp is not sufficient grounds for the removal of this family from among its obvious relatives and the establishment for it (with the Salviniaceae) of an independent major group differing greatly from other fern-like plants.

Hymenophyllaceae. The Hymenophyllaceae are a group specialized in relation to humid habitats. In general they represent a reduction group, the small size, delicate texture, and filamentous gametophytes being the result of simplification. The family, however, still retains many primitive characters— dichotomy of leaf and of venation, sessile or short-stalked sporangia with a large number of spores and transverse, or oblique, complete annulus, with longitudinal dehiscence. The gametophyte, though specialized, still shows the abundant adventitious lobes characteristic of primitive families. The number of sporangia in a sorus is increased, and, accompanying this, has come gradate development. The relationships of the filmy ferns are not clear because reduction has obscured many characters, but the family belongs in the marginal series and seems to be closer to the Schizaeaceae than to any other family.

Salviniaceae. The Salviniaceae, like the Hymenophyllaceae, are a reduction group. In adaptation to a floating habit, they have in size and in structure progressed much further in specialization. Heterospory brings in further modifications, especially in the gametophytes which show reduction comparable in many ways to that in other heterosporous groups. As compared with the Marsileaceae, heterospory has advanced much further: the sori of the Marsileaceae are bisporangiate; those of *Salvinia* are monosporangiate, those of *Azolla* in a transitional state. *Azolla*, has, moreover, progressed very far in the reduction of the sporangia of a sorus to one.

The sporocarp of the Salviniaceae is biologically similar to that of the Marsileaceae, but morphologically is wholly unlike it. There is clearly no relation between these two heterosporous fern families; neither the possession of heterospory and of sporocarps, nor of an aquatic habit ties them together. The outstanding character is of course heterospory, but this is seen as a character attained independently in many groups of vascular plants. The affinities of the Salviniaceae are obscure, but their characters seem to associate them most closely with the Hymenophyllaceae.

Dicksoniaceae. Belonging also to the marginal series and clearly related to the Schizaeaceae are the Dicksoniaceae. This family belongs at a level definitely higher than that of the group of families so far discussed. The sorus is gradate but shows in some forms transitions to mixed. The sporangia are small and long-stalked with an annulus which is nearly vertical and may show a stomium. The spore number is small in general, as in the highest (homosporous) families. The antheridium is intermediate in complexity between that of the lower and that of the highest types. The Dicksoniaceae are related, without much doubt, to schizaeaceous stock.

Cyatheaceae. Standing at about the same level in advancement as the Dicksoniaceae, and resembling this family in many ways, is the larger family Cyatheaceae. The stage of advancement in this family—to the dendroid habit; to the gradate sorus, with transitions to mixed; to the small, flat sporangium with nearly vertical annulus; to a spore number of 64 to 16—is closely the same. These ferns, however, belong definitely to the superficial series, and their ancestral relationships are clearly with the Gleicheniaceae. They are, therefore, regardless of similarities, not close to the Dicksoniaceae; the resemblances result from parallel advancement to the same level. In taxonomic treatments the Dicksoniaceae are often included in the Cyatheaceae, since the two groups possess in common characters which have been used as a basis for classification. From a morphological standpoint they do not seem, however, to be closely related.

Polypodiaceae. The most complex as well as the largest group is the Polypodiaceae. In this family a high level of specialization has been attained in many characters: the sorus is superficial and mixed; the leptosporangiate sporangia are small, flattened, borne on slender stalks, and contain few spores; the annulus is elaborate in type, and in form and position is such as to bring about not merely efficient transverse dehiscence but an active scattering of the spores (a feature attained also in somewhat lower families); the gametophyte is small, delicate, and short-lived; the antheridia are simple, with few sperms; the primary organs of the embryo are definitely limited at the quadrant stage.

That the advance in these characters has taken place independently along several or many lines is clear, since a study of all characters shows that the subgroups of the family are clearly allied to unrelated stocks. The family is an excellent example of a highly polyphyletic group. The expression of the same tendency in various lines of fern stock has resulted in the attainment of certain stages in form and structure which are those chosen as a taxonomic basis for the limitation of the family. That these steps are still in process of making is evident in the transitions present in several groups, and in the fact that some of the steps may be seen to be taken in ontogeny in some forms, though in closely related types they are now fixed. The Polypodiaceae are therefore a heterogeneous group, an unnatural family. The relationships of its members are complex; as in any large and specialized group there is no 'highest group'— there are several subgroups about equally advanced when all characters are considered; the phylogenetic 'tree top' of the ferns consists of several branches attached at different levels.

It is evident that the leptosporangiate ferns are an advancing group; that they are progressing today in evolutionary modification; that they are not to be looked upon as a mere remnant of an ancient group. They occupy, in respect to present-day progressiveness, a position comparable in many ways to that held by the angiosperms. The fossil record bears out this conclusion, which is derived from the study of living forms.

FILICINEAE

Important Characters: Evolutionary History and Bearing on Classification

SPOROPHYTE

Body. The body of the Ophioglossales is simple and unspecialized: it is unsupported by sclerenchyma and largely unprotected by dermal appendages; its tissues are simple, and the plant is more or less fleshy throughout. The body of the Filicales is complex: its tissues are of many types and of elaborate structure, and it is protected, often elaborately, by hairs and chaffy scales. Support is given by sclerenchyma, which is varied in type and complex in distribution. The Marattiales are intermediate in these characters, with small amounts of supporting tissue and a simple, more or less fleshy body. Specialization in body structure accompanies advance in other features.

Habit. In habit both the largest types (dendroid) and the smallest (filmy) seem to be derived. The rhizome type appears primitive for the group; at least it is clear that arborescent forms have developed from rhizomatous types—and that this advance has been made in several groups, although in only two, the Cyatheaceae and the Dicksoniaceae, has it reached full expression. [This statement is not to be interpreted as implying that the arborescent habit is only of recent development in this group; some of the ancient ferns (Chap. XVI) were tree-like.] It is difficult to determine the primitive-habit type, but dorsiventral stems have clearly been derived from radial; tree types, in some cases at least, from smaller types; and the smallest forms from larger ones by reduction. There may well have been among the earliest ferns diverse habital types—arborescent, climbing, creeping.

Reduction in size has resulted from adaptation to epiphytic habit and hygrophytic habitats. The rhizome habit is retained. The effects of reduction are prominent in size, and especially in leaf structure. Only rarely has the aquatic habit been acquired, and still more rarely the annual. The aquatic group, Salviniaceae, represent extreme reduction and modification in relation to habitat. The annual species are members of the most advanced families.

Throughout ferns there is evidence that an original, rather extensively branched stem has been simplified by the suppression of most of the forkings. This is evident in all three major groups. (Among primitive ferns unbranched types also undoubtedly existed; see Chap. XVI.) Dichotomy in branching is clearly primitive, as in other groups. Progressive modification has led in many lines to unbranched, or sparsely branched, rhizomes and erect stems. Groups which are characterized by dichotomous branching are in general also primitive in other respects. The attainment of the unbranched condition is to be found in various groups—from the primitive *Botrychium* and *Angiopteris* to the higher genera of the Polypodiaceae.

Leaf. The leaf, like the stem, was undoubtedly originally complex in form. Comparative study of living forms points clearly to this, and the evidence from fossil forms points in the same direction. [The fact that the fern leaf represents a branch system (Chap. XVII) provides the strongest support for this opinion.] It is unfortunate that in descriptive terminology the frond is "divided," "dissected," etc., since fusion and reduction of its parts, rather than division, have undoubtedly occurred in phylogenetic development. Without doubt the small leaf and the simple leaf represent the advanced types in this group. The archaic large and complex leaf persists, however, even in some of the most advanced groups—most tree ferns and many polypodiaceous genera. In contrast, in the most primitive group, species of *Ophioglossum* have a small simple leaf. (The primitive members of the closely related *Botrychium* have a highly complex leaf.) The tendency in some primitive groups (Schizaeaceae, Gleicheniaceae) toward great length and indeterminate growth is further evidence that the ancient leaf was very large.

In the leaf, as in the stem, dichotomy is primitive. It is seen in divisions, lobes, and veins. As in the stem it has given place to monopodial branching and thus to the characteristic pinnate condition. Dichotomy, prominent in nearly all the lower groups, still persists, however, to some extent in the highest. In venation the simple open dichotomous type has been replaced by the closed reticulate—a type clearly more efficient mechanically and physiologically; yet dichotomous venation still persists in some most advanced genera.

The leaves of the Filicales are exstipulate; those of the other groups are stipulate, but the stipules are of different types. There is no obvious relationship of leaf type based on stipules.

Among epidermal appendages the simple uniseriate hair is clearly the ancient type (Chap. XVI); more complex hairs and chaffy scales (which are probably broadened hairs) are advanced types. There is no definite evidence that an appendageless state preceded that with simple hairs, but the lower groups have few appendages, especially when mature.

Leaf Dimorphism. The segregation of vegetative and reproductive functions in different parts of the leaf, or in separate leaves, represents undoubtedly a primitive condition (Fig. 175*A*,*B*); from this ancient dimorphism there has developed the condition—often called monomorphism—found in the majority of ferns, a blade serving for both vegetative and reproductive functions (Fig. 175*D*). And from this there has been derived a new dimorphic condition—fertile and sterile leaves separate (Fig. 175*E*); this change has taken place independently in various genera and is at present occurring in the higher families.

It is commonly stated, as though inclusively, that dimorphism between fertile and sterile leaves represents a condition derived from monomorphism; that in the fertile frond the blade has been reduced or lost, and in the sterile frond the reproductive function has been lost. But it is clear that there are two kinds of this

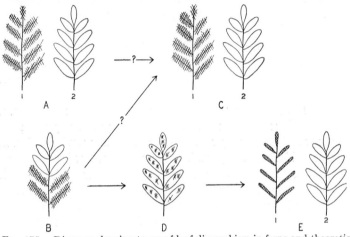

Fig. 175.—Diagram showing types of leaf dimorphism in ferns and theoretical relationships of these types. *A*, *B*, archaic types; *C* to *E*, modern types. (Cross hatching indicates fertile parts of leaves.) *A*, perhaps represented among living forms (*C*) by *Osmunda cinnamomea, O. lancea, Schizaea dichotoma, S. pusilla,* etc.; *B*, represented by *Botrychium, Anemia, Osmunda Claytoniana* and *O. regalis; D*, represented by the majority of modern ferns, for example, *Cyathea, Dicksonia, Asplenium; E*, represented by such genera as *Onoclea, Woodwardia, Cryptogramma.*

dimorphism, one ancient, the other modern. The latter type differs from the former in that in the fertile leaf there is present the reduced blade, as, for example, in *Onoclea sensibilis* (Fig. 99). There is abundant evidence, partly from comparative structure, partly from the fossil record, that the dimorphism of members of primitive families—Ophioglossaceae, Osmundaceae, Schizae-aceae—is of the ancient type and was present perhaps in fern stocks from the beginning; that that of the Polypodiaceae is modern and derived. In the modern type the fertile frond is contracted or reduced, and in most cases still serves in some small measure as a vegetative leaf. In this type transitional forms are common.

Evidence from living forms that the ancient type gave rise to monomorphism is found only in such series as *Osmunda-Todea* and *Anemia-Schizaea-Lygodium-Mohria* (Fig. 176). In the latter group fertile segments are seen in stages transitional to the monomorphic.

Leaf dimorphism in its highest expression is found in *Osmunda cinnamomea* and *O. lancea*—the fertile frond being ephemeral and never green. (A similar extreme dimorphism exists among the branch systems of species of *Equisetum*.) Whether this dimorphism among entire leaves represents the persistence of an ancient similar condition or whether it has been derived from the ancient dimorphism between leaf segments is uncertain.

The relations between fertile and sterile leaf types among the ferns are complex; they can best be understood only when the morphology of early types of vascular plants is discussed (page 309).

Sporangium. *Position.* The sporangium is primitively terminal upon a leaf segment, or marginal (terminal upon a minor segment?)—*Botrychium, Anemia, Schizaea;* from this position there has been a migration to the dorsal surface (superficial). This change has taken place in different groups at different times and in some forms is in process of taking place at the present time. The development of a blade on fertile leaf segments is closely connected with this change in sporangium position, the expanding sides or margins extending beyond and above the sporangia which are left on the lower surface. The "phylogenetic slide" is thus primarily a passive change.

Form and Structure. The early type of sporangium in the fern group is large, and in form and structure crude. Its wall is massive, without even a simple opening apparatus. The formation of a special nourishing layer for its many spores is in its earliest stages. In development it is eusporangiate, and a vascular bundle leads to its base. Among living ferns, *Botrychium* presents the best example of such a sporangium. This archaic sporangium is sessile or with a short, stout stalk and is definitely oriented; the advanced type has a long, slender stalk and is irregular and indefinite in orientation.

The resemblances of this sporangium, morphologically, to the tip of a leaf lobe are important: early stages are alike; vascular

tissue leads to the base; stomata occur on the sides.   That this
massive sporangium is the primitive type—a fact borne out not

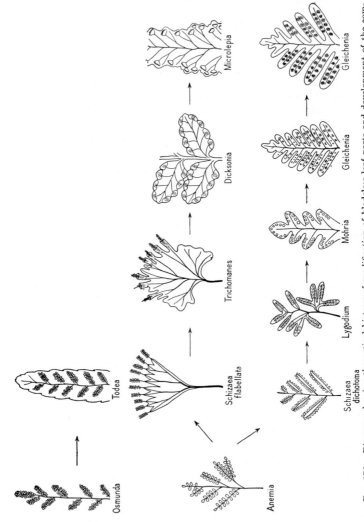

Fig. 176.—Diagram showing theoretical history of modification of bladeless leaf parts and development of the common, modern, fertile fern pinna with superficial sori. Series *Osmunda-Todea*, the axis tips expanded ventral to the sporangia, the sporangia of each leaf segment becoming a sorus; series *Anemia-Schizaea flabellata-Trichomanes-Dicksonia-Microlepia*, the axis tips below the sporangia expanded and fused, the fertile tips becoming marginal clusters, these clusters becoming first marginal sori, then, by the expansion and fusion of the ventral indusial lips, superficial sori; series *Anemia-Schizaea dichotoma-Lygodium-Mohria-Gleichenia*, the axis tips so expanded that the sporangia are marginal, the blade margin gradually developed beyond the sporangia, the sporangia, now superficial, multiplied, forming sori; ...

merely by comparative studies of the series but by its lack of
elaboration as a spore-developing and spore-dispersing organ—
suggests that the resemblance to a leaf apex is significant, that
the sporangium and the leaf tip are homologous (Chap. XVII).

The primitive fern sporangium is an integral part of the leaf, not an appendage.

This archaic sporangium, under specialization, was reduced in size; its spore number greatly cut down; its wall thinned to a single layer; a long, slender stalk and efficient dehiscence developed. Large and crude sporangia are found in the Ophioglossales and the Marattiales; the more primitive families in the Filicales —Osmundaceae, Gleicheniaceae, Schizaeaceae—have large sporangia, but the walls are thin and the annulus is unspecialized. The most advanced sporangium type, with hair-like stalk and small body, suggesting an appendage, is surely an extreme modification from the early type in form, position, and relation to leaf.

Annulus. The annulus developed from a simple, poorly differentiated and poorly limited cluster or several-seriate row of cells to a uniseriate ring. This ring, at first transverse and, like the cluster, associated with longitudinal dehiscence, became— through an oblique stage—vertical and responsible for transverse dehiscence. At first complete, as a ring, and uniform throughout, it became incomplete when vertical (being then necessarily interrupted by the stalk) and elaborate in structure by the formation of a special opening region, the stomium. In function the annulus served at first merely to tear open the sporangium wall, allowing the spores to escape; in its highest form it serves not merely to open the sporangium but to aid in the dispersal of the spores by mechanical scattering.

As the sporangium was reduced in size, it became flattened. The flattened condition is associated perhaps partly with crowding of the sporangia in sori but doubtless also with the formation of the uniseriate annulus which finally became marginal on the flattened spore sac.

Tapetum. The development of a tapetum as a special means of nourishing the maturing spores is seen in various stages among ferns. In the large thick-walled sporangium the tapetum is irregular in thickness and indefinite in limits; in higher types it becomes sharply limited and uniform in thickness, the number of layers being reduced to one. In the earlier types the tapetum is formed from wall layers, in the later ones from sporogenous tissue itself.

Attachment. The large sporangium is sessile or has a short, thick stalk; the small sporangium has a long, slender stalk. In some of the most advanced types the stalk consists of a single row of cells. With a long stalk the sporangium is apparently in a position more favorable for spore dispersal, especially if crowded with others in a sorus.

Spore Number. The number of spores per sporangium shows progress from very many and indefinite to few (mostly 32) and definite—and in heterosporous forms to one.

Sorus. The sorus shows extraordinary diversity of form and structure. The history of its modification has already been discussed at some length (page 163).

The relation of sporangium and sorus is complex and obscure. Structurally a sorus is a cluster of sporangia. (Solitary sporangia are, in some groups, unfortunately called "monangial sori.") The cluster may have arisen by the segmentation of a single large sporangium, by the aggregation of originally more distant sporangia, by multiplication of a solitary sporangium, and by the transformation of tassels; perhaps all of these methods have been followed. The uniseriate clusters of the Marattiaceae and the Gleicheniaceae are cited as examples of sori belonging to primitive groups which show in the form and arrangement of their members evidence of their derivation from a single sporogenous mass. The synangial members of these groups, under this theory, are examples of forms in which division is not yet completed. There seems, however, to be no evidence of value in support of sorus formation by the division of an original single sporangium. The synangial condition seems to have resulted from fusion and not to be evidence of division.

From the tassel condition the sorus has perhaps arisen in several ways: (1) By the development of a lateral blade on the axis, ventral to the sporangia, the tassel becomes directly a superficial sorus. This may be seen in the *Osmunda-Todea* series (Fig. 176). (2) By a similar expansion of the axis, but along the lines of sporangial attachment, a blade with marginal 'monangial' sori is formed. The solitary sporangia later become multisporangiate sori by increase in number. This condition may be seen in the *Anemia-Schizaea-Lygodium-Mohria* series (Fig. 176). (3) By the webbing of the sterile stalks of the fertile tips the tassels become marginal sori, such as those of the Hymenophyllaceae (Fig. 176). It is apparent that whatever the origin of a sorus, its members may be increased greatly in numbers. The method followed in the case of the simple radiate sorus can be seen in *Gleichenia*.

Indusium. That the sorus was primitively naked is evident from the absence of an indusium in the Marattiales—an indusium could hardly exist in the nonsoral Ophioglossales—and in the more primitive families of the Filicales. The indusium is a special organ of leptosporangiate ferns, within which group it has apparently arisen many times and in different ways. In the eusporangiate groups the only type of protection for the sporangia is a sinking in the leaf tissue (*Ophioglossum, Danaea*); this method is found also in a few cases among primitive leptosporangiate ferns (species of *Gleichenia*).

Heterospory. Two families of the advanced group are heterosporous. These families seem not to be related, and it is evident that heterospory has arisen independently in each. As a homoplastic character it cannot be used to hold the families together; the group Hydropteridineae is an unnatural one and should not be maintained in morphological treatments. The Marsileaceae and the Salviniaceae are to be considered members of the Filicales, far advanced along the line of spore and gametophyte specialization and representing end products of two lines of elaboration. In respect to these features they are far more advanced than those other highly specialized ferns, the Polypodiaceae; but the Polypodiaceae have advanced further in certain sporangial and soral characters. One line has advanced far in one direction, the other in a different one.

GAMETOPHYTE

The gametophytes of the ferns are of two markedly different types: that of the Ophioglossales is fundamentally a cylindrical, branched structure with the sex organs generally distributed; that of the Marattiales and Filicales is a dorsiventral thalloid structure with the sex organs largely restricted to the lower surface. Among the Ophioglossales a flattened type exists in *Botrychium*, but this is obviously derived from the radial. Accompanying the change in form is limitation of distribution of sex organs—to the upper surface in contrast with the lower in the other groups. (A similar derivation of a flattened gametophyte from a cylindrical one, with restriction of the sex organs to the upper surface, is found in *Lycopodium*.) The position of sex organs on the upper surface is doubtless the result of a biological relation to fertilization underground.

The presence of sex organs on the upper surface in the Marattiaceae may possibly be considered evidence of derivation of the flattened gametophyte of this group from a cylindrical one in which the sex organs are distributed over the entire body, as in *Ophioglossum* and the Psilotales; but such a condition may equally well have been derived from a flat thalloid type with antheridia and archegonia uniformly distributed over the surface. (The sex organs in a plant living prostrate on the soil surface under dry conditions would tend to become limited to the moist lower surface.)

The gametophyte of the Marattiales and Filicales is fundamentally an elongate ribbon-like structure branching dichotomously rather sparsely. There is clear progress from a slow-growing, rather massive, branched, and long-lived type to a rapidly developing and maturing, delicate, unbranched, and short-lived type. [Progress in specialization of gametophyte habit and body may be likened to that in the sporophyte where simple, early maturing, and short-lived types (annuals) represent high specialization.] The prothallia of the more primitive Marattiales and those of the lower families of the Filicales are of the earlier type; those of the advanced families of the Filicales are of the specialized type. It has been stated, and apparently with good reason, that the cordate gametophyte represents merely the juvenile stage of the ribbon-like type; the prothallium does not attain greater size or the form characteristic of the group because of the development of early sexual maturity and the demands for support of an embryo with consequent exhaustion. The filamentous and the lobed types are undoubtedly derived.

The ribbon-like types show not only the slower growth and longer life which are characteristic of archaic gametophytes in other groups of vascular plants but also vegetative reproduction by fragmentation and budding, another characteristic of gametophytes in primitive groups. Such multiplication is largely lacking in the higher families. Apogamy is not known to occur in the lower groups but becomes increasingly common in the higher ones.

Sex Organs. The antheridium of the Ophioglossales and Marattiales is large and variable in size, contains many sperms, and is sunken; that of the Filicales is smaller and is superficial and projecting. The former is crude, the latter specialized. Within the Filicales there is progress from a large antheridium of complex structure, with many sperms, to one that is small and simple, with few sperms. There is a rather close parallel between reduction in spore and in sperm number.

The archegonium differs little among ferns in an important way. There is considerable variation in length of neck, and it is apparent that, as in other groups, the long neck is primitive. There is among the Filicales progress from a rather long straight neck, which is sometimes curved forward, to a shorter neck markedly curved backward. The reduction of the neck canal cells has reached the stage of a single cell, usually with two nuclei. Only in some of the lower Filicales is there found a two-celled condition (a wall between the nuclei).

EMBRYO

Like the gametophyte, the embryo develops slowly in the primitive Ophioglossales and Marattiales and rapidly in the Filicales. In the first two groups the first division is transverse to the long axis of the archegonium, and later segmentation is indefinite in relation to the primary organs (Fig. 177*A,B*); in the last group the first division is longitudinal, and quadrants are more clear-cut and in the higher groups are definitely related to the organs (Fig. 177*C*). The presence of a suspensor has often been considered an archaic feature in the embryogeny of vascular plants. In the two more primitive fern groups a suspensor may indeed be present, and in the highest group it is absent. Yet the very irregularity of appearance of the suspensor (variable even within a species) lends strength to the growing view that this organ is of little or no morphological significance.

It has been suggested that the position of the first division in the zygote is related, at least in part, to the presence or absence of a suspensor; that is, the division is necessarily transverse when a suspensor is formed, since the suspensor must be an outer cell in order that it may thrust the embryonic cell deep into gametophytic tissues. But in the Ophioglossales and Marattiales the division is transverse even where no suspensor is present, and it is longitudinal in the Filicales, where also there is no suspensor. The difference in position of this first wall is apparently a feature more fundamental than that of dependence upon the presence of a suspensor.

There is in the two primitive groups no relation—or at most an obscure and indefinite one—between early segmentation of the embryo and limitation of organs, but in the advanced group quadrant segments definitely limit organs. The possession of a definite relation is perhaps an advance in specialization correlated with early differentiation and rapid growth of the embryo in the last group; that is, with a shortening of embryonic stages, organ delimitation is brought in very early. It is becoming increasingly evident that, from the standpoint of morphological interpretation, too much emphasis has been laid (in vascular-plant studies) upon early segmentation of the embryo (and also upon that of

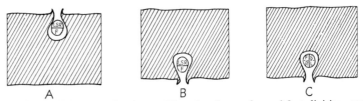

A   B   C

Fig. 177.—Diagrams showing position of embryo, plane of first division, and relation of early segmentation to first organs in the three major fern groups. *A*, Ophioglossales; *B*, Marattiales; *C*, Filicales. (The type without a suspensor is used as a basis for *A* and *B*.)

the apical growing point); that in many cases efforts have been made to read the structure of higher types downward into lower, and to find morphological significance where none exists. Definite quadrant function is not to be expected in the lower ferns.

The position of the embryo during its later stages of attachment to the gametophyte varies greatly among ferns (Fig. 178); this variation is due to the fundamental orientation of the embryo, the plane of the first division wall, and the form of the gametophyte. When the embryo is erect (whether or not deep-seated through the development of a suspensor) and the gametophyte is flat, the developing sporophyte pierces the prothallium vertically—the root breaking through, downward, when the archegonium is on the upper surface (*Botrychium*, Figs. 90; 178*C*), and the leaf and stem pushing through, upward, when the archegonium is on the lower surface (Marattiaceae, Figs. 95*K*; 178*D*). When the embryo is prostrate [a position for which the oblique, rather than vertical, orientation of the embryo axis (root stem)

(Fig. 178*E*) is perhaps responsible], both apices grow outward laterally at first. The axes of the young sporophytes of leptosporangiate ferns are thus at first horizontal. In most families the leaf and stem tip grow up through the notch, but in the Osmund-

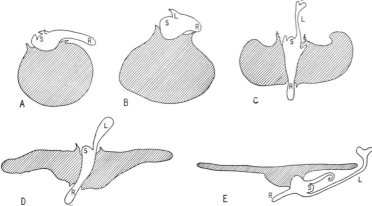

Fig. 178.—Diagrams showing position of developing embryo and relation to gametophyte. *A, Ophioglossum; B, Botrychium virginianum; C, B. dissectum; D, Marattiales; E, Filicales.*

aceae growth out from under the prothallus is usually lateral (Fig. 179). This difference is perhaps accounted for by the fact that the plane of the first division of the zygote in most leptosporangiate ferns is at right angles to the long axis of the prothallium, whereas in the Osmundaceae it is usually parallel to this

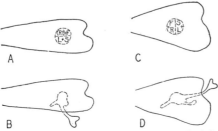

Fig. 179.—Diagrams showing position of segments and of developing embryo in leptosporangiate ferns. Prothallium seen from above. *A, B,* Osmundaceae; *C, D,* other families.

axis. The stem and leaf quadrants are in the first case anterior and thus directed toward the notch. Although in the Osmundaceae the position of leaf and stem initials in the embryo is obscure, they are in many cases lateral.

Relations of the Major Groups

The three major groups—Ophioglossales, Marattiales, and Filicales—differ from one another in several important ways (Table 3, page 302). The leaf is circinate in the Marattiales and Filicales but not in the Ophioglossales. In the first and last groups it is stipulate, but the stipules are of different types, thin and sheathing in the Ophioglossales and thick, fleshy, and nonsheathing in the Marattiales. The Filicales are exstipulate, although in the Osmundaceae the petioles are wing-margined.

The body of the Ophioglossales is fleshy and without sclerenchyma; the appendages are simple hairs. The Marattiales are more or less fleshy with small amounts of sclerenchyma, and the hairs are simple. The Filicales are characterized by abundant hairs or chaffy scales, are not fleshy, and have much sclerenchyma.

The sporangium of the Ophioglossales and the Marattiales is large and thick-walled and develops from a group of initials; that of the Filicales is small and thin-walled and develops from a single initial. In the Ophioglossales the sporangium is terminal (fundamentally) on leaf divisions and there is a vascular supply at its base; in the other groups the sporangium is marginal or superficial and has no vascular supply.

In the Ophioglossales there is no annulus; in the Marattiales there is none or only a most unspecialized cluster of cells; in the Filicales the annulus ranges from an unspecialized group of cells to a highly specialized row with a stomium. The tapetum in the Ophioglossales and Marattiales is derived from the inner layers of the heavy wall; in the Filicales it is formed from sporogenous tissue. In the first group it is usually irregular and indefinite in limit, and of two to three rows of cells; in the others it becomes a rather uniform layer of one or two rows of cells.

The gametophyte of the Ophioglossales is radial (cylindrical fundamentally) and thus differs greatly from that of the other groups which is dorsiventral. In the latter type that of the Marattiales is massive, that of the Filicales is thin. The gametophytes of the Ophioglossales and Marattiales develop slowly, are long-lived, may bear several embryos, and continue to live and develop after embryos are formed; those of the Filicales develop rapidly, are short-lived, and (in most cases) bear only one embryo, the development of which exhausts the prothallium and limits its life. In the Ophioglossales the sex organs are borne all around the gametophyte; in the other two groups they are borne on the underside (antheridia, and rarely archegonia, on the upper side in the Marattiales). The antheridia of the Ophioglossales and Marattiales are large and sunken, with many sperms; those of the other group are small and projecting, with few sperms.

The embryo of the Ophioglossales and Marattiales is erect and that of the Filicales is prone. The first division of the zygote in the first two groups is transverse; that of the Filicales is longitudinal.

In some ways the Ophioglossales and Marattiales seem to stand together—eusporangiate development and the accompanying massive, crude sporangium; the possession of stipules; the large sunken antheridia; the erect embryo. In other ways the Marattiales and the Filicales seem related—the circinate leaf; the superficial sori; the dorsiventral gametophyte. So distributed are the differences that it is apparent that the three groups are not closely related, and that no one of them represents an ancestral stock from which the others may have been derived. When all characters are taken into consideration, the Ophioglossales are clearly the most primitive group. The Marattiales also possess many primitive characters but stand as a whole above the Ophioglossales. The Filicales are definitely an advanced group. The classification as Eusporangiatae and Leptosporangiatae brings together the two more primitive groups; but the basis, eusporangiate development, is merely an archaic character, which is found in other ancient vascular plants. The two eusporangiate fern groups are not closely related, and the classification, though a convenient one, does not express natural relationship.

"Ferns" consist of three distinct stocks; they are, therefore, if considered a unit group, polyphyletic. The interrelationships of the three groups are further discussed later (Chap. XVII). It is evident that ferns are complex in their relationships—polyphyletic both in large groups (Filicineae, Filicales) and in small (Polypodiaceae).

Table 3.—Important Characters of the Major Fern Groups

	Ophioglossales	Marattiales	Filicales
Sporophyte			
Body	Fleshy, without sclerenchyma	Somewhat fleshy, with little sclerenchyma	Not fleshy, with much sclerenchyma
Leaf	Non-circinate; 'stipulate'; 'stipules' thin, sheathing	Circinate; stipulate; stipules thick, not sheathing	Circinate; exstipulate
Anatomy:			
Secondary growth	Present (in one genus)	Absent (one exception?)	Absent
Xylem:			
Tracheids	Round-pitted	Scalariform-pitted	Scalariform-pitted
Vessels	Absent	Absent	Rare
Sorus	Nonsoral	Soral	Nonsoral and soral
Sporangium:			
Position	Terminal or marginal	Superficial	Marginal or superficial
Attachment	Sessile or with short, stout stalk	Sessile	Sessile to long-stalked
Vascular supply	Present at base	None	None
Origin	Eusporangiate	Eusporangiate	Leptosporangiate
Size	Large	Large	Large to small
Wall	Thick	Thick	Thin
Tapetum	Irregular, from wall tissue	1 or 2 layers, from wall tissue	1 or 2 layers, from sporogenous tissue
Annulus	Absent	Absent or unspecialized	Unspecialized to elaborate
Spore number	Many (thousands)	Many (thousands)	Many (hundreds) to few, to 1 (heterospory)
Gametophyte			
Position	Subterranean	Surface-living	Surface-living
Form	Radial, branched, fleshy	Dorsiventral, sparsely branched, massive	Dorsiventral, unbranched, delicate
Color	Nongreen	Deep green	Bright green
Development	Slow-growing, long-lived	Slow-growing, long-lived	Fast-growing, short-lived
Sex organs:			
Distribution	Unrestricted (fundamentally)	Both surfaces (♀ lower only)	Lower surface (♂ rarely on upper)
Antheridium	Large, variable, sunken	Large, variable, sunken	Small, constant, projecting
Archegonium:			
Neck	Long, 7 to 8 tiers, projecting; or short, 4 tiers, sunken	Short, 2 to 3 tiers, broad, almost completely sunken	Long, 5 to 8 tiers curved, projecting
Neck canal cells	1, 2-nucleate	1, large, 2-nucleate	1, usually 2-nucleate
Ventral canal cell	Obscure or ephemeral	Large, prominent	Large, prominent
Embryo			
Orientation	Erect; leaf and stem from outer or central part	Erect; leaf and stem from inner part	Prone; leaf and stem from lateral part
Development	Slow	Slow	Rapid
First division	Transverse	Transverse	Longitudinal
Suspensor	Present or absent	Present or absent	Absent

TABLE 3.—IMPORTANT CHARACTERS OF THE MAJOR FERN GROUPS—
(*Continued*)

	Ophioglossales	Marattiales	Filicales
Embryo—(*Continued*)			
Quadrants or octants....	Mostly obscure; correlation with organs in most cases uncertain or impossible	Obscure; not definitely related to organs	Mostly definite; with constant relation to organs
First organ to develop...	Root	Leaf	All together
Foot.................	Well developed	Not definite	Well developed
Leaf.................	Slow growth, laterally or upward through prothallium	Slow growth, upward through prothallium	Rapid growth, laterally and upward through notch

Comparison with Other Groups

The groups of ferns, when compared with the other groups thus far discussed, stand together. The leaf of ferns is large in comparison with the stem and with the plant as a whole, and is complex in form and in structure; that of the other groups is small, and is simple in form and structure. The fern leaf develops apically and over a long period; the small leaf, after early stages, develops throughout and is mature in a short time. The fern leaf trace is large, often complex, and is accompanied by a gap; the trace of the small leaf is small and simple, and there is no gap. The sporangia of ferns are borne on the margins or on the dorsal surface of the leaf; in the other groups they are borne on the axis, on sporangiophores, or on the ventral surface of the leaf. Although ferns are themselves a diverse lot with no close interrelationships, they form a unit group when compared with the Psilopsida, Lycopsida, and Sphenopsida. They stand clearly far apart, morphologically, from these plants which are commonly and most unfortunately known as "fern allies." They are to be placed, therefore, in another group, the Pteropsida.

Bibliography

FILICALES

ATKINSON, G. F.: "The Biology of Ferns," New York, 1894.

BAKER, J. G.: "Handbook of the Fern-Allies (Rhizocarpeae)," London, 1887.

BOWER, F. O.: Is the eusporangiate or the leptosporangiate the more primitive type of fern?, *Ann. Bot.*, **5**: 109–134, 1891.

———: Studies in the morphology of spore-producing members. IV. The leptosporangiate ferns, *Phil. Trans. Roy. Soc. London*, **192B** : 29–138, 1899.

————: Studies in the phylogeny of the Filicales. I–VII, *Ann. Bot.*, **25–32,** 1911–1918.

————: The dermal appendages of ferns, *Ann. Bot.*, **40**: 479–490, 1926.

BROWNE, I.: The phylogeny and inter-relationships of the Pteridophyta: a critical résumé. VI. Filicales, *New Phyt.*, **7**: 230–253, 1908; **8**: 13–31, 1909.

CHRIST, H.: "Die Farnkräuter der Erde," Jena, 1897.

————: "Die Geographie der Farne," Jena, 1910.

CHRISTENSEN, C.: "Index Filicum," Hafniae, 1906.

CZAJA, A. T.: Über Befruchtung, Bastardierung und Geschlechtertrennung bei Prothallien homosporer Farne, *Ztschr. Bot.*, **13**: 545–589, 1921.

DRACINSCHI, M.: Über das reife Spermium der Filicales und von *Pilularia globulifera*, *Ber. deutsch. bot. Gesells.*, **48**: 295–311, 1930.

FARMER, J. B., and L. DIGBY: Studies in apospory and apogamy in ferns, *Ann. Bot.*, **21**: 161–199, 1907.

HANNIG, E.: Über das Vorkommen von Perisporien bei den Filicineen nebst Bemerkungen über die systematische Bedeutung derselben, *Flora,* **103**: 321–346, 1911.

HARTMAN, M. E.: Antheridial dehiscence in the Polypodiaceae, *Bot. Gaz.*, **91**: 252–276, 1931.

HEIM, C.: Untersuchungen über Farnprothallien, *Flora,* **82**: 329–386, 1896.

HOOKER, W. J., and F. BAUER: "Genera Filicum," London, 1842.

HOOKER, W. J., and R. K. GREVILLE: "Icones Filicum," London, 1831.

HORVAT, I.: Die Bedeutung des Gametophyten für die Phylogenie der Filicineen, *Glasnik d. kroatischen naturwiss. Gesells.* J **33**: 137–157, 1921.

JAKOWATZ, A.: Vergleichende Untersuchungen über Farnprothallien, *Sitzber. Akad. Wiss. Wien.*, Math.-naturw. Kl., Abt. I, **110**: 479–506, 1901.

KUPPER, W.: Über Knospenbildung an Farnblättern, *Flora,* **96**: 337–408, 1906.

LAGERBERG, T.: Zur Entwicklungsgeschichte des *Pteridium aquilinum, Ark. för Bot.*, **6**: 1–28, 1906.

LANG, W. H.: On apogamy and the development of sporangia upon fern prothallia, *Phil. Trans. Roy. Soc. London*, **190B**: 189–238, 1898.

LUERSSEN, C.: Die Farnpflanzen, *in* L. Rabenhorst, "Kryptogamen-Flora," Leipzig, 1889.

MARTIUS, C. F. P.: "Icones Plantarum Cryptogamicarum," Monachii, 1828–1834.

MOTTIER, D. M.: Development of sex organs of fern prothallia under prolonged cultivation, *Bot. Gaz.*, **91**: 218–223, 1931.

SCHLUMBERGER, O., Familienmerkmale der Cyatheaceen und der Polypodiaceen, usw., *Flora,* **102**: 383–414, 1911.

SCHNARF, K.: Beiträge zur Kenntnis des Sporangienwandbaues der Polypodiaceae und der Cyatheaceae und seiner systematischen Bedeutung, *Sitzber. Akad. Wiss. Wien*, Math.-naturw. Kl., **113**: 549–573, 1904.

SLOSSON, M.: "How Ferns Grow," New York, 1926.

STEIL, W. N., New cases of apogamy in certain homosporous leptosporangiate ferns, *Bot. Gaz.*, **95**: 164–167, 1933.

VLADESCO, A.: Sur les premiers cloissonnements du zygote des fougères leptosporangiées, *Compt. rend. Acad. Sci., Paris*, **195**: 1415–1416, 1932.

CHAPTER XIV

PALEOBOTANY AND THE FOSSIL RECORD

The thorough comparative study of a group of living plants is believed to provide a reasonably sound basis for opinions as to their phylogeny, since, naturally, the history of a group is expressed in high degree in its form and structure. But as information concerning the phylogenetic development of organisms grows, it is more and more clearly seen that conclusions as to the fundamental morphology of living plants, and especially as to their origin and relationships, cannot in many cases be drawn from living plants alone. Resemblances in structure may not represent similarity of origin and close relationship: the part played by parallel evolution has been a most important one; reduction brings about a simplicity of form often difficult to separate from the simplicity of primitiveness. With the recognition of these facts the great value of information as to the actual form and structure of ancestral plants—as a check on the theoretical conclusions drawn from living plants—is obvious. Such information comes only from fossils. The remains of plants of past times provide actual facts, not theories, as to the form and structure of ancestral groups and therefore as to the history of modification. Past history is the certain key to the present. A knowledge of fossil plants is, therefore, in the determination of phylogeny, of the greatest importance.

The study of the plants of the past is usually considered a separate field of botany, *paleobotany*. The aim of paleobotany has been defined as "an understanding of the succession of floras that have existed on the earth, their composition, distribution in space and time, and their relationships and evolution." As such, paleobotany covers a wide field. Botany, unfortunately, is usually looked upon as the study of a single flora, that of the present. Paleobotany covers what botany should cover, for the study of existing plants from any viewpoint, if sound, rests upon that of ancestral forms. Morphology and taxonomy especially must include much paleobotany.

To understand plants of the past it is necessary to learn something of the nature of fossils, of the system of nomenclature applied to them (which differs in some ways from that applied to living plants), and of historical geology.

Fossils.   Plant fossils consist of the remains of plants that lived in the past, and of replacements, of impressions, of casts and molds, and of any mark or trace of such plants.   Actual remains form only a part of the fossils left by a group of plants. These and those in which the tissues have been replaced— apparently molecule by molecule—so that their form is preserved in minute detail are of course the most valuable.

Where structure is still present, it has been destroyed in varying degrees—the tissues may have been partly decayed before preservation began or they may have been distorted by compression and chemical changes.   Where replacement has occurred, the structure of even delicate tissues is often preserved, in many cases in an amazing way (Figs. 198, 212).   Impressions give information as to form and texture, and sometimes as to minute surface details.   Casts and molds have none of the plant tissues present but show form and often features of structure.

Only part of the abundant plants of past ages left remains; of these a large part has been destroyed by geological and geographical changes.   Of those surviving such destruction, many are inaccessible; and of those so situated that they may be available, only a very small part has been discovered and studied. Yet a surprising amount of information has been obtained concerning the plant life of most geological periods, and this is being constantly increased.   The chief advances in an understanding of the morphology and phylogeny of vascular plants in the past 50 years have been the result of the study of fossil types; and the last 20 years have seen most important progress.

Nomenclature of Paleobotany.   Since fossils are formed largely from debris, they are in most cases fragmentary— leaves, twigs, seeds, spores, pieces of wood, roots, casts of trunks, of pith cavities, etc.   The study of such material is the study of isolated organs or parts of organs.   Such fossil plant parts are named, as are living plants, according to a binomial system. Generic names are, however, applied, first of all, to groups of fossils on the basis of general similarity in form; that is, genera are *form genera* only; definite identification of the relationship of the given organ to others is uncertain or impossible, and a temporary classification is made. Most genera are therefore artificial and provisional, established merely for convenience in description and study. For example, leaves with a certain form and venation are placed temporarily in the same genus; cones with a certain structure, tree trunks with certain surface markings constitute other form genera.

Under these form genera, species, based on less important characters, are described. It therefore happens that parts of the same plant, their connection unrecognized, may be placed in several genera—the leaf in one, the cone, the seed, the bark, the wood, etc., in others. For example, of a certain plant the stems were placed in the genus *Lyginopteris*, leaf blades in *Sphenopteris*, petioles in *Rachiopteris*, seeds in *Lagenostoma;* roots in *Kaloxylon*, microsporangia in *Crossotheca*. Similarly, plants distantly related or unrelated may be placed in the same genus.

Proof may later be obtained that several plant parts placed in as many genera belong together, and the relation is recognized; yet the fossils are still, for convenience, known by the original name, for example, *Lagenostoma Lomaxi* is now known to be the seed and *Sphenopteris* the leaf of *Lyginopteris Höningshausi;* yet these fossils retain their original names. Such a method may at first seem clumsy and confusing, but so slowly are the connections between organs made, and so uncertain must many of these be for an indefinite period, that it is soon seen to be the only possible method. Further, it has, in practice, proved satisfactory.

Historical Geology. An understanding of the plant life of the past is necessarily bound up with historical geology, which "deals with the changes through which the earth has passed— the history of continents and oceans as physical structures, the history of life upon them, and the conditions under which this life has developed and changed." Much of the field of paleobotany is indeed included in historical geology. To supply an outline of some phases of the subject, particularly the "time table," the accompanying Table 4 (page 308) and Fig. 180 are provided.

In the descriptions, conclusions, and theories of the preceding chapters, only the living members of the groups have been considered. The fossil forms are now to be discussed; information

TABLE 4

Era and years duration	Major division	Period and years back from present	Epoch	Advances in life	Dominant life
Cenozoic (60,000,000)	Quaternary	(2,000,000)	Recent	Rise of civilization	Age of man and herbaceous plants
			Pleistocene	Periodic glaciation; extinction of great mammals and many trees; rise of modern herbs	
	Tertiary	Late Tertiary	Pliocene	Continued cooling of climate; increasing restriction of plant distribution and of forests; appearance of man	Age of modern life—mammals, birds, flowering plants
			Miocene	Climate changing greatly, becoming cool and semi-arid; restriction of distribution of plants; beginning of forest reduction; culmination of mammals	
		Early Tertiary	Oligocene	Climate warm, humid; culmination of Eocene floras; world-wide distribution of tropical forests; primitive mammals disappear; rise of higher mammals and birds	
		(60,000,000)	Eocene	Climate cool, semi-arid, then warm, humid; modernization of flowering plants; development of extensive forests, reaching polar regions; modern birds and marine mammals appear	
Mesozoic (125,000,000)		Upper Cretaceous		Climate fluctuating; angiosperms dominant in floras; gymnosperms dwindling; rise of primitive mammals	Age of reptiles and higher gymnosperms
		Middle Cretaceous		Climate fluctuating; rapid development of angiosperms; many living genera appear; specialization and extinction of great reptiles	
		Lower Cretaceous (125,000,000)		Climate very warm; rise of angiosperms; conifers and cycads still dominant	
		Jurassic (157,000,000)		Climate warm; first known angiosperms; conifers and cycads dominant; cordaites disappear; primitive birds and flying reptiles	
		Triassic (185,000,000)		Climate warm, semi-arid; floras not luxuriant; higher gymnosperms increase; seed ferns disappear; first mammals; rise of giant reptiles	

TABLE 4.—(*Continued*)

Era and years duration	Major division	Period and years back from present	Epoch	Advances in life	Dominant life
Paleozoic (368,000,000)	Late Paleozoic	Permian (223,000,000)		Climate dry, with periodic glaciation; dwindling of ancient groups; extinction of many; rise of land vertebrates	Age of amphibians, lycopods, and seed ferns
		Pennsylvanian (upper Carboniferous) (271,000,000)		Dominant lycopods; primitive gymnosperms, seed ferns, and horsetails; extensive coal formation	
		Mississippian (lower Carboniferous) (309,000,000)		Dominant lycopods, horsetails, seed ferns; rise of primitive reptiles and insects	
	Middle Paleozoic	Devonian (354,000,000)		Early land floras: lycopods, horsetails, seed ferns, primitive gymnosperms, sphenophylls; first forests; rise of amphibians and fishes	Age of fishes and early land plants
		Silurian (381,000,000)		Algae dominant; first known land plants; rise of lungfishes and scorpions (first air-breathing animals)	
	Early Paleozoic	Ordovician (448,000,000)		Rise of corals, armored fishes (and land plants?); marine algae dominant	Age of higher invertebrates and algae
		Cambrian (553,000,000)		Climate warm, uniform over earth; first abundant fossils; many groups of invertebrate animals; dominance of trilobites; marine algae	
Proterozoic (900,000,000)		(1,500,000,000)		Rocks chiefly sedimentary, of enormous thickness; glaciation; first fossils: worms, crustaceans, brachiopods; algae (?)	Age of primitive marine invertebrates; fossils rare
Archeozoic (550,000,000+)		(2,000,000,000)		Igneous rocks: lavas, metamorphosed rocks; few sedimentary; no direct evidence of life	Age of unicellular life (?); fossils unknown

derived from them adds vastly to an understanding of them and their phylogeny, and of the basic morphology of vascular plants.

PSILOPHYTALES

In recent years there have come to be known a group of ancient vascular plants which are of the greatest importance to the morphology and phylogeny of vascular plants. Interest in these ancient plants lies in their great age and in their simplicity of

structure: they are the oldest known land plants—of Upper
Silurian and Lower and Middle Devonian age—and this and their
simple form suggest that they may represent the beginnings of a
vascular land flora and supply information as to the origin of these
plants.

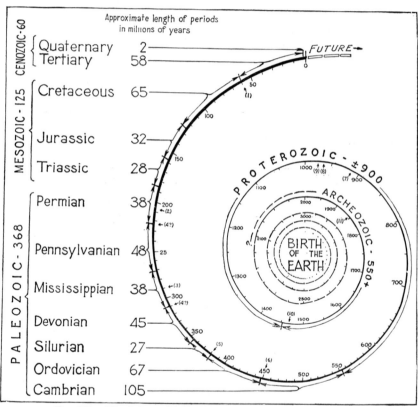

FIG. 180.—The "time table" of historical geology. (*After Moore.*)

Although the group has already been known though imperfectly
since the middle of the last century, a real acquaintance with it
has been acquired only in the past 20 years. During this period,
owing to the fortunate discovery of well-preserved material, and
to special interest in Devonian fossils, awakened in part by this
discovery, advance in knowledge of the Psilophytales has been
rapid.

Several genera—*Rhynia, Hornea, Psilophyton, Asteroxylon, Pseudosporochnus, Drepanophycus* (*Arthrostigma*), and *Baragwanathia*—can now be said to be well known; a number of others are as yet insufficiently known. *Drepanophycus* was described in 1852 and *Psilophyton* in 1859, but these genera (with others less well understood) received little attention during the following decades because their peculiarities of structure and classification suggested possible misinterpretation. Continuing interest in Devonian plants at the end of the nineteenth and the beginning of the new century culminated in the description, in 1917 and succeeding years, of a group of three new genera from excellently preserved material from the Lower Devonian of Scotland. The group was then well established and its importance evident. New genera and new species in considerable number have since been described, extending greatly the knowledge of the group and showing its distribution to have been world-wide—Norway, Great Britain, Germany, Czechoslovakia, Nova Scotia, Wyoming, China, Australia. At the present time (1935), with definite extension of these plants well back into the Upper Silurian, interest continues and further important discoveries will undoubtedly soon be made.

The three new genera described from Scotland are *Rhynia, Hornea,* and *Asteroxylon.* These were simple herbaceous plants, resembling in habit, size, and habitat species of rush, *Juncus.* Their debris formed beds of peaty material which, with living plants, was buried beneath layers of sand and preserved by infiltration and replacement by siliceous material. The preservation is remarkably perfect, and the structure of these genera was learned in much detail. To this knowledge has been added that from other stations where new species have in some cases been found.

The genera of this group vary in important characters and therefore need separate description.

RHYNIA

Habit. *Rhynia* (Fig. 181), of which two well-defined species have been described, is the simplest genus. Borne on a slender rhizome were erect cylindrical stems which branched dichotomously, though sparsely. The rhizomes bore rhizoids, but there were no roots. The stems were naked, with blunt apices. The

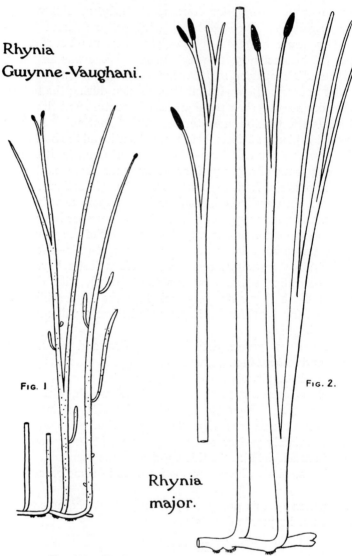

Rhynia
Gwynne-Vaughani.

FIG. I

Rhynia
major.

FIG. 2.

FIG. 181.—Habit of *Rhynia*. (*After Kidston and Lang.*)

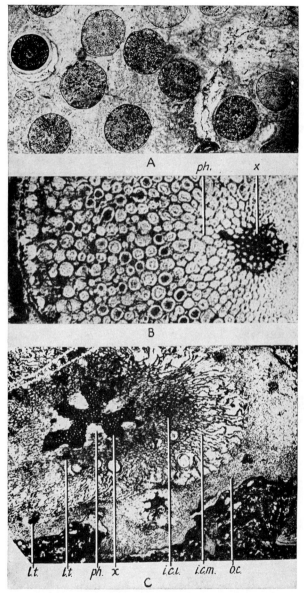

FIG. 182.—Anatomy of the Psilophytales. *A, B, Rhynia Gwynne-Vaughani;*
C, Asteroxylon Mackiei. A, cross sections of several stems in siliceous matrix;
B, cross section of part of one stem; *C,* cross section of stem. *ici,* inner zone of
inner cortex; *icm,* middle zone of inner cortex; *lt,* leaf trace; *oc,* outer cortex;
ph, phloem; *x,* xylem. (*After Kidston and Lang.*)

body of the plant was therefore merely a branched cylindrical axis.

The stems of *R. major*, the larger species, were about 50 cm in height and 1.5 to 6 (chiefly 5) mm in diameter; those of *R. Gwynne-Vaughani* were 2 to 3 mm in diameter and up to 20 cm in height. The latter species bore on its smooth stems hemispherical or oval protuberances the nature of which is not clear. These projections were mere parenchymatous bulges or cushions, somewhat lenticel-like in form and structure. When situated at the base of the stem they apparently, in some cases, bore rhizoids. Some seem to have grown out into small lateral branches which were easily detached—a possible means of vegetative reproduction.

Anatomy. The axis had a slender, central protostele, with a cylindrical strand of xylem (Fig. 182*B*). About the xylem was a sheath of elongate cells with oblique ends, probably very simple phloem. The cortex was thick. The delicate epidermis had stomata similar to those of other vascular plants, and a heavy cuticle. The tracheids were all annular, and the central ones were the smaller.

Reproduction. The sporangia were cylindrical structures borne terminally on the branch tips (Figs. 181, 183*B*). They were continuous with the stem, but a slight constriction at the base formed an indefinite short stalk. Those of *R. major* were large, about 12 mm long by 4 mm in diameter. Their walls were massive—of several layers of cells, the outer ones thick-walled, and there was no means of dehiscence (Fig. 183*A*). The many spores, all alike, cutinized, were borne in tetrads, and filled the sporangium chamber. The inner wall cells probably formed an indefinite tapetum.

HORNEA

Habit. *Hornea* was similar to *Rhynia*, but was a smaller, more slender plant with somewhat more freely branched stems (Fig. 184), which were without appendages of any sort. The rhizomes were shorter and jointed, with thick, tuberous segments.

Anatomy. The stele of the stem was similar to that of *Rhynia*, but the rhizome was apparently without vascular tissue, consisting wholly of parenchymatous cells. The steles of the attached aerial stems passed into the fleshy mass, expanded

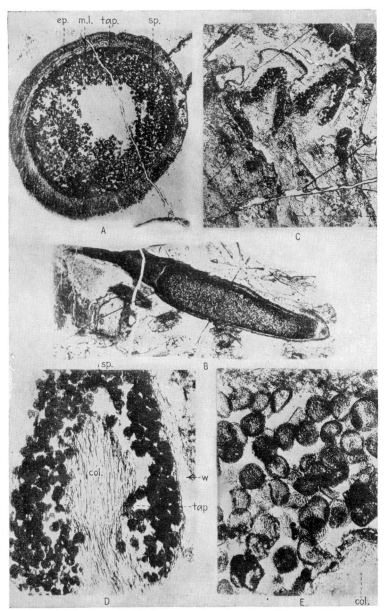

FIG. 183.—Reproduction in the Psilophytales. *A, Rhynia major; B, R. Gwynne-Vaughani; C* to *E, Hornea Lignieri. A,* cross section of sporangium; *B,* longitudinal section of sporangium; *C,* longitudinal sections of two sporangia, one dichotomously forked; *D,* central portion of sporangium in *C* showing columella and spores; *E,* mature spores. *col,* columella; *ep,* epidermis; *ml,* middle layer of wall; *sp,* spores; *tap,* tapetum; *w,* wall. (*After Kidston and Lang.*)

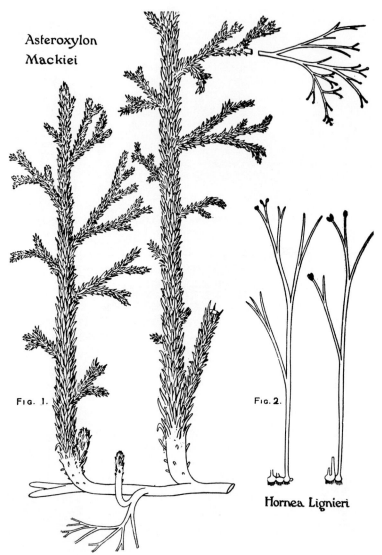

Asteroxylon
Mackiei

Fig. 1.

Fig. 2.

Hornea Lignieri

FIG. 184.—Habit of *Asteroxylon* and *Hornea.*   (*After Kidston and Lang.*)

bell-like, and faded out. These rhizome joints have been likened to protocorms in their anatomy and in their relation to the vascular axes.

Reproduction. The small sporangia were terminal on the stem tips and sessile, being continuous with the stem (Fig. 184). They had no uniform shape, being merely fertile stem tips; in many cases they forked dichotomously, like the stem (Fig. 183*C*). The wall was thick and without evidence of a means of dehiscence. The spores (Fig. 183*E*) lay in a dome-shaped cavity around and above a central columella, which seems to represent a continuation of the phloem of the stele (Fig. 183*C,D*).

ASTEROXYLON

Two species are now well known in this genus: *A. Mackiei* (Fig. 184) from Scotland, and *A. elberfeldense* from Germany. The former was first known; the latter, a larger and stouter species, has added important facts to a knowledge of the genus.

Habit. The plant body in *Asteroxylon* was much more complex than that of *Rhynia* and *Hornea*. A naked, branching rhizome sent up freely branching erect stems clothed with small *Lycopodium*-like leaves. At the base of the leafy axes there was a transition to a naked region below. The more slender underground branches of the rhizome were like roots in appearance and behavior, some of them burrowing into the decaying tissues of other plants.

The leaves were about 5 mm in length and closely crowded, apparently without regular arrangement, although there are suggestions of spiral order. In form they were more spine-like than leaf-like, being conical or awl-shaped; in cross section oval or round-triangular.

Anatomy. The vascular cylinder, like the plant body, was more complex than that of *Rhynia* and *Hornea*. The stele, in cross section, in the smaller species is a stellate protostele (Fig. 182*C*), in the larger species a "polystellate" stele with a central pith. From the arms of the stele small vascular strands extended obliquely upward to the bases of the leaves; these bundles, however, did not enter the leaves, which were veinless. The tracheids of the smaller species were like those of *Rhynia;* those of the larger included scalariform types and some had more or less rounded pits. The smallest cells were near the outside, giving a mesarch or exarch structure.   There was no secondary growth.

Reproduction.   No sporangia were at first found in connection with the plants, but associated with the leafy stems were slender, naked, dichotomous branches bearing terminal sporangia. These naked branches owing to their method of occurrence and to the similarity of their stomata and other anatomical structure, were suspected of being the deciduous fertile branchlets

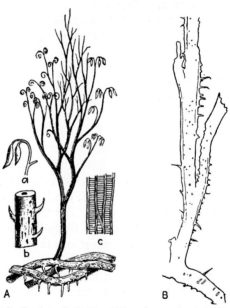

FIG. 185.—*Psilophyton.   A*, habit of *P. princeps* (*a*, axis tip with terminal sporangia; *b*, portion of axis, with spines; *c*, tracheids); *B*, *P. wyomingense*, portion of base of plant.   ×2.   (*A, after Dawson; B, after Dorf.*)

of *Asteroxylon*, but it was not until *A. elberfeldense* was well known that proof of their nature was found.   In this second species (where the leafy stems and the naked ones were at first placed in the form genera *Thursophyton* and *Hostimella*), occasional connections of the two types of stems have been found, and it is evident that the leafy branches passed into spiny ones and those into naked, fertile tips.

The sporangia were ovoid or ellipsoid, minute (about 1 mm long) and show a simple annulus and apical, longitudinal dehiscence.

Psilophyton

This genus, although one of the first of the group to be described, is not so well known as the preceding genera because of the fragmentary nature and poor preservation of its remains. Slender, upright, dichotomous stems somewhat similar to those of *Rhynia major* rose from creeping rhizomes (Fig. 185). Their tips were circinate, and they bore on their lower parts short (0.3 to 2.0 mm long), spine-like projections. The spines were flattened in the vertical plane and had no vascular supply and no stomata. They were therefore emergences and not leaves. Sporangia were borne, suspended, mostly in pairs at the tips of the branches, probably terminal on an ultimate dichotomy. They were obovoid and proportionately large (4.0 to 6.5 mm long by 1.0 to 1.5 mm thick).

Pseudosporochnus

Plants of this genus (Fig. 186) were in habit markedly different from the preceding genera. They were much larger, attaining a height of 2 to 3 m and possessed a trunk-like main stem. The trunk rose unbranched and gradually tapering from a rounded, sometimes swollen base. Simple root-like structures extended apparently horizontally from the base. The trunk gave rise at the top to a crowded group of branches, all of about the same size. These main branches, which were decurrent on the trunk or fused laterally to it, forked freely, forming a bushy crown of slender dichotomous tips. Some of these tips were filiform; others were thickened (reaching a diameter of 0.6 mm) and formed the sporangia. Spores, all of one type, have been found in these club-shaped tips.

Pseudosporochnus has been called a "small tree" and "a form transitional from the herbaceous to tree types." Though pieces of trunk up to 35 cm long and 5 to 6 cm in diameter have been found, the plant is hardly to be called a small tree. Whether secondary growth was present is not known. The ultimate branchlets have been called leaves, and in function, they doubtless so served. Such "leaves" were, however, morphologically very different from the simple lateral outgrowths of other genera of the group; they were the ultimate lateral parts of the axis system, with branches in more than one plane and with some

of the tips transformed into sporangia.   There were no appendages of the enation type.

FIG. 186.—*Pseudosporochnus Krejcii.* Habit.   × about ¼.   (*After Kräusel
and Weyland.*)

DREPANOPHYCUS (ARTHROSTIGMA)

One of the earliest genera described in this group was *Drepanophycus*, a plant whose stems had spine-like, rigid projections

(Fig. 187). These emergences were stouter and longer than those of *Psilophyton* and more abundant. In form they resembled thorns rather than leaves, being more or less falcate, with broad bases. In arrangement they were largely irregular but approached in some cases the spiral or whorled. The stems were stout, up to 2 or 3 (rarely 5) cm in diameter, with a very slender vascular stele and with traces supplying the spines and continuing as a definite vein. In a few cases sporangium-like bodies

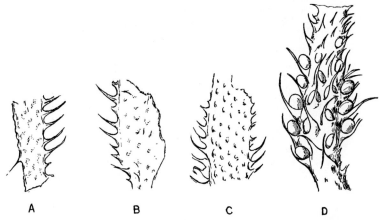

FIG. 187.—*Drepanophycus* (*Arthrostigma*). *A* to *C*, portions of axis showing shape and arrangement of emergences; *D*, fertile portion of axis. (*After Kräusel and Weyland.*)

have been found on the sides of the stems among the spines. The spines were commonly about 1 cm in length but ranged up to 2 or 3 cm.

PROTOPTERIDIUM

Another small plant, *Protopteridium* (Fig. 188), deserves especial attention because of its fern-like habit. The lateral branch systems were sterile or fertile. The latter bore terminal, suspended sporangia resembling those of *Psilophyton* and were in form remarkably like fern fronds.

BARAGWANATHIA

In the last few years information concerning these ancient plants of the Lower and Middle Devonian periods has been

increasing rapidly: long-known but doubtful genera are becoming
well established and new species added; new genera have been dis-

Fig. 188.—*Protopteridium.*   Branching axis with determinate fern-frond-like
lateral branches, those on the upper left fertile.   × about ⅓.   (*After Kräusel
and Weyland.*)

covered.   One of the latest contributions (1935) to our knowledge
of the group is a most important one, since it presents a Silurian

land flora and thereby extends vascular plants much farther back in geological time. It is important, also, because it adds another genus whose characters are rather completely known—*Baragwanathia* (Fig. 189).

Fig. 189.—*Baragwanathia.* 1, portion of leafy axis, about natural size; 2, axis tip with terminal bud and spirally arranged sporangia, about natural size; 3, portion of axis, enlarged, showing sporangia. (*After Lang and Cookson.*)

The stems were stout (1 to 5 cm in diameter) and clothed with abundant long, lax leaves. In general appearance the leafy stems resemble the spiny stems of *Drepanophycus*, but the appendages of the Silurian genus were definitely leaf-like—long (up to 4 cm in length by 0.5 to 1 mm in width) and soft, not stiff and emergence-like; of uniform width throughout, not tapering from a broad base; arranged in spirals, not irregularly. The branching was dichotomous, and the lateral branches were more slender, being perhaps rhizomes; the habit of the plant is, however, unknown.

The slender vascular cylinder (3 to 8 mm in diameter) was of the *Asteroxylon* type, stellate with many (up to 12 or more) arms which widened distally. The tracheids were all of the annular

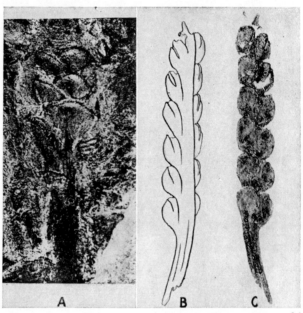

Fig. 190.—*A, Zosterophyllum australianum,* fertile axis tip, ×1¾; *B, C, Bucheria ovata,* fertile axis tip bearing marginal sporangia (?), dorsal and ventral views, ×2½. (Note resemblance to fertile leaf tips of *Botrychium* and *Ophioglossum*.) (*A, after Lang and Cookson; B, C, after Dorf.*)

type without differentiation into proto- and metaxylem. Epidermal structure has not been preserved, and information as to stomata and cuticle is lacking. The leaves had definite traces and veins.

The sporangia were borne in a fertile zone near the ends of leafy branches, apparently sessile on the stem between leaf insertions (Fig. 189, 2, 3). In position they are related to the leaves, but in just what manner is not clear; they form spiral series, in some cases seeming to be in the axils of the leaves, in others possibly on the stem itself or adaxial on the leaf at the base. They were reniform, about 2 mm wide, with spores of one kind, round-oval in outline.

Baragwanathia was thus the most complex of the genera of this group; it is also much older than the others. With it are fragmentary remains of other, probably even more complex plants. Among those Devonian genera as yet inadequately known there are also plants with elaborate structure—with sporangia borne in spike-like clusters on elongate stalks—for example, *Bucheria* from Wyoming and *Zosterophyllum* from Scotland and Australia (Fig. 190). A large and varied flora of complex and simple plants of the *Psilophyton* group lived in Upper Silurian and Lower and Middle Devonian times, and among those thus far known the more complex types are at least as old as the simpler.

DISCUSSION AND SUMMARY

In these ancient genera the simplicity of the plant body is the outstanding character. In *Rhynia* the body is a simple axis differentiated only into a creeping portion, which bears rhizoids, and an erect, aerial, photosynthetic portion. There are no roots or leaves. On the aerial stem of *Psilophyton* are sparse, spine-like emergences. In *Asteroxylon* there are abundant, more leaf-like appendages with stomata; these projections are, however, fleshy and thick, being only slightly flattened and they have no definite arrangement. The appendages of *Baragwanathia* are definitely leaf-like in form, arrangement, and structure (though information as to stomata is lacking). The spines of *Psilophyton* have no vascular supply; the somewhat larger ones of *Drepanophycus* have a simple vein. The more leaf-like structures in *Asteroxylon* are without veins, but traces are present in the form of stubs of vascular tissue which extend to the base of the appendages. The leaves of *Baragwanathia* have well developed leaf traces and veins. The various genera show a possible upgrade series in the development of leaf-like appendages as enations of the axis.

The genus *Pseudosporochnus* is in habit very different from the other members of the group, yet the plant body is, as in the other genera, a branching axis. There is greater elaboration among the axis branches—a trunk; a tufted, photosynthetic group of fine branchlets; spreading, root-like underground parts.   The sporangia were not so advanced, being merely thickened axis tips.   *Protopteridium* shows still more marked differentiation among branch systems and a close approach to fern-frond shape in the fertile segments.

The simplicity of the body is continued in the sporangium which is seen to be merely an axis tip.   In *Hornea* the sporangium is not recognizable as such externally; only sections demonstrate that some of the stem tips are fertile.   The axis nature of the sporangium is further evident in the presence, in this genus, of a columella, the continuation of the stele, and in the dichotomy of the sporangia.   In *Pseudosporochnus* the sporangia are fertile axis tips which differ from the sterile ones externally only in their greater thickness.   In *Rhynia* the sporangia are somewhat more differentiated, though still clearly mere stem tips; the sporangium has fairly definite form and is set off from the stem below by a weakly differentiated stalk, and there is no columella.   In neither genus is there a means of dehiscence. The sporangia of *Psilophyton* and *Asteroxylon* have definite form and are sharply distinct from the axis; those of the latter genus have an annulus and apical dehiscence.   In sporangium differentiation in form and dehiscence the genera show a series parallel in general with that in body differentiation.   A somewhat similar series is seen in living forms where a massive wall and the absence of an annulus are primitive.   Dehiscence, where present in the fossil types, is longitudinal as in the more primitive living groups.

The sporangium in all these genera is a terminal part of the axis.   In *Drepanophycus* and *Baragwanathia* the relation to the axis is not so clear: in these genera the sporangium is a lateral, apparently sessile structure related in position to the leaves. The sporangia of *Zosterophyllum* and *Bucheria*, terminal on short lateral branches, suggest a possible derivation for this condition, but some other origin is perhaps as likely.   Interpretation depends upon the discovery of other and possibly older types.

In anatomy the protostele is characteristic, as in primitive living plants; a pith is probably present in *Asteroxylon elberfeldense*.   Secondary growth is lacking throughout the group. The xylem consists of annular tracheids in most forms; other types appear only in the plant whose stele is advanced in the possession of a pith. Xylem of annular tracheids only is characteristic of this group. The slenderness of the vascular stele is remarkable, especially as there is no evidence of other supporting tissue.

A likeness has been seen between the fleshy joints of the rhizome of *Hornea* and the protocorms of *Lycopodium* in the lack of vascular tissue, and in the fact that from the parenchymatous masses arise stems with vascular tissue. The presence of protocorms in such very early and simple plants, and in a group some of which resemble *Lycopodium*, would doubtless provide strong support for the "protocorm theory" (Chap. XVII) of the origin of the vascular sporophyte; but the arrangement and number of the tuberous parts and a comparison with the similar *Rhynia* demonstrate that these structures are merely segments of a rhizome. A similar lack of apparent vascular tissue is found in tubers among angiosperms.

The group as a whole show structure in all features as simple as can be imagined for vascular plants—a structure that matches the hypothetical picture of "first land plants": a mere axis or thallus, carrying on all vegetative and reproductive functions with little or no elaboration of form, and provided with those features essential to existence on land and in the air—a conducting system, stomata, cuticle, and cutinized spores. There is no differentiation into "fundamental parts—root, stem, leaf, sporangium, emergence, hair."

The extremely simple form of such genera as *Rhynia, Hornea,* and *Psilophyton* and the fact that they are so old have led naturally to the suggestion that these are the most primitive of vascular plants. The body is alga-like in some ways, and these plants have therefore been looked upon as forms transitional between algae and higher vascular plants—representatives of the stage through which vascular plants passed when first developing on land. As such, plants of the *Psilophyton* stock would be the ancestors of higher vascular plants. That land plants came from aquatic ancestors can hardly be doubted; that early land plants were of simple structure is probable. But that the known genera of this group, or their relatives, represent these first air-living vascular plants is an open question.

The group is the oldest one yet known, and it was surely large and varied and of world-wide distribution. The fact that among the oldest known forms are some of the most complex ones suggests that there must have been a still older land flora and a long preceding period of evolution. Here, as in several other groups of vascular plants, the oldest members yet known are complex; simpler forms are later. Such simpler forms may be surviving primitive types or reduced members of the series. The interpretation of this situation in the Psilophytales is most difficult. Some reduction has doubtless occurred since the group was in existence well before the end of the Silurian period, and since the simplest known genera were bog or marsh plants, and, further, lived apparently in the neighborhood of volcanic activity. Their specialization is evident in their thick cuticles and in the tuberous rhizome of *Hornea;* further, many, perhaps all of the group, lived in wet places—a habitat where vascular plants become reduced. Above all, the most complex genus is among the oldest. On the other hand, the fact that a whole series of these plants with the same general characters is now known suggests that it is hardly likely that all members of a large group have been reduced. Further, the structure of the sporangium in the simplest genera presents strong evidence for primitiveness—the massive, unspecialized wall; the columella; the lack of an annulus and perhaps of any dehiscence; and especially the lack of external differentiation of the sporangium. It seems hardly likely that these genera, if greatly reduced, would still show the crudest possible type of sporangium.

The presence in the immediately following geological period, Upper Devonian, however, of large (arborescent) and complex types of several widely different groups, including seed-bearing plants and trees with thick cylinders of secondary wood, demands surely for such plants "a long antecedent period of development," and suggests that the Lower and Middle Devonian psilophytalean types can hardly have been the ancestral stock from which the many advanced types arose with great rapidity. This fact has led to an opinion that a land flora perhaps existed "as far back of the Devonian as the Devonian is back of the present time." For such an opinion there is at present no certain foundation in fossil remains; such a long period of early existence and modification would provide, however, a basis for the advanced specialization and the great variety of the floras of the Upper Devonian and the lower Carboniferous.

The Psilophytales are indeed "ancient and simple"; that they are also "archaic and ancestral" is surely not known. That they are alga-like and show structure intermediate between algae and advanced vascular plants is evident. As a group they can hardly have been reduced in extreme fashion. If not ancestral, they seem to represent types of possible first vascular land plants. Knowledge of the group is probably only beginning, and the problem may well increase in complexity before solution, as the newly discovered Silurian flora has added to, rather than solved, the difficulties of interpretation of the Devonian flora.

The known genera are apparently but few of an extensive world group of similar plants; an attempt to classify naturally and to determine interrelationships is, therefore, with the present information about the group, almost valueless. The genera may all be placed in one family, recognized as broadly inclusive, the Psilophytaceae; each well-known genus may form a family— Rhyniaceae, Horneaceae, etc.; *Pseudosporochnus* may be set apart in the Pseudosporochnaceae, the others forming the Psilophytaceae; *Drepanophycus* and *Baragwanathia* are closely related and may be placed in a separate family. Any treatment is of course provisional. Regardless, however, of the disposition of the genera in families, all may be placed provisionally in a single order, Psilophytales.

The similarity of these plants and the living Psilotaceae is close. The latter group has until recent years been generally considered reduced; *Tmesipteris* and *Psilotum* have been called "reduced lepidophytes." Although these genera have undoubtedly been modified to some extent by the adoption of a xerophytic and epiphytic habit, the recently acquired knowledge of their gametophytes (the gametophytes, antheridia, and sperms of the two groups being wholly unlike) and the details of embryogeny and vascular anatomy make such an interpretation of relationships no longer possible. The Psilophytales and the Psilotaceae are alike in many important ways: the body an axis without roots, with emergences rather than leaves; the sporangium an axis tip, with massive and undifferentiated wall, with a central stelar columella; the emergences flattened in the vertical plane and decurrent, without vascular supply or with traces extending only into the cortex.

330 MORPHOLOGY OF VASCULAR PLANTS

These characters are not found in any other group, and the Psilotaceae and Psilophytales therefore seem to belong together in a major group in a natural classification. The Psilotaceae have been treated (page 114) as belonging in the major group Psilopsida; the Psilophytales should be placed in the same group. The Psilotaceae with their chambered sporangia and elaborated histological structure form an independent order the Psilotales. The relationship of the two groups is obscure, and the living family has left no fossil remains which have thus far been found. There can be little doubt, however, but that the Psilotaceae represent surviving remnants of the ancient psilophytalean stock, retaining the major morphological features of the ancestral types. As such they are living examples of the oldest known vascular plants.

Bibliography

ARBER, E. A. N.: "Devonian Floras," Cambridge, 1920.

BERRY, E. W.: Devonian floras, *Amer. Jour. Sci.*, **14**: 109–120, 1927.

DAWSON, J. W.: The fossil plants of the Devonian and Upper Silurian formations of Canada, *Geol. Survey Canada*, I, 1871; II, 1882.

DORF, E.: A new occurrence of the oldest known vegetation from Bear-tooth Butte, Wyoming, *Bot. Gaz.*, **95**: 240–257, 1933.

HALLE, T. G.: Lower Devonian plants from Röragen in Norway, *Kgl. Svensk. Vetensk. Akad., Handl.*, **57** (1): 1–46, 1916.

KIDSTON, R., and W. H. LANG: On Old Red Sandstone plants showing structure from the Rhynie Chert Bed, Aberdeenshire, Pts. I–V, *Trans. Roy. Soc. Edinburgh*, **51–52**, 1917–1921.

KRÄUSEL, R.: Wesen und phylogenetische Bedeutung der ältesten Gefässpflanzen, *Ber. Deutsch. Bot. Gesells.*, **50**: 5–12, 1932.

—— and H. WEYLAND: Beiträge zur Kenntnis der Devon-flora, I. *Senckenbergiana*, **5**: 152–184, 1923; II. *Abh. Senckenb. Naturf. Gesells.*, **40**: 115–155, 1926; III. *ibid.*, **41**: 317–359, 1929.

——: Über Pflanzenreste aus dem Devon Deutschlands, I. *Senckenbergiana*, **12**: 217–221, 1930.

——: Die Flora des deutschen Unterdevon, *Abh. Preuss. Geol. Landesanstalt*, **131**: 1–92, 1930.

——: Die Flora des böhmischen Mitteldevons, *Paleontographica*, **78** (B): 1–46, 1933.

LANG, W. H.: Contributions to the study of the Old Red Sandstone Flora of Scotland, I–VIII, *Trans. Roy. Soc. Edinburgh*, **54, 55, 58**, 1925–1934.

——: On the spines, sporangia, and spores of *Psilophyton princeps* Dawson, shown in specimens from Gaspé, *Phil. Trans. Roy. Soc. London*, **219B**: 421–442, 1931.

——, and I. C. Cookson: Some fossil plants of early Devonian type from the Walhalla series, Victoria, Australia, *Phil. Trans. Roy Soc. London,* **219B**: 133–163, 1930.

——: On a flora including vascular land plants, associated with *Monograptus*, in rocks of Silurian age, from Victoria, Australia, *Phil. Trans. Roy. Soc. London*, **224B**: 421–449, 1935.

Zimmermann, W.: Die Spaltöffnungen der Psilophyta und Psilotales, *Ztschr. Bot.*, **19**: 129–170, 1926.

CHAPTER XV

LEPIDODENDRALES

Among extinct plant groups the lepidodendrids are outstanding because of the abundance and excellent preservation of their fossil remains. These ancient plants were one of the dominant plant groups of the Paleozoic. There were surely many genera and doubtless a great number of species. (Many genera and several hundred species have been described; some of the genera are, of course, form genera, and many species will doubtless be united; yet the group was certainly a great and diverse one.) The habitat was low, wet ground, and the roots were perhaps at times under water.

Habit. Most of the genera were tree-like in size and habit; if the living club mosses, maintaining their structural features, be imagined increased in size to that of large trees, an excellent picture of the probable appearance of the lepidodendrids will be obtained. As trees, most of them were large—up to 30 (perhaps to 45) m in height, varying in habit—richly branched, sparsely branched, or unbranched. In most cases the trunks were straight and columnar (Fig. 191), extending unbranched for more than half of the height of the tree. In proportion to the size of the tree the trunks were slender, averaging perhaps 1 m in diameter, but reaching 2 m in some cases. The branching was dichotomous, the main branches being thick and trunk-like; where branching was free, a dense crown of small branchlets was formed. At the base the trunk forked dichotomously into thick, spreading, root-like parts (Figs. 192, 193), which, tapering rather abruptly, bore slender, lateral roots. To both these appendages and the main-root-like divisions of the trunk is given the generic name *Stigmaria*. These organs are much the same in all members of the group, and *Stigmaria* is therefore a form genus for the root-like parts of the lepidodendrids. The appendages— "stigmarian rootlets"—were slender, elongate, cylindrical structures, spirally arranged and dichotomously forked.

Fig. 191.—Restoration of plant life of the Carboniferous period. The columnar trunks at the left and the leaves and cones in the upper left corner are those of lepidodendrids. The trees with whorled branches at the right are calamites. The small plants in the foreground are sphenophylls. (*After Dahlgren by permission of the Field Museum of Natural History, Chicago, Ill. Copyright by the Museum.*)

Leaves. The younger branches were thickly clothed with abundant linear or acicular leaves (Fig. 191) commonly from 2 to 10 cm long, frequently up to 15 or 18 cm and in some species to about 1 m. Their length varied on the same plant, a condition perhaps due to long-continued growth. Probably all were ligulate, though, as the ligules were small and sunken in pits, this is not readily determined. In section the leaves were rhombic and suboval, and they were attached by a broad spreading base of similar outline (Fig. 194). Though apparently

Fig. 192.—*Stigmaria ficoides.* Base of a lepidodendrid with thick, tapering dichotomously branched 'roots'. (*After Williamson.*)

persisting for a long time the leaves were ultimately shed by abscission above the thickened base, leaving the base attached as a projecting truncated cone or pyramid, the *leaf cushion*. (A similar condition is seen in some living conifers, for example, *Picea.*) In the majority of forms the leaves were arranged in close spirals; in some they stood in alternating whorls. In many forms the leaves were closely placed, and the branches therefore were covered, after the leaves fell, with an armor of leaf bases. As the stem increased in diameter, the cushions in many of these forms kept pace with the growth, so that the

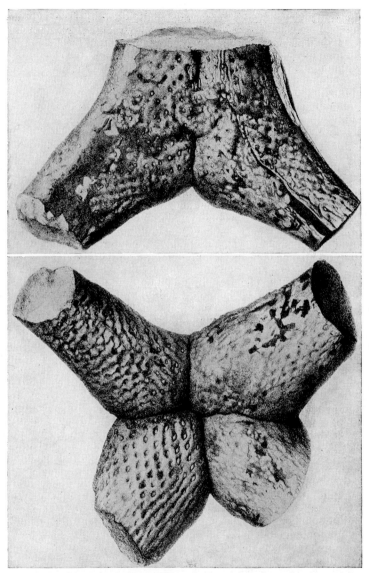

FIG. 193.—*Stigmaria ficoides.* Views of young plant from the side and from below showing dichotomies and rootlet arrangement. Note resemblance to rhizomorph of *Isoetes.* (*After Williamson.*)

trunk and large limbs were encased in the armor. These
cushions, because of their firm texture and projecting character,

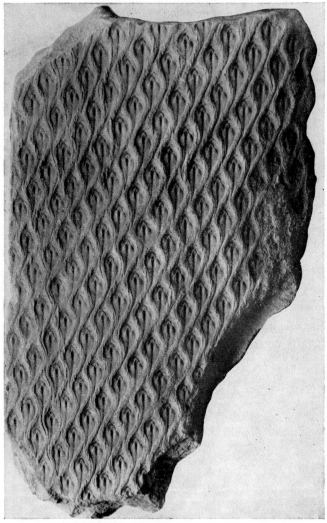

Fɪɢ. 194.—*Lepidodendron obovatum.*   Impression of surface of trunk.   (*After
Dahlgren by permission of the Field Museum of Natural History, Chicago, Ill.*)

readily formed fossils, especially molds and casts (Fig. 194);
such fossils are the most abundant remains of the lepidodendrids

and are among the most perfect and striking of all paleozoic fossils. The arrangement, form, and structure of the cushions are taxonomically one of the most important structural features of the group.

Anatomy. The stele was small, the woody cylinder occupying only 9 to 14 per cent of the cross-sectional area of the stem

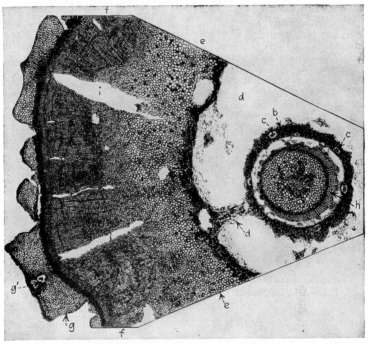

Fig. 195.—*Lepidodendron selaginoides.* Portion of cross section of small branch. *b,* innermost cortex; *c,* leaf trace; *d,* middle cortex; *e,* outer cortex; *f,* periderm; *g,* leaf cushion; *g',* bundle in leaf base; *h,* secondary xylem; *i,* break in tissue. (*After Williamson.*)

(Fig. 195); that of conifers and angiosperms, in contrast, occupies 80 to 90 per cent. Secondary growth was present, but even in large trunks the proportion of wood was small. The persistent cortex was thick and differentiated into an inner soft layer and an outer hard layer; in the latter, secondary growth developed a thick periderm with much sclerenchyma (Fig. 195). Support for the tree was provided largely by the hard outer tissues of the cortex. The stele of some forms was protostelic; that of the majority had a pith of either simple or mixed nature.   The xylem was typically exarch.   The vascular cylinder was terete with slight ridges from the sides of which arose the simple leaf traces which, leaving no gaps, passed obliquely upward through the cortex to the broad leaf bases.   The leaf vein is simple except in *Sigillaria* and related forms where it is double for part of its extent.   On the leaf scar the broken trace forms the central structural feature.   Forming a row on the scar with this bundle end are two rounded or triangular areas, one on each side, known

Fig. 196.—A lepidodendrid cone (*Lepidophloios cliftonensis*).   (*After Dawson.*)

together as the *parichnos*.   These represent cross sections of strands of soft, parenchymatous (aerating or secretory) tissue, extending from the cortex into the leaf.   On the cushion below the leaf scar, two other similar areas may appear; these are the outer ends of similar parenchyma columns, probably connected in a system with those that enter the leaf.   Above on the cushion, centrally, is the ligular pit.   The ligule is small and shrunken, resembling in form and condition the ligule of *Selaginella* rather than that of *Isoetes*.

Reproduction.   *Cones.*   The sporangia were borne ventrally at the base of sporophylls which in nearly all cases formed cones. These strobili resembled superficially those of living conifers (Figs. 196, 197): the more or less leaf-like sporophylls were in close spirals, or, less commonly, in alternating whorls.   The cones were mostly large—bearing in size much the same relation to those of *Lycopodium* and *Selaginella* as do the leaves and stems. They may be compared in size and general appearance with the seed-bearing strobili of the conifers: some were a few centimeters

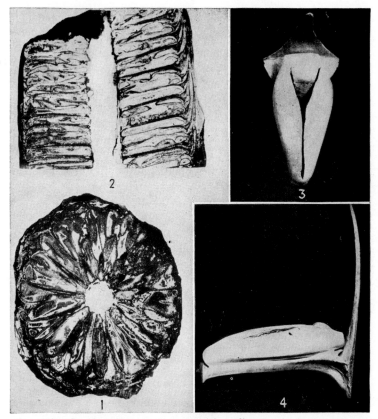

FIG. 197.—*Lepidostrobus.* 1, 2, cross and median longitudinal sections of cone, about natural size; 3, 4, views of model of sporophyll with sporangium: 3, ventral view showing method of dehiscence; 4, lateral view showing slender sporophyll base and attachment of sporangium, distal lobing of sporophyll, and position of ligule. (*After Coulter and Land.*)

long by 1 cm in diameter; most of them were much larger, up to 3 cm in diameter (resembling ears of maize in size and form); in a few cases they reached nearly 1 m in length. They were borne terminally on the lateral branches of the crown, or, in the sparsely branched and unbranched genera, solitary or clustered on short deciduous branchlets which arose directly from the trunk or the main branches.

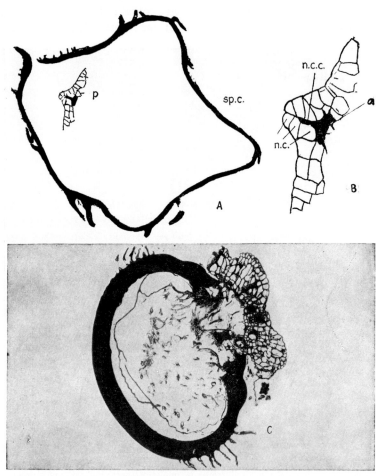

Fig. 198.—Gametophytes of the lepidodendrids. *A*, *B*, *Lepidodendron Veltheimianum; C, Bothrodendron mundum. A*, cross section of spore with included gametophyte, only the archegonial cushion of the prothallium preserved; *B*, the cushion enlarged; *C*, cross section of spore with protruding prothallium showing archegonia cut obliquely. *a*, archegonium; *nc*, neck cell; *ncc*, neck canal cell; *sp.c*, spore wall; *p*, prothallium. (*A*, *B*, *after Gordon; C, after McLean.*)

Sporophylls and Sporangia. The sporophylls had slender bases with leaf-like tips upturned at right angles, and in some cases with downward projecting flaps which covered the sporangium below (Fig. 197). They resembled, except in the long narrow bases, the sporophylls of species of *Lycopodium*. The large sporangia were radially elongate and attached for their full length to the sporophyll below. Most of the genera were heterosporous, with the megasporangia at the base of the cone; in a few, only one kind of spore has been found and these were doubtfully homosporous. Homosporous forms were doubtless present, but the homosporous condition is, of course, difficult to demonstrate in fossil plants. In rare forms sporangia have been found in zones, or, irregularly placed, on leaf-like sporophylls along the stem, as are sporangia in some species of *Lycopodium*.

Spores. The microspores were minute—from 0.02 to 0.03 mm in diameter—and were borne in enormous numbers in the large sporangia. The megaspores were large—0.5 to 2.0 mm in diameter—and there were in most cases 8 to 16—occasionally 4— in a sporangium. Enormous spores—up to 6.5 mm in diameter— have been reported. The microspores were usually smooth; the megaspores were covered with spines which were often forked, or curved and hooked, and in some cases had wings and other extensive projections. Heterospory attained its highest development in a few forms which bore seeds.

Gametophytes. Megaspores are occasionally found bearing well-grown gametophytes. The prothallium filled the spore projecting in some cases to some extent from the spore wall, resembling thus very much those of *Selaginella* and *Isoetes* (Fig. 198). Where archegonia are preserved, there is further resemblance to these living genera.

Embryo. No embryos are known.

ILLUSTRATIVE TYPES

A brief description of some of the more important generic types will give a better picture of the group.

PROTOLEPIDODENDRON (see also *Archaeosigillaria*)

This Middle Devonian plant is of much interest, because it is perhaps the oldest of the lepidodendrid types. It is unfortunately poorly known as yet—only as stems, possibly of an herbaceous plant, with attached leaves and oval or rhombic leaf scars without cushions. The leaves present in their dichotomous tips a character which sets this genus far from others.

Lepidodendron and Sigillaria

These are the two outstanding genera of the group. Though both were trees of somewhat similar size and habit, *Lepidodendron* branched freely, whereas *Sigillaria* branched once or twice, or not at all, and its leaves were longer than those of the former genus; it resembled in general habit certain living, tree-like monocots, such as *Xanthorrhoea, Cordyline,* and *Yucca.* The leaf veins of *Sigillaria* forked once, and the branching occurred at different points, so that the leaf scar shows one or two bundle scars. Its cones were borne on the trunk and main branches and were larger than those of *Lepidodendron.* The character and arrangement of the leaf cushions are, however, of the greatest value in separating the genera. The cushions of *Lepidodendron* were rhombic or oval, tending to be vertically elongated, and were arranged in spirals. Those of *Sigillaria* were rounded or hexagonal, tending to be transversely elongated, and stood in vertical rows; the cushions were less extensive, lower, and farther apart, with the scar covering most of the cushion. In *Sigillaria* the vertical rows of leaf scars often stood well apart on ridges, and the areas between the scars were in some cases strongly wrinkled suggesting that the trunks were fleshy.

Lepidostrobus

This is a form genus for the fertile branch tips and cones of the lepidodendrids. In only very few cases have the cones of this group been found attached to the branches of *Lepidodendron* and other genera, but of their relationship to the group there can be no question because of similarity in anatomy and other features. Only rarely can a species of *Lepidostrobus* be connected definitely with the species of trunk to which it belonged. The characters of this genus are essentially those given above for lepidodendrids as a whole. The sporangia show an important feature in the presence, in some forms at least, of strips of sterile tissue radiating among the spores from an attachment to a pad at the base along the line of attachment to the sporophyll.

Sigillariostrobus and Mazocarpon

A few lepidodendrid cones have been definitely associated with *Sigillaria* and are therefore known as *Sigillariostrobus. Mazo-*

carpon, a name given to *Sigillariostrobus* when structure is preserved, or to the sporophylls and sporangia of this genus, shows structural features of much morphological interest. A lateral and distal flap of tissue projected shovel-like from the sporangium wall (Fig. 199). Within the large sporangium the fertile tissue was greatly restricted: the megasporangium had

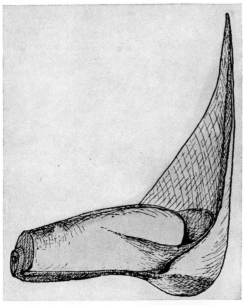

FIG. 199.—*Mazocarpon.* Restoration of sporophyll with sporangium. The sporangium has a lateral and distal, shovel-like, projecting flap of tissue. (*After Benson.*)

only eight spores, and these lay embedded in cushions of sterile tissue; in the microsporangium the sterile tissue was more extensive and restricted the spores to small pockets. A close resemblance is seen in the presence and distribution of this sterile tissue, which is much larger in amount than that in *Lepidostrobus*, to the condition in *Isoetes*, where trabeculae divide the sporogenous tissue.

LEPIDOCARPON

Two types of seeds were borne by the lepidodendrids; one of these is *Lepidocarpon* (Fig. 200). The name is applied to cones in which seeds of a certain type were formed, and to the isolated seed-bearing sporophylls of such cones. Little is known of the plant which bore the cones, but all evidence points to a *Lepi-*

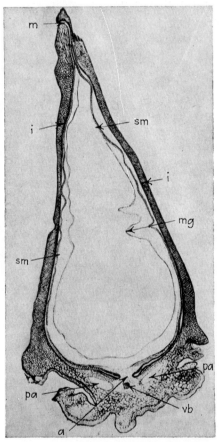

Fig. 200.—*Lepidocarpon.* Cross (vertical) section of detached "seed" (as seen in tangential section of cone). A large megasporangium containing a single megaspore is enclosed by an integument-like upgrowth of the narrow sporophyll base. The integument is closed about the megasporangium except at the top where a narrow slit forms a micropyle. *a,* attachment of megasporangium to sporophyll; *i,* integument; *m,* micropyle; *mg,* megaspore wall; *pa,* cavities perhaps representing parichnos; *sm,* megasporangium wall; *vb,* vascular bundle. (*After Scott.*)

dodendron-like plant. The cones were like those of other lepidodendrids, but each megasporangium contained one large megaspore which filled the cavity, except for space occupied by three abortive spores. About the sporangium the upturned sides of the sporophyll formed an integument-like covering which enclosed it except for a longitudinal slit along the top. This opening served probably as a crude micropyle. The sporophyll was shed from the cone with its enclosed spore within which a prothallium developed. The seed was therefore a sporophyll

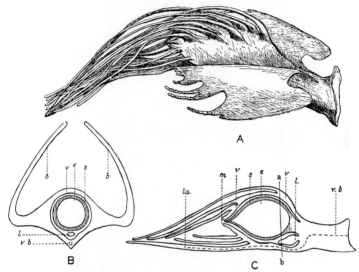

Fig. 201.—Seed of *Miadesmia*. *A*, restoration, lateral view; *B*, cross section on line *ab* in *C*; *C*, median longitudinal section. A complex upgrowth of the sporophyll encloses the sporangium except at the distal end where a micropyle is formed. *b*, wings of the sporophyll; *e*, cavity of sporangium; *l*, ligule; *lc*, tip of sporophyll; *m*, micropyle; *s*, sporangium wall; *v*, "velum," the upgrowth of the sporophyll which encloses the ligule and the sporangium; *vb*, vascular bundle. (*After Benson.*)

enclosing a sporangium which held a single megaspore within whose walls a gametophyte had developed.

MIADESMIA

The second seed-bearing lepidophyte is better known. *Miadesmia* was a delicate herb with the habit of a *Selaginella*. Its seeds, though in general like those of *Lepidocarpon*, were more advanced in type (Fig. 201). No abortive sister spores have been found; an upgrowth of the sporophyll formed an elaborate integument with many lobes and processes; the micropyle was not a slit but a rounded pore, distal in position; the sporangium was

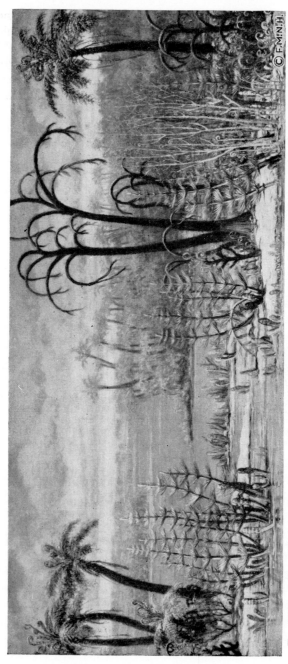

FIG. 202.—A Late Devonian Landscape. The sparsely branched trees with arching limbs are *Archaeosigillaria*; the palm-like trees, a seed fern, *Eospermatopteris*; the trees with whorled branches, calamites. (*By permission of the Field Museum of Natural History, Chicago, Ill.; Charles R. Knight, artist: copyright by the Museum.*)

attached proximally, as on a stalk, rather than along a dorsal ridge (Fig. 201*C*). The many teeth of the integument perhaps served to hold microspores in the neighborhood of the micropyle.

Both these seeds differ from the seeds of all other groups in that the entire sporophyll is concerned in the formation of the reproductive structure, and is shed as a part of it.

Archaeosigillaria (*"Protolepidodendron"*)

One of the oldest members of this group is *Archaeosigillaria primaeva*, a small tree of the Upper Devonian (Fig. 202). Though known in several parts of the world, the best example comes from New York state—"the Naples tree"—a remarkable tree trunk. It occurs also in eastern New York with the earliest seed plants, *Eospermatopteris*. The genus is of particular interest in that the trunk shows the characters of both *Lepidodendron* and *Sigillaria*, the scars at the base being vertically placed and those above spirally. The trees were of peculiar habit, slender, tapering, and sparsely branched, with small leaves. The base of the trunk was enlarged but did not fork; rootlets with stigmarian structure were attached directly to the rounded base.

Pinakodendron

In this genus no cones were formed; the sporophylls were like the leaves and borne in zones along the stem much as are the sporophylls in *Lycopodium lucidulum*. The megasporangium bore only four spores.

Lycopodites and Selaginellites

Among paleozoic fossils there are a few herbaceous plants which in habit resemble the living club mosses. Among these is *Miadesmia*, a seed-bearing type, which has already been discussed. Others resemble rather closely *Lycopodium* and *Selaginella* and have been placed in the genera *Lycopodites* and *Selaginellites*—those which are apparently homosporous in the former, those heterosporous in the latter. The presence or absence of a ligule is in most cases not determinable; hence the assignment is uncertain, for *Lycopodium* in Paleozoic times may have had heterosporous, and *Selaginella* homosporous forms. In *Selaginellites*, in most cases, the megaspore number ranged from 16 to 32. In both genera, forms with sporophylls free and in cones are known, with various types of leaf and sporophyll arrangement. A few fossils (*Lycostrobus*) indicate that plants of this type lived through later geologic periods and serve to connect, loosely, the ancient with the living forms.

PLEUROMEIA

The lepidodendrids as a group flourished especially in the Carboniferous; most of them became extinct at the end of this period, a few of the Sigillarias alone surviving into the Permian. In the Triassic there lived, however, a remarkable *Sigillaria*-like plant, *Pleuromeia* (Fig. 203). This genus is known from Europe and eastern Asia, but unfortunately still largely from structureless fossils. Its stem was an unbranched trunk over 1 m in height and about 10 cm in diameter. The base of the trunk was divided dichotomously into four (sometimes six or eight) short, fleshy, *Stigmaria*-like lobes which were upturned at the end as in *Isoetes* (Figs. 203; 204*A,C*). Over the surface of the lobes were borne rootlets in type and arrangement like those of *Lepidodendron* and *Isoetes*.

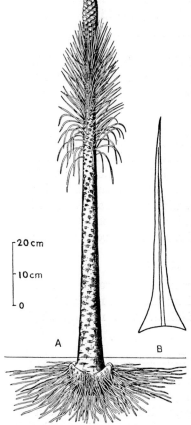

Fig. 203.—*Pleuromeia. A*, restoration; *B*, leaf. (*A, after Hirmer; B, after Mägdefrau.*)

The leaves were linear-lanceolate (about 11 cm long) with a broad, flanged base (1.4 to 3.0 cm wide) and a prominent double midvein (Fig. 203*B*). The leaf scars show that they were closely arranged in spirals. The cone was terminal and apparently long; pieces 10 cm long have been found. The "sporophylls" (Fig. 204*D,E*) were circular, reniform, or oval structures without tips

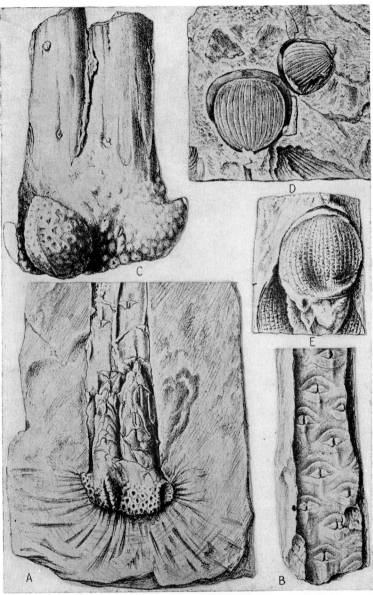

Fig. 204.—*Pleuromeia.* *A*, base of plant showing stem with leaf scars and rhizomorph arms with rootlets and rootlet scars; *B*, impression of piece of stem showing leaf scars; *C*, base of plant showing rhizomorph arms with rootlet scars; *D*, 'sporophyll' seen from above; *E*, 'sporophyll' seen from below. (*After Solms-Laubach.*)

(in one species 1.5 to 2.5 cm long by 2.0 to 2.7 cm wide) and were closely packed on the axis.   They bore, apparently on the abaxial side, sporangia nearly as large as the sporophyll.   The plants were heterosporous, the megaspores tetrahedral, the microspores reniform.   Internal structure is poorly preserved, but there was apparently a small stellate stele and no secondary vascular tissue.   The roots were in structure closely like stigmarian rootlets and the roots of *Isoetes*.

There is evidence in the apparently fleshy trunk and thick leaves that *Pleuromeia* was a fleshy xerophyte or halophyte.   The peculiar, *Isoetes*-like base, and the presence, in some cases, of a marine fauna with the remains suggest that the genus lived on the borders of pools or marshes.

GAMETOPHYTE

Among heterosporous fossil plants the female gametophytes are frequently found.   It is of course remarkable that such delicate structures should have been preserved, and especially that the preservation should sometimes be excellent (Fig. 198).   The identification of the genus to which the prothallia belong depends upon the structure of the spore in which the gametophyte is borne, a matter of much difficulty unless the spores can be connected with the cones that bore them.   Among the lepidodendrids the gametophytes of several genera have, however, been identified.   Those of *Lepidocarpon* are not infrequently found, and those of *Mazocarpon* and *Lepidostrobus Veltheimianus* are known in part.   In the latter the gametophyte apparently did not project beyond the spore wall.   The archegonium was of the usual type with a neck of three rows of cells.   In the seed-bearing genera *Lepidocarpon* and *Mazocarpon* the gametophyte was borne similarly within the spore wall.   Perhaps the most beautiful specimen of a paleozoic gametophyte known is that of a lepidodendrid, probably *Bothrodendron mundum* (Fig. 198).   In this form the gametophyte projects from the spore as a cushion, much as in *Selaginella*.   Low down on this cushion were borne the archegonia.   The oval openings on the right side of the cushion probably are the cavities of archegonia; no necks are seen because the plane of section did not pass through them.   It is apparent that the gametophyte in this case developed after the spore left the sporangium.

Discussion and Summary

The lepidodendrids were a prominent group of paleozoic plants with characters which place them with the lycopsid groups Lycopodiaceae, Selaginellaceae, and Isoetaceae. Though predominantly large trees, there were in the groups small trees and herbaceous forms. The latter types are the older—Middle and Upper Devonian—and were probably not abundant. The group flourished in the Carboniferous, reaching the climax of its development at that time, then rapidly died out, with only *Sigillaria* and related forms persisting into the Permian. The very many species showed great diversity in habit, leaf, leaf cushion, form, structure and attachment of cone, and anatomy.

The leaves were of uniform type, simple, ligulate, deciduous, with a single gapless trace. The forked vein of *Sigillaria* is the only departure from simplicity. The leaf base, with its variety of form and structure, is a prominent character. The leaves of *Protolepidodendron* differ greatly from those of all other forms in their forked tips and thereby raise an important morphological question (Chap. XVII). The cushions were low and oval, and the leaf itself very slender. The resemblance of the leaves of this genus to the spine-like enations of some of the Psilophytales, especially in the form of the base and its lateral flattening, is close.

The cones were like those of living forms in type, but were in most cases of huge size. The sporangia and the number of spores were proportionately large. Though some forms were perhaps homosporous, it is difficult to determine this question; the great majority were surely heterosporous. The ligule is more readily seen in the sporophyll than on the leaf base, and its presence is known in many cone genera. Whether there were forms without ligules (*Lycopodium*-like) among the lepidodendrids is unknown; "there is no definite evidence that eligulate heterosporous forms ever existed."

Heterospory is dominant in the group, and heterosporous forms are as old as homosporous. Within the lepidodendrid line, and among the forms allied to it, there is no evidence that heterospory developed from homospory. Already by late Devonian and early Carboniferous times an elaborate and diverse heterospory had developed, and this had led to the seed habit.

It cannot be too strongly stated that heterospory and the seed habit are ancient features among vascular plants—not those which appeared in late geologic time and were responsible for the later dominance of gymnosperms and angiosperms.

The large sporangia were radially elongated, in contrast with the broad, short types of *Lycopodium* and *Selaginella*, and were attached by a long narrow base rather than by a stalk-like pad. In the megasporangia the number of spores was much greater than that in *Selaginella*. The presence of plates of sterile tissue isolating the spores in pockets suggests the semidivided sporangia of *Isoetes*.

The spores much resemble those of the living heterosporous genera in size and form, though some were apparently gigantic, and the 'ornamentations' were much more prominent and complex. In a few forms at least progress reached the seed habit. The seeds were, however, crude as compared with those of other groups; they have been called "an unsuccessful attempt in seed formation." The success of the seed-bearing forms as compared with that of the others cannot, of course, be determined since all became extinct at about the same time. Resemblance to living forms is continued in the gametophyte, both in the seed-bearing and non-seed-bearing forms.

The gametophytes of the lepidodendrids were similar to those of living heterosporous lycopsid forms—further evidence that the living forms are surviving members of the ancient group, unchanged in many features. There were forms in which the gametophyte developed after the spore was shed, and in which it projected markedly from the spore wall, and others in which it was retained within the spore wall; advance in gametophyte reduction and retention within the spore wall had already in Paleozoic times progressed far.

Mingled with the lepidodendrids were herbaceous plants closely resembling the living *Lycopodium* and *Selaginella*. Structural fossils of these plants are rare, and important characters are uncertain; whether a ligule was present is in most cases not determinable. It is therefore not possible to say that plants very close to these living genera existed in the Paleozoic. But certainly plants with the habit of the living club mosses were present in Carboniferous times. The *Selaginella* habit—leaf and cone—is clear, with a megaspore number, however, much larger than that of present-day forms; and one type, *Miadesmia*, bore seeds. If these forms represent the ancestral stock of the modern club mosses, the group had already in Paleozoic times advanced to the seed habit (a character attained this early in other groups also); and the living forms are representatives of the less specialized members.

Among the various fossil lepidophyte groups, the one standing apparently farthest from the others in morphological features is *Pleuromeia*. This genus has many lepidodendrid characters, especially those of *Sigillaria:* the leaves are ligulate and in form and proportions similar; the general characters of leaf cushion and leaf scar are the same; the rootlets are anatomically of the same type. But the 'sporophylls' are not leaf-like, and the sporangia are believed to have been dorsal rather than ventral. This last character is one not found elsewhere in plants of this general type, and the position of the sporangium (dorsal or ventral) is now recognized as one of the greatest importance in determining relationships among the major vascular plant groups. *Pleuromeia* resembles in many ways *Sigillaria* and *Isoetes*. It seems most unlikely that a plant so clearly a member of a group with adaxial sporangia should have abaxial sporangia. Some other interpretation of the anomalous position of the sporangia will doubtless be made when better preserved material is obtained. In *Isoetes* the sporangia are so deeply sunken that but little sporophyll tissue lies below them, and in a fossil state they might appear dorsal; a similar, more extreme condition may have obtained in *Pleuromeia*, with only delicate, fleshy tissues below the sporangium. The absence of a midvein, which should lie below, makes, however, this interpretation unlikely. On the other hand, no midvein is apparently present above (Fig. 204). In this absence of a midvein and in shape—broad, rounded, apexless—the 'sporophyll' of *Pleuromeia* is so unlike the sporophylls of all allied plants, which are elongate, with pointed tips, that it seems likely that the structure that apparently bears the sporangium is not a sporophyll. The two sides of the sporophyll and sporangia (if correctly interpreted) look much the same (Fig. 204), and from such evidence the sporangia could as well be ventral as dorsal. The sporangium of *Mazocarpon* (Fig. 199) perhaps provides the clue to the nature of this pseudosporophyll: the apparently fertile structure may be the rounded lateral and distal flange of the sporangium wall, and the sporophyll may have been reduced and nearly or quite lost. A sporangium of *Mazocarpon*, if seen from above, would appear like the fertile appendage of *Pleuromeia*. Since the flange is lateral and somewhat above the center of the sporangium, the position of the sporangium would appear to be dorsal. Such a highly hypothetical interpretation is supported by the fact that *Pleuromeia* seems to represent a stock descended from *Sigillaria* types where sporangia were flanged.

The lepidodendrids present a feature unusual among the vascular plants thus far discussed—a permanent 'root system.'

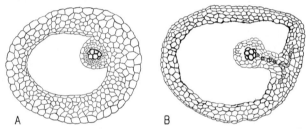

Fig. 205.—*A*, cross section of root of *Isoetes; B*, cross section of stigmarian rootlet. In both the stele is monarch and excentrically placed in a central cavity. ×30. (*B, after Weiss.*)

Among the living groups other than the gymnosperms and angiosperms, only *Isoetes* has such a structure; roots are adventitious in origin and temporary in function. In the lepidodendrids and *Pleuromeia*, parts of the main axis (*Stigmaria*) were given over wholly to rootlet bearing and were capable of indefinite increase by meristems. These did not have typical root structure, and the term rhizomorph is probably best applied to them. Functionally these plants had, however, the equivalent of a main and permanent root system. In this the lepidodendrids and *Pleuromeia* stand with *Isoetes* and apart from the living and fossil club mosses.

The morphology of these rhizomorphs provides valuable evidence of probable relationships among these groups. The peculiar rootlet anatomy (a small monarch stele usually excentrically placed in a large central cavity) (Fig. 205), together with the arrangement of the rootlets, is convincing evidence of the close relationship of the lepidodendrids, *Pleuromeia*, and *Isoetes*, even were other characters more diverse. The rhizomorphs of the lepidodendrids, in their considerable length and remote dichotomy, differ, however, greatly from those of *Pleuromeia* and *Isoetes* where the arms of the axis base are short, fleshy, sparsely branched, and upturned. In *Isoetes* the lobes of the 'corm' base are not equivalent to rhizomorph branches; they are rather the masses of tissue formed on the sides of the shortened and laterally flattened axes. The rhizomorph axes themselves are buried, and their form is seen only in the stele (Fig. 40); they lie along the furrows. If the outer parenchymatous tissues (temporary food-storage layers) are removed, the stele of *Isoetes* and that of *Pleuromeia* are so closely alike as not to be separable. (The soft cortical tissues have doubtless not been preserved in *Pleuromeia*, and of the rhizomorphs merely the steles are seen.) It has been remarked that the upraised basal lobes of *Pleuromeia* show no evidence of meristematic apices. If these grew in 'length' as do those of *Isoetes*, the apical meristem was a line along the underside, and the morphological puzzle of their growth disappears. So close is the resemblance of the base of *Pleuromeia* to that of *Isoetes* that there can be little doubt of the close morphological similarity of the two. These genera then stand together in this character as against the lepido-dendrids. That this extraordinary form of rhizomorph could have arisen by a shortening of the type found in the lepido-dendrids seems unlikely; such a peculiar structure could more readily have been derived directly from the short tuberous base of *Archaeosigillaria*.

The resemblances of *Pleuromeia* to *Isoetes* extend to other features: the leaves are of the same type and shape, with broad bases and wing-like flanges; the microspores are reniform; the sporangia are among the largest in vascular plants. The supposedly dorsal position of the sporangia would keep them apart, but this is probably a misinterpretation.

The genus *Sigillaria* was apparently a more or less fleshy xerophyte. For this reason it perhaps survived under the more difficult conditions of the Permian after other genera had disappeared. *Pleuromeia*, like *Sigillaria* in its unbranched habit, smaller, doubtless more fleshy in axis and leaf, may perhaps be a survivor of sigillarian stock adapted to the still more difficult conditions of the Triassic—even perhaps, as has been suggested by those who have studied it in detail, to the borders of oases and salt marshes—a habitat to which its peculiar structure seems adapted. *Isoetes*, in structure, if closely related to *Pleuromeia*, represents then but a further step in reduction and adaptation to life on the borders of pools, in the water, and even in a few species, to desert habitats. The morphological structure of *Isoetes* speaks for just such a telescoping and reduction. The axis of most individuals is simple but occasionally is dichotomous, a retention possibly of the simple branching of sigillarian stock. That the Triassic genus and the living one represent the surviving remnants of the ancient lepidodendrid stock, there can be little doubt; that they are direct descendants of *Sigillaria* and that the quillworts have been derived from *Pleuromeia* is unlikely, but that this is the general line of relationship is probable. The unique method of apical growth of the later forms unites these genera as against the ancestral group.

The relationship of *Pleuromeia* to the lepidodendrids and to *Isoetes* seems fairly close. For this reason and for convenience in discussion *Pleuromeia* has been included under Lepidodendrales in this treatment. From the standpoint of classification it seems best, however, to treat these three groups as separate orders, at least until closer relationship is demonstrated. The lepidodendrid line therefore consists of the Lepidodendrales, Pleuromeiales, and Isoetales.

Lycopodium and *Selaginella* stand away from these other forms in several strong characters: the sporangia are axillary or cauline, fundamentally, and not foliar; the leaves are without enlarged bases, are not deciduous; the sperms are biciliate (in the other group only those of *Isoetes* are of course known); they had no permanent 'root system'; they were herbaceous in habit (a feature probably of little importance). These genera, however, are unlike in that one is liguleless. If *Lycopodites* and *Selaginellites* represent members of an ancient stock from which the living forms have descended, one type is as old as the other, and no connection can be seen other than that the two are probably closer to one another than either is to the lepidodendrid line.

Bibliography

BENSON, M.: *Miadesmia membranacea*, Bertrand: a new palaeozoic Lycopod with a seed-like structure, *Phil. Trans. Roy. Soc. London*, **199B** · 409–429, 1908.

————: *Mazocarpon* or the structure of *Sigillariostrobus*, *Ann. Bot.*, **32**: 569–589, 1918.

BISCHOF, G. W.: "Beitrag zur Kenntnis der *Pleuromeia* Corda aus den oberen Schichten des bunten Sandsteins zu Bernburg," Mägdesprung, 1852.

BROWN, I. M. P.: The phylogeny and inter-relationships of the Pteridophyta, a critical résumé, *New Phyt.*, **7**: 93, 103, 150, 181, 230, 1908.

COULTER, J. M., and W. J. G. LAND: An American *Lepidostrobus*, *Bot. Gaz.*, **51**: 449–453, 1911.

DAHLGREN, B. E.: "A Forest of the Coal Age," Leaflet 14, Field Museum of Natural History, Chicago, 1933.

DAWSON, J. W.: On the genus *Lepidophloios* as illustrated from the Coal Formation of Nova Scotia and New Brunswick, *Proc. Trans. Roy. Soc. Canada*, ser. 2, **3** (IV): 57–78, 1897.

GORDON, W. T.: Note on the prothallus of *Lepidodendron Veltheimianum*, *Ann. Bot.*, **24**: 821–822, 1910.

HALLE, T. G.: Einige kräutartige Lycopodiaceen paläozoischen und mesozoischen Alters, *Arkiv för Bot.*, **7** (5): 1–17, 1907.

HILL, T. G.: On the presence of a parichnos in recent plants, *Ann. Bot.*, **20**: 267–273, 1906.

HIRMER, M., Paläophytologische Notizen. 1. Rekonstruction von *Pleuromeia Sternbergi* Corda, nebst Bemerkungen zur Morphologie der Lycopodiales. *Palaeontographica*, B. **78**: 47–56, 1933.

KRYSHTOFOVICH, A.: *Pleuromeia* and *Hausmannia* in Eastern Siberia, etc., *Amer. Jour. Sci.*, 5th ser., **5**: 200–208, 1923.

MÄGDEFRAU, K.: Zur Morphologie und phylogenetischen Bedeutung der fossilen Pflanzengattung *Pleuromeia*, *Beih. Bot. Centralbl.*, II, **48**: 119–140, 1931.

McLEAN, R. C.: Two fossil prothalli from the Lower Coal Measures, *New Phyt.*, **11**: 305–318, 1912.

SCOTT, D. H.: The seed-like fructification of Lepidocarpon, etc., *Phil. Trans. Roy. Soc. London*, **194B**: 291–333, 1901.

————: The present position of palaeozoic botany, *Prog. Rei Bot.*, **1**: 139–217, 1907.

SOLMS-LAUBACH, H.: Ueber das Genus *Pleuromeia*, *Bot. Ztg.*, **57**: 227–243, 1899.

WALTON, J.: The absence of eligulate heterosporous Lycopodiales in the fossil record, *Proc. Roy. Soc. Edinburgh*, **51**: 114–115, 1931.

WEISS, F. E.: The vascular branches of Stigmarian rootlets, *Ann. Bot.*, **16**: 559–573, 1902.

WHITE, D.: A remarkable fossil tree trunk from the Middle Devonic of New York, *Bull. N. Y. State Museum*, **107**, 1907.

WILLIAMSON, W. C.: On the organization of the fossil plants of the Coal Measures, Pts. 2, 3, 9, 10, 11, *Phil. Trans. Roy. Soc. London*, **162, 169, 171, 172**, 1872–1881.

————: A monograph on the morphology and physiology of *Stigmaria ficoides*, *Palaeontogr. Soc. London*, 1887.

CHAPTER XVI

CALAMITALES

Living with the lepidodendrids in the Paleozoic and, like the ancient club mosses, forming a prominent element in the floras of those times were the gigantic horsetails, or calamites. If in this plant group, as in the case of the club mosses, living forms be imagined as increased in size to large trees, an excellent picture of these plants is obtained. Like the lepidodendrids the calamites were a large and diverse group, with many genera and species, and similarly they lived in swampy habitats—perhaps as a whole in wetter places and often in the water. Because of the jointed structure and less solid nature of the stems the fossil remains of these plants are more fragmentary than are those of other groups, and large parts of the plants are rarely found; yet the group has long been known in most of its morphological features.

Habit. There were probably both herbaceous and arborescent forms in the group, though the existence of small types is difficult to determine because the young stems of arborescent forms cannot be distinguished from the mature stems of small plants. Most of the calamites were, however, undoubtedly trees (Fig. 191). Their size is not so readily determined as is that of the lepidodendrids. Casts of the pith cavity give, however, much information, and the trunks were, at least in some cases, 20 to 30 m high with a diameter of 1 m. All the habital types found in *Equisetum* were present: the *E. arvense-E. sylvaticum* type, with whorls of branches at every node; the *E. hyemale* type, with unbranched or rarely branched trunks, rising two or three together; the *E. fluviatile* type with whorls of branches at a few nodes only. All were rhizomatous, and the rhizomes were very large, themselves tree-trunk-like. The roots were like those of *Equisetum* except in size; they arose adventitiously between the leaves on the stem bases and rhizomes.

Leaves. The leaves were in most cases small and simple, free or more or less fused at the base. On the larger stems there

358

were many in a whorl, more than 100 in extreme cases. In shape they were linear or linear-lanceolate; some were stiff and spreading (Fig. 206), others erect and more or less appressed, as in *Equisetum;* still others were apparently soft and curved upward. Most of them at least were photosynthetic organs. In the older forms the leaves, and consequently the ridges of the stem, did not alternate at successive nodes; in later forms a uniform alternation prevailed.

Anatomy. In anatomical structure, as in general form, the calamites were merely huge horsetails. The possession of secondary vascular tissue is the only important feature of difference. The young stems, before the development of cambial activity, are hardly to be distinguished in anatomy from those of *Equisetum.* Even in the trunks the large pith cavity and wide cortex were prominent features. Casts of the pith cavity up to 33 cm in diameter have been found. Surrounding the pith was a ring of primary collateral bundles, with protoxylem lacunae. Secondary xylem formed a complete cylinder, uniting the primary strands. The cortex in large stems was as wide as the xylem and formed a bark thicker proportionately than that of present-day trees; it con-

FIG. 206.—*Annularia radiata,* the tip of a calamite branch with leaves. (*After Dahlgren, by permission of the Field Museum of Natural History, Chicago, Ill.*)

tained large amounts of periderm and served doubtless in considerable measure for support of the tree. Externally the bark was smooth (Fig. 191), showing in some cases on old trunks longitudinal cracks.

The leaf and branch traces arose as in *Equisetum*, and the leaves had a single vein. The secondary wood was complex, containing tracheids, fibers, parenchyma, and large rays.

Reproduction. The sporangia were borne on sporangiophores in most cases like those of *Equisetum*, and the sporangiophores were grouped in cones. Though in some genera the cones resembled those of the horsetails, in the majority of forms they were more complex, leaf-like bracts being mingled in the cone

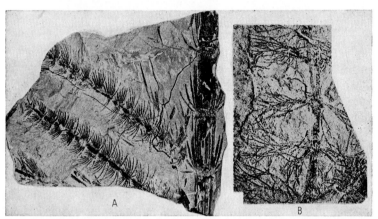

Fig. 207.—Twigs and leaves of the calamites. *A, Calamocladus equisetiformis; B, Asterocalamites scrobiculatus.* (*A, after Noë; B, after Walton.*)

with the sporangiophores. There were four sporangia on each sporangiophore. At least part of the genera were heterosporous, and the distribution in the cone of the two types was indefinite; both were present even on the same sporangiophore. The difference in size between microspores and megaspores was not so great as that in the lycopsid forms, the diameter of the megaspore being only about three times that of the microspore. "Elaters" were not present.

ILLUSTRATIVE TYPES

A description of a few of the important genera—in part form genera—is necessary.

Asterocalamites (Archaeocalamites)

This genus, one of the oldest members of the group—from the Upper Devonian and lower Carboniferous—differs greatly from later forms in that its leaves were large—10 to 12 cm perhaps to 40 cm long—and forked dichotomously several times (Fig. 207*B*). The plant was probably tree-like, with the leaves and ridges not alternating at successive nodes. The cones were probably without bracts.

PROTOCALAMITES

Interest in this lower Carboniferous genus lies chiefly in the fact that, unlike the other genera, it possessed centripetal wood.

CALAMITES

This genus has long been a broadly inclusive form genus for structural material, especially stems. It is used as a basic name for typical members of the group.

ANNULARIA AND ASTEROPHYLLITES

These are form genera for leafy twigs in the true calamites. In the former the leaves were short, probably rigid, and often fused at the base; in the latter they were more slender and softer, curved upward, and free at the base. In *Annularia* the leaf whorl in the older forms stood at right angles to the twig; in the later forms it was oriented with relation to light, coming in horizontal twigs to lie in the plane of the twig (Fig. 206).

CALAMOSTACHYS

The cones of the calamites fall into four groups based on the relationship of bracts and sporangiophores. In *Calamostachys*, whorls of these two kinds of organs alternated. In some species the number of organs in each whorl was the same; in others there were twice as many bracts as fertile organs. The bracts were fused into a saucer-like structure and bent upward, *Asterophyllites*-like so that their tips enclosed the sporangia as do the sporophyll tips in *Lycopodium* and the lepidodendrids. In this type of cone some were heterosporous.

PALAEOSTACHYA

In cones of this genus the peltate sporangiophores, which bore four sporangia, stood in the axils of bracts. That this position was one of modification from that in *Calamostachys* is evident from the vascular anatomy (Fig. 208); the bundle supplying the sporangiophore bends downward from an internodal position to the bract axil. The cone structure of this genus is obviously derived.

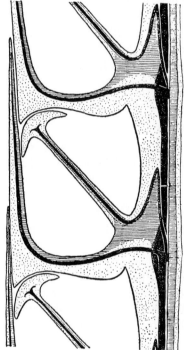

FIG. 208.—*Palaeostachya.* Portion of radial section of cone showing course of vascular tissue. The strand to the peltate sporangiophore (sporangia not shown) bends downward from an internodal position. (*After Hickling.*)

CINGULARIA

The sporangiophores of this genus were not peltate but strap-like, once forked, and bore their four sporangia on the lower surface near the ends. The cones were further unusual in that the sporangiophores stood close below the bracts. It is possible that here the sporangiophores have migrated upward to the bracts above (as in *Palaeostachya* they have moved downward) but structural proof of such a change is lacking.

The fourth type is that found in *Asterocalamites* and in *Equisetum* where there are no bracts in the cone.

EQUISETITES

Remains of plants closely resembling *Equisetum* are frequent as Mesozoic and Tertiary fossils. These are in some respects transitional between the ancient and the living genera. A Triassic form had stems 20 cm in diameter with 120 leaves in a whorl; other later forms were smaller. Whether these intermediate forms had secondary growth is unknown.

DISCUSSION AND SUMMARY

The calamites were a group of giant horsetail-like plants which lived in the Paleozoic. Apart from their large size they differed from *Equisetum* structurally chiefly in the possession of secondary growth. Among the many forms there were probably herbaceous types, but the fragmentary condition of the fossils makes this uncertain. There is no evidence, however, that any of them lacked secondary growth.

In habit the various types of branching seen in *Equisetum* existed. The leaves, though small and simple, were much larger than those of the living horsetails and served as photosynthetic organs. The cones were diverse in structure with different arrangements and relations of bracts and sporangiophores. There were typically four sporangia on each sporangiophore, which, except in one small group, were of the peltate type found in *Equisetum*. Heterospory was present in some genera.

Anatomically these plants were complex, resembling closely in most features—the hollow pith, the nodal diaphragms, the carinal canals, the thick cortex with supporting tissue, the leaf traces—the living horsetails. In only one genus was centripetal xylem present. Secondary growth in both cortex and vascular tissue added to the complexity of structure; and the secondary xylem was itself complex in structure, with cells of several types and apparently with the various functions found in the specialized wood of conifers and angiosperms. In anatomical specialization the group had progressed far by upper Carboniferous times.

The oldest types show an absence of alternation of leaves and stem ridges in succeeding nodes, and it seems probable that the alternating condition was derived from the non-alternating.

In the cones the variety of relationship between bracts and sporangiophores presents a puzzling situation; a discussion of this is perhaps best postponed to the discussion of the structure of the plant body in general. The fact is clear, however, that the sporangiophore, whatever its nature, changed its position on the cone axis relative to the neighboring bracts in one and probably in two directions. (Similar migrations are seen in angiosperms in the case of inflorescences and flowers.) The constancy in the form of the sporangiophore and in the number of sporangia is remarkable. Only in *Cingularia* and related forms is the peltate tip not found.

Heterospory, though present, had apparently not advanced far, since the two types of spores were not extremely different in size or form.

The closeness of the calamites to *Equisetum* in relationship is clear. *Equisetum* is itself an ancient genus; its remains, known as *Equisetites*, can be followed back through the Mesozoic and perhaps as far as the Carboniferous. The calamites themselves probably died out in the Permian.

The history of *Equisetum* seems to be one of reduction in size and specialization in certain structural features. In habit the segregation of function among the branches (page 91) has been developed, probably as a recent feature, since it is in process of taking place at the present time in some species. The spores are provided with an elaborate outer layer which was absent in the older forms. The leaves have largely lost their photosynthetic function and have become appressed and strongly fused. Secondary growth has apparently been lost; there are probably vestiges in the cone axes and in the nodes, which are conservative regions. *Equisetum* may, of course, have been derived from an ancient type which was without secondary growth. The type of cone is that found in the older groups of calamites, and in *Hyenia*, a plant representing a group possibly ancestral for the line.

The calamites with articulate stems, and with sporangia borne on sporangiophores, are members of the Sphenopsida. That *Equisetum* was derived from the great mass of paleozoic members of this stock is certain; that it is a reduced calamite not so. It bears the cone type of the oldest calamites, not that of the most advanced ones; it is homosporous, not heterosporous as were many of the later genera. It does not possess the important character of non-alternating ribs and leaves, and must therefore be assumed either to have advanced in this respect independently or to have been derived from the more specialized alternating forms. It is especially worthy of note that in this group, as in others, the surviving member is one of small size and is not a representative of the more advanced types of the line.

Family lines are difficult to draw among these plants, for the calamites, though diverse in characters of family rank, are largely known only as form genera. It is evident that the Equisetaceae should form a separate family, and that forms with divided leaves and non-alternating ribs should be placed in the Asterocalamitaceae. Others may be grouped together for the purposes of this discussion in a loose family, the Calamitaceae; to arrange the remaining forms in more natural families involves the description of several form families and detailed classification beyond the purpose of this treatment. The various families are commonly placed in a single order, the Equisetales. A separate order Calamitales is sometimes maintained for the calamites, but this is not justified on morphological grounds. The classifica-tion of these plants therefore stands

Equisetales $\begin{cases} \text{Calamitaceae} \\ \text{Equisetaceae} \\ \text{Asterocalamitaceae} \end{cases}$

HYENIALES

Among members of the Devonian flora which have come to be known in the last few years are *Hyenia* and *Calamophyton*. These genera, like other Devonian forms, are of the greatest interest morphologically and phylogenetically. Their characters place them close to the calamites and *Equisetum* and yet suggest the Psilophytales. Both genera were small, shrub-like plants (Fig. 209), with short, dichotomous appendages arranged in whorls of few members. The sterile appendages, which forked two or more times, were leaf-like. The fertile appendages, which forked but once, with the tips spreading or recurved, bore terminal clusters of two or three anatropous sporangia. On some branches the fertile tips were grouped distally, forming a sort of loose cone. The stem of *Calamophyton* was jointed, that of *Hyenia* was not. Little is known of the internal structure.

DISCUSSION AND SUMMARY

The Hyeniales, because they are among the earliest known land plants, and because they are simple, are most important phylogenetically. In their characters they form a transition group between the Psilophytales and the calamites. The sporangia are borne terminally on branches of the axis which are recurved, with the sporangia anatropous and suspended— a condition suggesting that seen in *Psilophyton* and related genera.

The character of the appendages provides a basis for the interpretation of the morphological nature of the sporangiophore —one of the most difficult problems connected with the morphology of vascular plants.   The similarity in form and position of the fertile appendages of *Hyenia* and *Calamophyton* and of

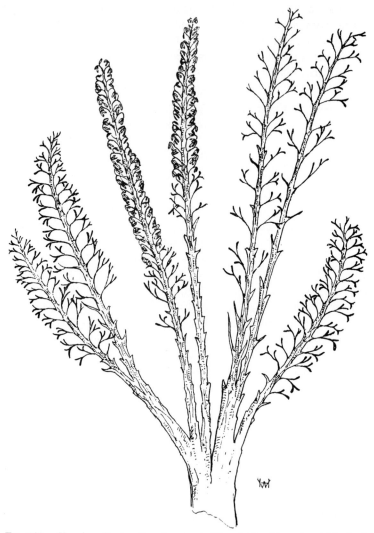

FIG. 209.—*Hyenia.*   Restoration showing habit.   (*After Kräusel and Weyland.*)

the sporangiophores of the calamites and *Equisetum* suggests that the organs are homologous.   An expansion of the tissues in the region of the forking in the two ancient genera would produce the peltate sporangiophore of later forms. And in these later forms the sporangia are known from their ontogeny to be terminal in position. Anatomical evidence is added in the fact that within the peltate tip a vascular bundle leads to the base of each sporangium, suggesting that each sporangium is terminal upon a branchlet. The presence of four sporangia throughout the calamites suggests two dichotomies of the fertile appendage.

From the evidence provided by *Hyenia* and *Calamophyton* it is apparent that the 'leaves' and the fertile tips in this group are homologous. This suggests that the same condition prevails in the Equisetales; the sporangiophore and the leaf are both lateral lobes of the axis, the leaf more simple, since it represents an undivided lobe.

The two genera are much alike, and the whorled appendages and the jointed stem of *Calamophyton* relate them to the calamites. The leaf of the group closely resembles that of *Asterocalamites*, the oldest of the calamites, and a further similarity may be seen in the cones, which in all three genera were without bracts. In *Asterocalamites*, however, the fertile appendage was peltate and bore four sporangia. A possible series may be seen leading from the Psilophytales through *Hyenia, Calamophyton*, and *Asterocalamites* to the calamites and horsetails.

Hyenia and *Calamophyton* are as yet unsufficiently known; they may form independent families or fall together in a single family. They should be placed, however, in the order Hyeniales, which because of its jointed stems and sporangiophores is a member of the Sphenopsida.

SPHENOPHYLLALES

The sphenophylls were a comparatively small group of ancient plants of which there are no surviving representatives. Like the ancient horsetails they flourished in the Carboniferous period, dying out after that time except for a few forms which lived on into the Triassic.

Habit. In contrast with the last two groups these plants were small and probably herbaceous. Their habit is somewhat uncertain, but their form and structure suggest that they were possibly climbing plants. They were formerly believed to be aquatic forms, but their anatomical structure indicates that they did not live in the water. The stems were slender and jointed, with whorls of wedge-shaped leaves (whence the name of the group) (Fig. 191). The leaves were superposed, and on the internodes were ribs which likewise did not alternate. In general appearance the sphenophylls have often been likened to the living angiosperm genus *Galium*, the bedstraws. Plants of the extinct group were of course much larger, with strong stems

FIG. 210.—*Sphenophyllum emarginatum.* Leafy twig showing leaf type and arrangement. (*After Noë.*)

which reached in some cases a diameter of 1 cm. Only one genus, *Sphenophyllum*, is distinguished in the group.

Leaves. The whorls of leaves consisted in most cases of six or nine members; where there were more, the number was a multiple of three (Fig. 210). The leaves were always cuneate and entire, or toothed, or cut or slit dichotomously in varying degrees. Two forms of leaf, one entire and one dissected, characterize some species. It was because of this condition that the sphenophylls were formerly believed to be aquatic plants, the dissected leaves being considered the submersed form; but the two types occurred on the stems with no regularity of position, the dissected ones intermingled with, or above, the entire ones. The leaf blade was complex, showing several veins which branched dichotomously.

Anatomy. The stems of these plants often show well-preserved structure. Though externally there is a resemblance to calamite stems, the internal structure is wholly different. The stele is without a pith, the primary xylem forming a solid, exarch, central rod, three-angled (rarely six-angled) in cross section. Secondary xylem formed a thick sheath about this primary core. In the cortex, periderm was formed in considerable quantity.

Reproduction. The sporangia in most species were borne on sporophylls in long, slender, terminal cones; in a few forms there were probably no cones, fertile leaves being scattered among the sterile. The cones consisted of many whorls of sporophylls, the members of each whorl fused at their bases into a saucer-like structure. Each sporophyll was divided into an adaxial and an abaxial lobe; the former was usually fertile, the latter sterile, but in occasional species both were fertile. The sporangia were borne terminally, either solitary or in pairs, on more or less peltate tips, or suspended anatropously. The fertile lobe branched in most cases so that each sporophyll bore three to six or more sporangia (twice as many when the dorsal lobe also was fertile). The various species were characterized by the number and arrangement of the sporangia on the fertile lobe. Because of the division of the sporophyll into adaxial and abaxial lobes, and the reduction of the ventral lobe to a stalk, the sporangia appear to be borne on a sporangiophore in the axil of the sporophyll. In a few species the stalk is reduced, and the sporangia are then sessile on the upper surface of the lower lobe. The sporangium wall is several layers thick. Most of the species were homosporous; a few are now known to have been heterosporous.

The cones of the sphenophylls were indeed diverse and complex in structure. *Cheirostrobus*, the cone of a more or less closely related plant, was, however, even more complex. As in *Sphenophyllum* the sporophyll in this plant was divided into dorsal and ventral lobes, and the former was sterile. Both lobes were divided into three parts. The ends of the ventral lobe were peltate with four sporangia, borne as in *Equisetum*. The divisions of the sterile lobe were longer, extending beyond the

sporangia, and there forking into upper and lower parts. Each
of these parts forked again, and the upward- and downward-
extending tips formed a protective layer about the cone. Each
sporophyll had, therefore, 15 tips. The cone was large (3 to
4 cm in diameter by 10 cm or more in length), and the sporangia
were homosporous. Nothing is known of the type of plant
which bore the cones. The anatomy of the cone axis and the
type of sporophyll indicate that *Cheirostrobus* belongs with the
sphenophylls or in some closely related group. The plant is
known only from lower Carboniferous strata.

<h2 style="text-align:center">DISCUSSION AND SUMMARY</h2>

The sphenophylls were one of the characteristic groups of the
paleozoic floras. They have, unfortunately, left no living
representative and are therefore less well known in detail than
other groups. Although their general habit is uncertain, most of
the important details of structure are well known. They
resemble the Equisetales in their jointed, ridged stem, whorled
leaves, and the manner in which the sporangia are borne. They
differ, however, from the horsetail group in their broader, more
complex leaves (with several branching veins); the uniform
number and three-merous plan of the leaves; the simple, protostelic central cylinder; the more complex sporophylls. The
lack of alternation of the stem ribs and leaves and the
dichotomy of the leaves are suggestive of the Hyeniales and
the oldest calamites.

The nature of the appendages—leaf and sporophyll—presents a
fundamental morphological problem, for in the latter there is
division into dorsal and ventral lobes, a condition not found in
other groups (with the probable exception of the calamites).
The leaf, in its dichotomous venation, suggests the dichotomously
lobed leaf of the Hyeniales; the sporophyll of the Hyeniales is
divided into two lobes which may well have been (so far as
ascertainable from published illustrations) dorsal and ventral.
In some species of *Sphenophyllum* both lobes of the sporophyll
are fertile, so that the resemblance to the sporophyll of *Hyenia*
is close. That *Hyenia*-like plants were ancestral for the sphenophylls seem probable; and since leaf and sporophyll in *Hyenia*
are homologous, it is probable that the leaves and sporophylls
of the sphenophylls are also homologous, and that the latter

are divided, with both lobes fertile, or with the lower, sterile, forming a protective bract.

The morphology of the sporangiophore, and therefore of the cone, of the horsetail and sphenophyll lines is most uncertain in some aspects. With little doubt the sporangiophore represents a minor lateral branch of the axis with terminal sporangia. It is probable that in some cases it is equivalent to a leaf; in other cases the lateral branch is divided, both parts becoming sporangiophores, or the lower a bract, the upper a sporangiophore.

For plants of so early a period the sphenophylls had advanced far in specialization, as indicated by the variety and complexity of cone structure. That a cone (*Cheirostrobus*) from so early a period as the lower Carboniferous should be by far the most complex cone in any group is an amazing fact. Such a condition is further evidence that vascular plants by mid-Paleozoic time had attained a high degree of specialization, and that some groups at least had already been in existence for a very long time.

In classification the sphenophylls belong close to the horsetails and calamites; they are therefore members of the same major group, the Sphenopsida. Among the sphenophylls themselves only one family, the Sphenophyllaceae, is usually distinguished. The position of *Cheirostrobus*—a form genus based on cone alone—is uncertain. It has been placed in the Sphenophyllaceae; in a separate family, the Cheirostrobaceae; and in an order Cheirostrobales, independent of the sphenophylls and parallel with them and with the Equisetales. Until more is known of 'he plant, it seems best to retain it at least for this discussion among the sphenophylls. The classification of this group then stands

$$\text{Sphenopsida} \begin{cases} \text{Equisetales} \\ \text{Sphenophyllales} \\ \text{Hyeniales} \end{cases}$$

COENOPTERIDALES ("PRIMOFILICES")

The remains of fern-like plants have always been among the best known of fossils. So abundant are these fossils in the Carboniferous beds that this period was known not many years ago as the "Age of Ferns." It is now well known that many of these fossils are not the remains of ferns but of seed-bearing plants, and that ferns were not at this time so abundant as formerly supposed. There was in the Paleozoic, however, a considerable group of true ferns. These ferns were distinct from living ferns in habit and general appearance, yet possessed characteristic fern sporangia, spores, and vascular anatomy. The fossil remains of these plants are fragmentary, and few of them are known except in part; the vascular structure, especially that of the leaves, and the sporangia are best known. A considerable number of genera have been described; most of these are, of course, form genera. These genera fall into a few small families, which, like the genera, are, of course, in part at least provisional. The group lived from the Upper Devonian to the Permian and flourished chiefly in the lower Carboniferous.

Habit. Most of these ferns were small plants, some erect, others probably creeping or climbing. A most important feature was a lack of definite differentiation between stem and leaf. The distal parts of the much branched axis doubtless served as leaves, but they were bladeless or nearly so. The stems forked in most cases dichotomously; one branch of the dichotomy became a determinate part of the system, a leaf; the other continued growth as the stem. It happened thus that the leaf base was in many cases as large as the stem. (A similar condition, at least as regards the vascular tissue, is sometimes seen in living ferns.) The leaves were large complex axis systems, sometimes with circinate vernation. Their branching was in some genera in many planes and the leaf therefore a bush-like structure; in other genera lateral divisions were in whorls of four, and leaves with a complex quadriseriate structure were formed. In a few cases the main divisions were in two rows. The divisions were terete, only the ultimate ones sometimes dorsiventral.

Anatomy. The vascular structure was simple—always a protostele with large simple leaf traces; in one group the stele became complex in form, but no pith was present. The complex forms included stellate, anchor-shaped, and many variations of an H-shaped type. A slight development of secondary wood was occasionally present.

Reproduction. All forms were apparently homosporous. The sporangia were large (1 to 2.5 mm long by 1 to 1.5 mm in diam-

eter) spherical, club-shaped, or pear-shaped (Fig. 211); in
arrangement they varied from solitary and terminal, through

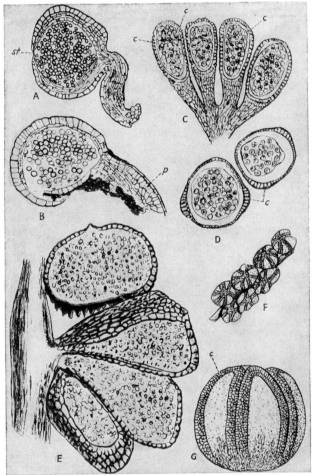

FIG. 211.—Sporangia and synangia of the Coenopteridales. *A, B, Stauropteris
oldhamia; C, D, Etapteris Lacattei; E, Botryopteris forensis; F, G, Corynepteris
corallioides.* *A, B,* sporangia terminal on divisions of the rachis; *C,* four sporangia, cut tangentially, on a common stalk; *D,* two sporangia cut transversely
showing annulus; *E,* group of sporangia with common insertion on axis; *F,* tip of
axis with synangia; *G,* synangium enlarged showing the annuli of the component
sporangia. *c,* annulus; *p,* palisade tissue; *st,* stomium. (*A, B, after Scott;
C, D, after Scott, from Renault; E, after Renault; F, G, after Hirmer from Zeiller.*)

clustered terminal (with the stalks more or less fused) and close
clusters borne on a single stalk, to a sessile, synangial group.

The close clusters were radiate, and the sessile groups and synangia closely resembled the sporangium clusters of the Marattiaceae. The synangium shows various stages of elaboration—from approximation only to complete fusion. Since the clusters were terminal, when the leaf tip on which they were borne was lost by reduction the cluster became lateral.

The sporangium wall was thick. Dehiscence was by an apical pore (Fig. 211*A*) or through a longitudinal slit produced by an annulus consisting of a band two to several cells wide, extending longitudinally on one or two sides of the sporangium. The number of spores was large, several hundred to 1000 or more.

Gametophyte. Germinating spores have been found in one genus within the sporangium (Fig. 212), as sometimes occurs abnormally in living ferns. The early stages of the gametophyte were like those of modern homosporous ferns. From this fact it is clear that these ferns were homosporous.

Fig. 212.—Germinating spores of *Stauropteris oldhamia.* (*After Scott.*)

Two groups stand out among these ancient ferns: one has simple, the other, complex anatomy. In the first group *Botryopteris* and *Grammatopteris* are the best known genera; among those in the second are *Stauropteris*, *Etapteris*, and *Zygopteris*.

Discussion and Summary

The ferns of the Paleozoic were true ferns in technical characters of leaf size and relation to stem, anatomy, sporangium, and spores. In appearance, however, they were hardly fern-like, since the fern-frond type of leaf had not yet appeared. The leaves were determinate, much-branched axis systems, bladeless except in a few forms where the flattened tips formed a narrow blade. The branching of the leaf segments was in two or more planes in most forms; only in a few where the branches are in two series—one plane—is the modern fern-frond type approached.

The fact that these ferns are the oldest known, that their characters are those recognized as primitive among ferns and other vascular plants, indicates that in these plants is to be seen the origin of the fern leaf. This leaf is therefore a simplified determinate major branch system with the branching restricted to one plane and the branchlets flattened and expanded, or connected by webs of tissue developed between. Morphologically the fern leaf thus differs greatly from that of the Lycopsida —where the leaf seems to be an enation—and from that of the Sphenopsida—where it appears to represent a minor lateral branch system. The large complex leaf of the Pteropsida is therefore an important morphological character of this major group.

The sporangia show the characters that, from the study of living forms, have been determined to be primitive: terminal position, large size, thick wall, terminal and longitudinal dehiscence, annulus band-like and indefinite or lacking, many spores, and a vascular supply. That the synangia represent fused clusters of sporangia is clear. The origin of the 'lateral' position of these synangia is seen to be by the shortening of the stalk which bears the cluster. The expansion and fusion of the leaf lobes around the synangium would leave the sporangium group in the superficial position. The position of the sporangia on the dorsal side and on a vein is thus attained directly; no 'slide' from the margin of a lamina to its surface, such as is seen in the higher leptosporangiate families, is involved. In the *Osmunda-Todea* series (page 178) the superficial position is acquired in this way.

The series of forms in this group of primitive ferns indicates that the sorus, in some forms at least (Marattiaceae and Gleicheniaceae), is a mere cluster of sporangia. It strengthens the evidence that the synangium of these families consists really of fused sporangia and is not a divided sporangium. That sporangium specialization had reached the synangial stage as early as Paleozoic times is further evidence of the advanced condition of the vascular plants of the time. Though these ferns were primitive types, they had advanced far in sorus elaboration.

The determination of relationships within the group is of course impossible since the forms are insufficiently known. The two groups mentioned above are often considered to form two provisional families, the Botryopteridaceae and the Zygopteridaceae. These two families, with others here omitted, form the order Coenopteridales, often known as the Primofilices. (The Archaeopteridaceae, commonly placed here, are, in the light of recent information and opinion, probably not ferns but pteridosperms.)

The relation of the Coenopteridales to other ferns is obscure. These ancient ferns are undoubtedly members of the ancestral stock of all ferns. That they left survivors beyond the Permian is doubtful, unless the Ophioglossales represent such a group. The Ophioglossales have no fossil record. The two groups show strong resemblances in sporangium form, structure, position, and vascular supply. Both groups have short simple hairs. The leaf of *Botrychium* suggests in its form and the manner of bearing the sporangia a lateral branch system of a coenopterid fern. The origin of the Ophioglossales, a group so unlike other ferns, is obscure, but it seems probable that they are descendants of some members of the Coenopteridales.

Resemblances of the synangia of the coenopterids to the synangia of the Marattiaceae, and the fact that marattiaceous ferns, similar to the living genera in essential features, were fairly common in late Carboniferous and Permian times, suggest that this second eusporangiate group is also related to the ancient primitive stock, though doubtless much less directly than the Ophioglossaceae. In their complex anatomy they form a line distinct from the simple coenopterids, though the two groups doubtless had a common origin in early fern-like plants. Marattiaceous ferns have a continuous fossil record back to the late Paleozoic; the Marattiaceae are therefore one of the oldest living families. The older members of this line differed in habit from the living ones in that some of them (*Psaronius*, *Megaphyton*, *Caulopteris*) were large tree ferns.

It is of course not possible to determine the method of sporangium development in the Coenopteridales, but the massive, thick-stalked, heavy-walled sporangia indicate eusporangiate development. With the eusporangiate living groups, Ophioglossales and Marattiales, they form an ancient and primitive section of the fern line. Modern leptosporangiate ferns show little evidence of relation to the paleozoic ferns. There is little evidence of definitely leptosporangiate ferns in the Paleozoic, and it is doubtful if the type had appeared at that time.

Among the leptosporangiate families, the Gleicheniaceae and the Schizaeaceae, both somewhat imperfectly leptosporangiate, go back to the late Paleozoic, as do also the Osmundaceae, which are intermediate in method of sporangium development. The sporangia of the royal ferns show many resemblances in position, form, and structure to those of the coenopterids. In anatomy this family is so distinct, however, that no close connection with the ancient group can be seen. These three families constitute the simplices group of leptosporangiate ferns—the group which from evidence secured by comparative study of living forms is primitive. The fact that according to the fossil record these are the oldest leptosporangiate families and the dominant families of the Mesozoic is evidence of the value and reliability of the conclusions drawn from evidence obtained from living forms.

The time of appearance in the fossil record of the filmy ferns is uncertain. Other gradate types are known as early as the Jurassic. The mixtae are chiefly Tertiary, though a few of the Polypodiaceae perhaps go back well into the Mesozoic. The heterosporous families are known only from the Tertiary. The fossil record provides striking confirmation of recent theories of stage of advancement and relationship among living ferns.

Bibliography

CALAMITALES

BROWN, I. M. P.: The phylogeny and inter-relationships of the Pteridophyta, II. Equisetales, *New Phyt.*, **7**: 103–113, 1908.
——: A new theory of the morphology of the calamarian cone, *Ann. Bot.*, **41**: 301–320, 1927.
HALLE, T. G.: On leaf-mosaic and anisophylly in palaeozoic Equisetales, *Svensk. Bot. Tidskr.*, **22**: 230–255, 1928.
HICKLING, F.: The anatomy of *Palaeostachya vera*, *Ann. Bot.*, **21**: 369–386, 1907.
HIRMER, M.: Zur Kenntnis der Organstellung und der Zahlenverhältnisse in der Gattung *Calamostachys* Schimper, *Flora*, **118–119**: 227–256, 1925.
JEFFREY, E. C.: Infranodal organs in Calamites and Dicotyledons, *Ann. Bot.*, **15**: 135–146, 1901.
MASLEN, A. J.: The relation of root to stem in calamites, *Ann. Bot.*, **19**: 61–73, 1905.

378   *MORPHOLOGY OF VASCULAR PLANTS*

Noë, A. C.: Pennsylvanian flora of northern Illinois. *Ill. State Geol. Survey,* *Bull.* 52.
Renault, B.: Notice sur les Calamariées, *Bull. Soc. Hist. Nat. d'Autun,* I, **8**: 1–54; II, **9**: 305–354; 1895, 1896.
Stur, D.: Zur Morphologie der Calamarien. *Sitzber. Akad. Wiss., Wien, Math.-naturw. Kl.,* **83**: 499–472, 1881.
Thomas, H. H.: On the leaves of *Calamites* (*Calamocladus* section), *Phil. Trans. Roy. Soc. London,* **202B**: 51–92, 1911.
Walton, J.: Contributions to the knowledge of Lower Carboniferous plants, VI, *Phil. Trans. Roy. Soc. London,* **219B**: 347–379, 1931.
Weiss, F. E.: Plant structure and environment with special reference to fossil plants, *Jour. Ecol.,* **13**: 301–313, 1925.
White, D.: Fossil flora of the Lower Coal Measures of Missouri, *U. S. Geol. Survey,* Monogr. 37, 1899.
Williamson, W. C.: Organization of the fossil plants of the Coal Measures, IX, *Phil. Trans. Roy. Soc. London,* **169**: 319–364, 1878; XIV, **179**: 47–57, 1888.
Williamson, W. C., and D. H. Scott: Further observations on the organization of the Coal Measures: I. *Calamostachys* and *Sphenophyllum, Phil. Trans. Roy. Soc. London,* **75B**: 863–959, 1894.

SPHENOPHYLLALES

Kidston, R.: Carboniferous lycopods and sphenophylls, *Trans. Nat. Hist. Soc. Glasgow,* n. s., **6**: 25–140, 1899.
Scott, D. H.: On the structure and affinities of fossil plants from the palaeozoic rocks: on *Cheirostrobus,* a new type of fossil cone from the Lower Carboniferous strata, *Phil. Trans. Roy. Soc. London,* **189B**, 1897.
———: A new type of Sphenophyll cone, *Phil. Trans. Roy. Soc. London,* **198B**: 17–39, 1905.

COENOPTERIDALES

Arber, E. A. N.: On the past history of the ferns, *Ann. Bot.,* **20**: 215–232, 1906.
Benson, M.: New observations on *Botryopteris antiqua, Ann. Bot.,* **25**: 1045–1057, 1911.
Bertrand, P.: L'étude anatomique des fougères anciennes et les problèmes qu'elle solève, *Prog. Rei Bot.,* **4**: 182–302, 1912.
Renault, B.: Recherches sur les végétaux silicifiés d'Autun et de Saint-Étiennes; étude du genre *Botryopteris, Ann. Sci. Nat. Bot.,* 6th ser., **1**: 220–240, 1875.
Sahni, B.: On the branching of the zygopteridean leaf, *Ann. Bot.,* **32**: 369–379, 1918.
———: On *Clepsidropsis australis,* a zygopterid tree-fern with a *Tempskya*-like false stem, from the Carboniferous rocks of Australia, *Phil. Trans. Roy. Soc. London,* **217B**: 1–37, 1928.

————: On a palaeozoic tree-fern *Grammatopteris Baldaufi* (Beck) Hirmer, a link between the Zygopterideae and Osmundaceae, *Ann. Bot.*, **46**: 863–876, 1932.

SCOTT, D. H.: The sporangia of *Stauropteris oldhamia*, Binney, *New Phyt.*, **4**: 114–120, 1904.

————: The occurrence of germinating spores in *Stauropteris oldhamia*, *New Phyt.*, **5**: 170–172, 1906.

CHAPTER XVII

THE PLANT BODY

In vascular plants the nature of the plant body and its parts has long been a basic morphological problem. The phase of this problem which concerns the relation of gametophyte and sporophyte can best be discussed after the structure of each of the generations has been considered.

Sporophyte

"Fundamental Parts." The body of the sporophyte of vascular plants is complex in form and structure. The comparative study of this body gave rise in early days of morphological study to an interpretation of structure based upon "fundamental parts"; that is, the body was looked upon as constituted of organs that were of different fundamental nature. The number of these parts was at first large; for example, stem, root, leaf, ovule, sporangium, sporangiophore, emergence, hair. This number was steadily reduced as more and more forms became known in detail, and as an understanding of morphological principles developed. In recent years the plant body has usually been considered to consist of root, stem, and leaf, these being distinct units of structure. Interpretations of the relations of these three organs have been various. In part they have related to the nature and origin of the sporophyte itself; these aspects are discussed elsewhere (page 392). The fact that root and stem have much in common in form, structure, and manner of growth, and that in some groups these organs formed a continuous structure with a transitional region, led to an interpretation of the body as fundamentally an axis differentiated into stem and root. The leaf, on this basis, is a major appendage of the stem. Under most theories of the origin of the sporophyte of vascular plants the sporophyte is considered to have been at first a simple structure with appendages developed as the body later became complex. The leaf is, according to one view, a lateral lobe of the stem, an outgrowth involving most or all of its tissues; according to another view, it is a lateral branch system, determinate in growth, reduced in size, and modified in form.   Under either view the leaf is merely a part of the axis—in one case an outgrowth from it, in the other an entire section of it.   The term *enation theory* has been applied to the theory that places the leaf as an outgrowth of the stem; the *overtopping theory* to that which holds the leaf to be a lateral, overtopped branch system which has become limited in growth while the main branch, or other branches, continue indefinite apical growth.

The recent discoveries of early land plants have been of the greatest importance to the interpretation of the morphology of vascular plants; they seem to have demonstrated the general nature of the plant body, that it is an axis simply or complexly branched and that all so-called organs are merely segments of this axis.   There are, under this interpretation, no fundamental parts.   Roots and leaves, as elaborated organs, are secondary structures.

The Leaf.   The primitive body condition is seen in Silurian and Devonian plants, in the simple axes of the Psilophytales and in their surviving representatives; in *Rhynia* and *Psilophyton*, and in *Psilotum* and *Tmesipteris*, there is no distinction of root and stem.   The underground part of the axis, with its rhizoids, represents perhaps a first stage in the differentiation of the lower end of the axis as the root.   In a group of genera—*Psilophyton, Drepanophycus, Baragwanathia, Asteroxylon*—a series may be seen showing the possible origin of the leaf as an enation: in *Psilophyton* the lateral emergences are small, spine-like, few in number, and restricted to certain parts of the axis; in *Drepanophycus* they are larger and stouter, but still spine-like or thorn-like in form; in *Asteroxylon* they are abundant, clothing the stem as do the leaves of *Lycopodium*, but the arrangement is indefinite and they are rounded in cross section; in *Baragwanathia* the appendages are much more leaf-like—large, numerous, probably flat, and arranged definitely in spirals.   Development of anatomical structure parallels, in part, that in size, external form, and arrangement: the spines of *Psilophyton* have no traces; the leaves of *Asteroxylon* have traces that reach only to the outer cortex; the leaves of *Baragwanathia* have well-defined leaf traces and veins.   In *Drepanophycus*, where a vein is present in a spine-like appendage, internal structure has progressed more rapidly than external. That the leaf has arisen in some forms as an enation seems probable. Leaves of this type remain in general small and simple. The close resemblance of the leaves of *Asteroxylon* and *Baragwanathia* to those of *Lycopodium*, together with anatomical resemblances in the stem, indicates that the leaf of the Lycopsida is of this type. In this major group the leaf departs from small size only in *Isoetes* and in the lepido-dendrids, and from simplicity only in *Protolepidodendron*. The minor forking at the leaf tip of this one genus possibly represents an expression of the tendency to dichotomy found throughout the plant body in primitive groups.

The features of resemblance between *Asteroxylon* and the other genera (except *Baragwanathia*) which seem to show the origin of the leaf as an enation in *Lycopodium* and related forms—habit, leaf form and arrangement, leaf trace, form of stele—may of course be merely superficial likenesses; the entirely different position of the sporangium supports such a view.

The theory that the leaf—at least the complex type of leaf—represents a branch system is not a recent one; it long precedes a general acquaintance with the Devonian flora now known. The structure of the Psilophytales and of contemporary forms such as *Hyenia* and *Protopteridium* strongly supports this theory by showing probable early stages in leaf formation by this method. Living plants add further strong evidence: the apical growth of the fern leaf; the great length and long-continued—almost indefinite—development of the leaf in primitive fern families; large size and complex structure; the large and complex leaf trace (in some cases equalling the stele in size), especially the presence of a gap with the trace (gaps occur in the Lycopsida only in association with branch, that is, stem traces); the terminal position of sporangia.

Among psilophytalean types, *Pseudosporochnus*, *Psilophyton*, and *Protopteridium* provide the best examples of a probable early stage in the formation of the large complex leaf. (Better examples are seen in the pteridosperm *Eospermatopteris* and in *Aneurophyton*, which is probably also a seed fern.) The lateral branchlets of *Pseudosporochnus* and *Protopteridium* form spreading determinate systems which serve as leaves. With a flattening and expansion of these axis tips, or with the development of lateral wings, a blade is formed and the axis system becomes a leaf of the fern-frond type.

The nature of the leaf in the Sphenopsida is not so clear. The leaf is simple, with simple trace and no gap, as in the Lycopsida, but there is evidence that the small leaf has been derived from a larger and more complex one: the oldest member of the group, *Asterocalamites* had rather large leaves, with slender dichotomous lobes; the leaf of *Equisetum* is surely reduced from the much larger leaves of the calamites; the leaf of the sphenophylls has a complex dichotomous venation or is divided dichotomously, suggesting a contracted *Asterocalamites* leaf; the fertile bract (which is apparently homologous with the leaf) is divided dichotomously in the horizontal plane. The sporangia are terminal on the lobes of the leaf. The position and method of attachment of the sporangia—which is much like that in the Psilophytales, terminal and anatropous—and the form, venation, and division of the leaf of *Asterocalamites* and *Sphenophyllum* suggest that the leaf in this group also represents a branch system, but a minor rather than a major one. *Hyenia*, the primitive member of the group, seems to provide important evidence: the lateral segments of its body are short, forking axes some of which serve as leaves, some as sporophylls.

Within the Sphenopsida, if *Hyenia* represents an ancestral form, the leaf has been simplified and reduced in size. The leaf of *Asterocalamites* was large [10 to 12 (40?) cm long]; that of *Equisetum* and many calamites is small. The dichotomy of the leaf in some species of *Sphenophyllum* and the forking venation of other species suggest derivation from complex leaves. Dichotomy is seen in the calamites only in the sporophylls.

If a reduction in size be seen as the history of development of the small leaf in the Sphenopsida, may not the story be much the same in the Lycopsida—*Protolepidodendron* in its forked leaf tip, and *Sigillaria* in its dichotomous vein alone retaining evidence of an ancestral complexity? Enation leaves may indeed be present only in the Psilophytales and Psilotales, but the resemblance of leaf form, sporangium position, and stelar structure of *Drepanophycus*, *Baragwanathia*, and *Asteroxylon* to *Lycopodium* is so close that it seems hardly likely that the leaf of the two groups is of a different nature.

The Telome Theory.   The interpretation of the plant body as a branched axis with its divisions specialized for various functions, but all alike in fundamental structure, is called the *telome theory*. A *telome* may be defined as a simple ultimate division of the plant axis (each telome ends at the point of union with other telomes). For example, a leaf or a sporangiophore consists of a single telome, or of a group of telomes fused in varying degrees.   A sporangium may be considered a fertile telome, or, when stalked, the tip of a telome.   Those telomes which are in function leaves are called *phylloids*.   The plant body is thus a branching axis, its specialized underground segments are roots, its aerial tips, if fertile, sporangia, if sterile, phylloids.   "Leaves" consist, under this interpretation, of one or more sterile telomes associated in many cases with one or more fertile telomes.   This treatment of the fundamental structure of the plant body is applicable to the Lycopsida only if the small leaf of the group be considered not an enation but a reduction from a larger structure.   The theory provides a basis of interpretation which removes outstanding morphological difficulties in the lower vascular plants.   It is built upon structure in the lowest known vascular plants; higher plants are safely interpreted only in this way.

   Leaf morphology thus supports the division of vascular plants into four major groups: the Psilopsida are leafless or show leaves only partly differentiated; the leaf of the Lycopsida is an enation enlarged and elaborated; that of the Sphenopsida is a minor branch system; that of the Pteropsida a major one.   The leaf is thus of different nature in vascular plants; the evolutionary development of a photosynthetic organ has come about in more than one way.

   Branching.   Branching of the axis is in most genera of the Psilophytales and in the Psilotales strictly dichotomous; in the Lycopodiales and Lepidodendrales and in the primitive ferns it is largely of this type.   But in *Asteroxylon, Lycopodium*, and some ferns it is best described as dichotomous with transitions to monopodial.   An origin, for one type at least, of monopodial structure can be seen in such forms; *Lycopodium* and *Selaginella* demonstrate this.   In the ferns the origin of a pinnate structure from dichotomy is often readily seen (*Lygodium, Marsilea*). In the sphenopsid group the whorled branching is not apparently reducible to a dichotomous system; these plants seem to possess a body structure—internal as well as external—fundamentally different from that of the other groups.

The development of determinate branch systems—short shoots —as units of structure is a marked feature of most groups. (Similar development is seen in gymnosperms and angiosperms.)

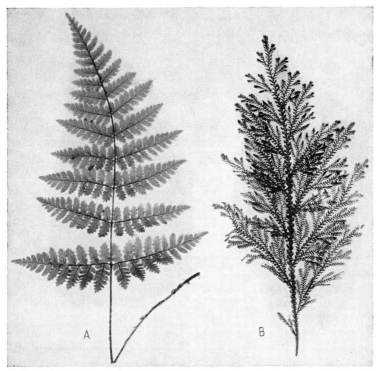

Fig. 213.—Determinate branch systems of different types. *A*, a fern leaf (*Dryopteris spinulosa*, var. *intermedia*), the photosynthetic portion developed by the expansion of the axis laterally; *B*, a leafy branch (*Selaginella* sp.), the photosynthetic portion developed by lateral emergences, leaves. × about ½.

These branch systems may be clearly such, as in *Lycopodium* and *Selaginella* (Fig. 213), or they may be differentiated as leaves, as in the fern frond (Fig. 213). They attain a maximum of simple leaf resemblance in small fern leaves (where reduced), as in the Hymenophyllaceae (and in the gymnosperm *Sciadopitys*). The fern frond and the *Selaginella* short shoot are closely alike in more than general appearance. Both are branch systems with photosynthetic lamina developed by the expansion of the axis tissue; in one case it is in the form of individual lobes—"leaves" —on a more or less limited axis; in the other it consists of the fused web-like margins of a definitely limited branch system.

The general relation of leaf and branch differs in the three groups: Lycopsida, leaf and branch relation indefinite; Sphenopsida, branch lateral to leaf; Pteropsida, branch in axil of leaf or without relation to leaf.

Branch (Leaf) Dimorphism. In the Psilophytales, sporangia were borne on the tips of groups of axes, and other axes were sterile; there were, therefore, before the leaf appeared, sterile and fertile branch systems. In both these systems blades appeared. Thus there were originally in the pteropsid and sphenopsid groups both sterile and fertile leaves or segments of leaves; neither type of leaf nor leaf segment arose originally by transformation from the other. The fertile, nongreen leaf segments of some living ferns—*Botrychium, Osmunda, Anemia* —have not originated by reduction from green, fertile segments; they represent the persistence of ancient conditions. In advanced fern families, especially the Polypodiaceae, non-blade-bearing fertile leaves or leaf segments usually represent reduction forms from green types. The sterile green leaf has not lost its sporangia, if evidence from Devonian plants is to be accepted. The relationship of leaf types in these groups is complex as already shown.

Leaf Venation. If the leaf blade has arisen by the webbing or widening of axis branches and the fusion of the ultimate divisions, the vascular supply of the branchlets becomes the veins of the leaf. As dichotomous branching is characteristic of primitive plants, the venation of primitive leaves would be dichotomous and open. This condition is seen in primitive ferns and is retained even in some genera advanced in other respects. As the leaf became specialized in function, a more efficient vascular supply developed by the formation of a network, at first coarse with few 'tie-ups' between the dichotomous main branches, then by the elaboration of the network by the development of a finer reticulum, with meshes within the original ones. This progress can be seen in living forms; it is supported by the fossil record. Devonian and lower Carboniferous plants show no reticulate venation; the first complexity in venation is said to be seen in middle Carboniferous leaves, and only in Mesozoic plants does a high type of venation become frequent.

Root System. The roots of most of the groups discussed are adventitious structures; only in the lepidodendrids, *Pleuromeia*, and *Isoetes* is a definite 'root system' present. Even here the roots are also perhaps to be considered adventitious, the 'main roots' being not specialized roots but basal axis trunks serving to bear the true roots—rhizomorphs rather than roots. Certainly in anatomy these structures are not roots. That such organs are restricted to one line is of especial interest, since it ties together even more closely three groups seen by other evidence to be related. (In *Selaginella*, rhizophores are present, but these are lateral structures and do not have indeterminate growth.) The presence of basal rhizomorphs secures support of a type different from that of other plants; such support may have been related to the attainment by the lepidodendrids of greater size than that reached by calamites—whose bases were huge rhizomes —or by ancient ferns which, when tree-like, had merely rounded, swollen bases. That the rhizomorphs were remarkable organs is evident in their peculiarities: the tips of the rhizomorphs of the lepidodendrids were stout and rounded, "like thick cucumbers"; and surely the axis tips in no plants but *Isoetes* (and probably *Pleuromeia*) grow by such extraordinary meristems and produce body structure of such unusual type. Only in one stock have rhizomorphs of this type appeared. It is one of the great good fortunes of morphology that there is still living an example which can be studied in detail.

The Sporangium. The sporangium has long been dropped as one of the fundamental parts. The correctness of this treatment is fully demonstrated by the Psilophytales where the sporangium is merely a fertile axis tip. The fact that the sporangium is terminal on lateral axis systems in such genera as *Psilophyton*, *Asteroxylon*, *Pseudosporochnus*, and *Hyenia* is in itself strong evidence that the complex leaf represents a branch system, for the study of living forms demonstrates that in leaves the terminal and marginal (that is, terminal on lateral divisions) sporangium position is primitive. Early fossil plants provide full support for the phylogenetic development of the fern-leaf type as followed in living forms.

A prominent character of the sporangium of the Psilophytales is its suspended and recurved position. This and the fact that the sporangium is an axis tip seem to solve the puzzle of the nature of the sporangiophore of the Equisetales and Sphenophyllales: the sporangiophore is a minor branch system, with the tips terminated by sporangia, a group of fertile telomes attached in a whorl. The peltate tip characteristic of the Equisetaceae, Calamitaceae, and part of the sphenophylls seems to represent the broadened and fused ultimate divisions of the fertile branch. In *Hyenia* the tips are not fused; in later forms the broad tip is present, doubtless a protective structure for the sporangia. In *Hyenia* the number of sporangia on a sporangiophore is 2 or 3, in the calamites 4, in the horsetails 6 to 10. This suggests that the branching of the sporangiophore is like that of the main stem, verticillate. The anatomy of the sporangiophore bears out the nature of the enlarged tip, since each sporangium has a separate bundle, leading from the stalk strand through the tip to its base. Ontogeny also supports this interpretation since the sporangia in *Equisetum* arise from a ring of 'terminal' independent initials (page 95).

The interpretation of sporangium position in the Lycopsida is not clear and awaits further evidence from very early fossils. In *Selaginella* and *Phylloglossum* the sporangium is cauline, axillary, or foliar; in *Lycopodium* only axillary and foliar positions occur; in the lepidodendrids and *Isoetes* the sporangia are foliar. Ontogeny indicates that in *Selaginella* at least the foliar position is secondary. If this is generally true for the Lycopsida, the sporangium of this group is a lateral cauline structure which has in most members migrated to the surface of the adjacent leaf. *Baragwanathia* is perhaps important in the understanding of the Lycopsida. This Silurian genus resembles *Lycopodium* in leaf form, structure, and arrangement; its sporangia were cauline and lateral and were spirally arranged, perhaps in the leaf axils. Such a condition is closely like that in *Selaginella* and non-cone-bearing species of *Lycopodium*. *Baragwanathia* offers (1) a possible ancestral type for the Lycopsida; (2) further evidence that the leaf of this group is an enation (since, if the leaves were lateral branchlets, the sporangia should be terminal upon them; evidence of the distinctness of the lycopsid types from the time of earliest land floras and therefore a possible polyphyletic condition in vascular plants).

The Silurian plants so far known do not aid in the solution of the interrelationships of the four chief lines of vascular plants; they add, rather, to its difficulties. The sporangium position of *Baragwanathia* is wholly different from that of typical Psilophytales. The earlier plants are more complex than the later ones. In this last fact lies perhaps some support for the opinion that such simple plants as *Rhynia, Hornea,* and *Psilophyton* are reduced. It would seem rather, however, that there are at least two distinct lines within the Psilophytales—one with lateral, and one with terminal sporangia. It is more and more certain that we know as yet but little about the Psilophytales; they were surely a vast and diverse group and the Lower Devonian does not represent the time of their origin.

Any discussion of the relationship of the condition where the sporangia were many and lateral on the stem to that where they were solitary and terminal is highly speculative: the two types may have been derived directly from algal types with similar general structure; or the large terminal sporangium may have been segmented and its sporogenous tissue restricted to lateral pockets beside which photosynthetic enations developed. Probably only fossils of Devonian, Silurian, or older periods will provide an answer to this.

Anatomy. A discussion in detail of the internal structure of the plant is beyond the scope of this book. Brief statements concerning stele and vessels will suffice here. The primitive stele is without question the protostele, a solid rod of vascular tissue. From this, more complex types have been evolved. First, accompanying an increase in size, a central parenchymatous pith is developed. A stele of such structure is a *siphonostele* or *solenostele.* This hollow cylinder of vascular tissue is unbroken or may possess leaf gaps which are closed before the departure of the trace next above. Two theories exist as to the method by which medullation came about: (1) by transformation (phylogenetic) of the innermost vascular tissue; (2) by the invasion (phylogenetic) of tissues from without the stele. The arguments and evidence for the intrastelar and extrastelar origin of the pith involve discussion of anatomical structure which cannot be included here.

The pith of lycopsid forms, and that of some of the more primitive ferns at least, are without doubt intrastelar in origin; that of higher ferns and other pteropsid groups is probably extrastelar.

Where, in a siphonostelic cylinder the leaf gaps overlap in their longitudinal extent, the stele is a *dictyostele*. In a dictyostele, breaks other than leaf gaps may be present. The vascular cylinder in such cases is a network of strands which in cross section appears as a circle of bundles. When in a stele of this type each bundle has the general structure of a protostele, the stele is often called a *polystele*. This term is inappropriate as it implies, falsely, that the axis has a multiple stelar condition; its use should be dropped. (For similar reasons the use of *gamostele* and *dialystele* should be discontinued.) The dictyostele, especially in its complex forms, represents an advance over the siphonostele. Protosteles in some few cases—as perhaps in the Hymenophyllaceae—may represent reduction stages.

In xylem there is progress from simple to complex structure. In the evolutionary specialization of this tissue the development of the vessel is an outstanding feature. The possession of vessels is a prominent character of angiosperms and high gymnosperms. Vessels are present, however, not only in ferns but in *Selaginella*, and in the latter the vessels are of the highest type. Such a distribution of vessels is an excellent example of parallel development in unrelated groups. It provides also an example of the high development of one structural feature in a group while others remain at a low level.

Secondary vascular tissues are present in nearly all groups, both in large and in small plants; their presence is not related to arborescent form. The possession of cambial growth does not indicate high development; many Devonian plants had secondary growth. It may be noted also that such growth is present in some of the large brown algae, and that in ancient algae (*Nematophyton*) a massive development of secondary tissues occurred.

Gametophyte

With the completion in recent years of a knowledge of the sexual generation of all groups of living vascular plants, it becomes possible to compare the gametophyte generally in these plants. Although it has been believed that because of simplicity of structure little information of value could be obtained from comparative studies of prothallia, it is apparent (now that the most primitive forms are known) that really important characters exist there. When a survey of the gametophytes of the various groups of lower vascular plants is made, a few significant differences stand out. In form there are two general types, the elongate radial (cylindrical) and the dorsiventral. The latter may be divided into a simple and a complex type. It is at once evident that this grouping coincides rather closely with classification based on sporophyte characters: the radial type occurs in the Psilotales, Lycopodiales, and Ophioglossales; the simple dorsiventral in the Marattiales and Filicales; the complex dorsiventral in the Equisetales. (Heterosporous groups are of course omitted.)

The cylindrical type is undoubtedly primitive: it is strongly developed in the most primitive group, the Psilotales; it is present in two other very primitive groups, the Lycopodiales and the Ophioglossales; flattened types develop from cylindrical in *Lycopodium* and in *Botrychium*. There is no evidence, however, that the dorsiventral type of the higher ferns and the horsetails has developed from a cylindrical one.

The fact that the cylindrical form is primitive is further evident from comparison of characters other than form. Among the gametophytes of all groups a series may be seen in which there is evident progress from large, dichotomously branching, slow-growing, long-lived, vigorous types, which may bear several embryos, to small, simple, rapid-growing, short-lived, delicate types, which rarely support more than one embryo. (A parallel series may be seen in the sporophyte, where the advanced type is an annual of small size.) That the series must be read toward the short-lived type is evident from the study of ferns, where such progress is clear. Perhaps the strongest evidence lies in the fact that there is in the Psilotales and part of the Ophioglossales no segregation of vegetative and reproductive regions. In the higher fern groups a restriction of the fertile region can be followed from both sides of the gametophyte to one side, accompanying a reduction in size, in thickness, and in time required to reach maturity.

The correlation of gametophyte type with sporophyte type strongly supports the classification which divides vascular plants into four major groups, and the ferns into three chief groups.

The complexity and variety of structure—external and internal—attained by the plant body as early as Devonian and lower Carboniferous are amazing. This is equalled or surpassed in reproductive methods: heterospory, with its accompanying gametophyte reduction, and the seed habit have arisen in independent lines; the most complex cone yet known in any group had been evolved. (Members of groups not yet discussed, seed ferns and gymnosperms, of arborescent habit, were also present.)   The Silurian period now shows a form (*Baragwanathia*) more advanced than the Lower Devonian types. All these facts suggest for vascular plants—at least for those of most groups—a considerable period of development before the Lower Devonian.

ALTERNATION OF GENERATIONS

The phenomenon of alternation of generations—so prominent and so important a feature of the morphology of plants and so much an object of discussion and controversy for many years—is still incompletely understood. The addition to our acquaintance with the sporophyte of vascular plants in recent years of a knowledge of the Psilophytales provides actual facts about simple and early sporophytes, probably not about the first sporophytes of land-living vascular plants but certainly about extremely old types which may well show the form of definitely early types. These plants should add much of value to the interpretation of the nature and origin of the sporophyte.   No detailed discussion of alternation of generations can be presented here; only the apparent bearing of recent information on the theories of the origin of the sporophyte can well be discussed.

Concerning the nature and origin of the sporophyte of vascular plants two theories have long existed: the *antithetic theory* and the *homologous theory*. The antithetic theory assumes that the two generations are essentially distinct, that the sporophyte is a new phase introduced into the life cycle of vascular plants in relation to life in the air; it assumes that the complex, independent, land-living sporophyte has evolved from the zygote of an ancestral algal form through a stage where it was merely a spore-bearing structure wholly dependent upon the gametophyte.

The homologous theory assumes that sporophyte and gametophyte are essentially alike in nature; that the sporophyte is not a new thing but a modified preexisting form; that sporophyte and gametophyte are correlative phases in the life cycle of the plants which have arisen by modification of an original single phase which was sexual. The origin of the two phases is in recent interpretations of the theory assumed to have occurred in the ancestral stock of vascular plants; that is, both gametophyte and sporophyte were already differentiated as separate generations in nonvascular plants.

New light has been thrown on the bases for these theories in the last few years, not only by the discovery of the simple sporophytes of Devonian and Silurian forms, but by a more complete acquaintance with the gametophytes of living groups.

The prothallia of the Psilotaceae have been known only for a few years. If this group is recognized as a surviving member of psilophytalean stock the nature of its gametophytes is of the greatest importance; if it is not admitted to be the most primitive living vascular family, it is surely one of the most primitive and the importance of its gametophyte structure nearly as great. Recent years have also seen a better knowledge of the gametophytes of the Lycopodiaceae and of the Ophioglossaceae and other ferns.

With the recognition of the Psilotaceae, Lycopodiaceae, and Ophioglossaceae as among the most primitive of living vascular plants, a comparative study of the gametophytes of all living groups seems to demonstrate that the history of the gametophyte in these plants is one of reduction in size and in length of life; of change in rate of development from slow to rapid; of change in form from cylindrical to dorsiventral. The primitive gametophyte of at least some groups (Psilotales, Lycopodiales, Ophioglossales) was an elongate, dichotomously branching cylindrical axis, with slow and long-continued apical growth. Within two of these groups the development of dorsiventral prothallia can be seen. In the Marattiales and Filicales there are no cylindrical gametophytes, but the prothallia of the more primitive group are not far in form from such a type: the body is thick and fleshy with a more or less cylindrical midrib, and dichotomous branching is prominent. Such a gametophyte may well represent a flattened cylindrical type. The more advanced Filicales seem to show a series from the type of the Marattiales to that of the Polypodiaceae—a series of reduction in size, of increasing rapidity of development, of decreasing midrib and increasing wings (the cushion of the highest families perhaps representing the remains of the midrib of lower forms).   The position of the sex organs in ferns is supporting evidence for the change from cylindrical to dorsiventral form.   The flattening of a cylindrical axis with sex organs on all sides would produce a structure with these organs on both sides; this condition is seen in the Marattiales and in the lower (even, rarely, in the higher) members of the Filicales. A gradual disappearance from the upper side would ensue as a biological response; evidence of this is seen in the leptosporangiate ferns.

There can be no doubt but that in the Psilotales, Lycopodiales, and Ophioglossales the cylindrical form is primitive for the gametophyte.   The above mentioned facts suggest that this may be true also for the Marattiales and the Filicales.

The dorsiventral gametophyte of the Equisetales, with its erect lobes, shows no evidence of derivation from a cylindrical type (however, only a single form, that of *Equisetum*, is known). Such a gametophyte is as distinct in type among gametophytes as is the sporophyte of the group among sporophytes.

There seems, therefore, to be strong evidence that the gametophyte of at least three groups of vascular plants was primitively a terete dichotomous axis with long-continued apical growth. Such a gametophyte resembles in these characters the sporophytes of the earliest and simplest land plants yet known.   A similar resemblance can also be seen in living plants: gametophytes of *Psilotum* and *Tmesipteris* (probably the most primitive living vascular plants) can be separated in form and appearance from pieces of the axis of the sporophyte (rhizome) only with difficulty (page 80); the roots and the prothallia of *Ophioglossum* are closely alike in form and in other features (page 127).

In these resemblances there is strong support for the homologous theory—for that interpretation of the theory which places the differentiation of gametophyte and sporophyte in ancient algal stocks, and assumes the origin of land-living independent sporophytes directly from independent aquatic sporophytes.   The alga-like body of the psilophytalean sporophyte is the best evidence for this view: in many genera—*Rhynia*, *Psilophyton*, *Zosterophyllum*, the form genus *Hostimella*, *Pseudosporochnus*,

Protopteridium, for example—the body is hardly more than that of an alga with vascular tissue, stomata, and cuticle. And among living algae sporophyte and gametophyte are well differentiated as independent generations. There are genera in which the two phases are closely alike, and others in which the two are markedly unlike in size and form. Even in a single series, as in the Phaeophyceae, this condition is found; and it is apparent that the condition of unlikeness has been derived from that of likeness.

The resemblances of the two generations seen in primitive living vascular plants make it more probable that in the ancestral forms the two generations were alike; the Psilotaceae and Ophioglossaceae provide strong evidence for this.

Not only is the homologous theory supported by the nature of the most ancient land plants and by similarity between the generations in the most primitive living groups, but much of the foundation upon which the antithetic theory has been built has fallen away in recent years. Forms which belong to primitive groups and which were looked upon as most primitive members within those groups are now recognized as advanced (even by the supporters of the antithetic theory), and their simplicity is seen as the result of reduction. *Ophioglossum, Isoetes,* and *Phylloglossum* were once looked upon as transitional forms demonstrating important stages or features in the early elaboration of the sporophyte. Of these *Ophioglossum* held the most prominent position. The resemblance of the sporophyte of *O. vulgatum* to the sporophyte of a moss provided a connecting stage between the dependent and the independent sporophyte, and a small and simple plant from which were seen developed large and complex forms. That the interpretation of the morphological relationship of leaf and fertile spike and of leaf and axis in *Ophioglossum,* which led to this view, was wholly erroneous is now clear. This species is an advanced one in the genus, and the sporophyte body of the genus as a whole is advanced as compared with that of *Botrychium,* which is complex in its fertile parts. The simplicity of *Ophioglossum* is the simplicity of reduction and not of primitiveness.

Isoetes, like *Ophioglossum,* is a highly specialized plant. The solitary sporangium, in the light of Devonian plant structure, is more primitive than the aggregation of sporangia in a strobilus;

and *Isoetes* is not merely a strobilus, it has stem and rhizomorph as definitely as have *Pleuromeia* and *Sigillaria*.

The protocorm has no basic morphological significance (page 397). *Phylloglossum* is not a "permanent protocorm." In the genus *Lycopodium* the protocorm is not restricted to a group of species which can be considered the most primitive. The resemblance of protocorms to *Isoetes* is superficial only.

Present-day views of the phylogeny of the bryophytes provide little or no support for the antithetic theory. This group of plants is now known in the fossil record only as far back as the Carboniferous period. There is no evidence that bryophytes preceded vascular plants in time. (Such evidence is of course negative and hence perhaps of little value.) Students of the phylogeny of bryophytes are apparently almost without exception of the opinion that the group is a highly specialized and complex line independent of relation to other land plants; that the mosses and the liverworts are separate groups, the former not derived from the latter. A recent view, which is becoming broadly accepted, is that the simplest types in the liverworts are reduction types; that the series in the group has in part been read in the wrong direction. *Ricciocarpus* is viewed not as a most primitive liverwort, but a highly specialized one—one that has become reduced as a result of adaptation to the floating habit, the reduction having affected both gametophyte and sporophyte. The Anthocerotales are considered by some students of the bryophytes to be independent of all other groups, to form a line parallel with other liverworts and with mosses. They are seen to be in their gametophytes the most primitive—most alga-like—of all bryophytes. The sporophyte is, however, held to be most nearly like that of vascular plants. It is of course possible that the lowest members of a group should show the closest approach in important features to the higher group seen as derived from the group, but it seems most unlikely. The interrelationships of the bryophytes indicate clearly a line of specialization of land plants which has developed far in a direction different from that taken by vascular plants.

The antithetic theory has been the theory most generally accepted in recent years and the one used as a basis in most elementary textbooks to demonstrate evolutionary progress in the rise and elaboration of vascular plants. Today the homologous theory seems to be supported by much the stronger evidence, and morphological interest is returning to its viewpoints. The question of the origin of the sporophyte in vascular plants must, however, remain open; further evidence relative to the question will doubtless come from early fossil types. Gametophytes of these plants may be found, for the preservation of soft structures is not improbable in the light of the remarkable preservation in *Rhynia* and *Hornea* and in the gametophyte of *Lepidodendron* (Fig. 198) and the germinating spores of *Botryopteris* (Fig. 212). If gametophyte and sporophyte were much alike in early land plants, some of the "sterile" fossil branching axes may perhaps be gametophytic!

THEORIES RELATING TO THE ORIGIN OF THE SPOROPHYTE OF VASCULAR PLANTS

The Protocorm Theory. This theory deals with a method by which the free-living state of the sporophyte of vascular plants may have been attained. The basis for the theory was the discovery in the club mosses of a structural condition apparently intermediate between that of gametophyte and sporophyte. Assuming that in ancestral forms the sporophyte was dependent upon the gametophyte (as in mosses and liverworts), and that the club mosses are very primitive vascular plants, it was believed that here was, surviving, a transition type with evidence of the method by which the tremendously important step to independence of the sporophyte was taken.

In some species of *Lycopodium* the embryonic sporophyte does not develop directly into a leafy plant (page 19), as in all, or nearly all, other vascular plants but forms a rounded fleshy body called the "protocorm." This protocorm is unlike a typical young sporophyte in a lack of roots and of vascular tissue, and suggests a gametophyte in shape and appearance, in its parenchymatous mass, and in its rhizoids and endophytic fungus. Though it bears green, leaf-like lobes, "prophylls," these are indefinite in position and of the simplest structure, without vascular tissue; they resemble lobes of a prothallium rather than true leaves. The young plant at this stage, though a sporophyte morphologically, looks and lives like a gametophyte. After the protocorm has lived for some time, nourished in part by the foot embedded in the gametophyte, a growing point arises laterally, or possibly internally, and a stem apex develops bearing true leaves and a root. It is easy to see that this structure could be looked upon as a primitive sort of sporophyte, as yet rootless, without conducting tissue, and partly dependent upon the gametophyte—the evolutionary forerunner of the leafy vascular sporophyte.

The resemblance of the mature plant of *Phylloglossum* to this protocorm greatly strengthened the theory, for in this small and simple club moss there was seen a permanent protocorm stage. In other words this plant seemed still to be in the most primitive stage of sporophyte independence and complexity. The individuals were believed not merely to pass through the protocorm stage, but to retain and repeat it annually; each season a new protocorm is formed and not a leafy vascular plant. According to this theory, *Phylloglossum* is a permanently embryonic lycopod.

In opposition to the theory it is stated that the protocorm is lacking in the more primitive species of *Lycopodium*, where it should be found if it is of significance; that it appears to be merely a resting stage in embryonic development related to environmental conditions; and that *Phylloglossum* is probably a reduced plant. Later studies have demonstrated that *Phylloglossum* is unquestionably a greatly reduced and specialized plant, one which has adapted itself biologically and structurally to a perennial, tuberous habit. The fact that it possesses vascular tissue throughout, that it has true roots, and that its leaves, having vascular traces and veins, are not prophylls is sufficient proof that this plant is not a permanent protocorm. Further, it has been shown that *Ophioglossum* and certain monocotyledons also possess a protocorm stage. The protocorm theory, therefore, is now merely of historical interest.

The Strobilus Theory. This theory is based upon the assumption that in the development of the complex sporophyte of higher vascular plants a primitive stage was passed through in which the sporophyte had the form and structure of a strobilus. The theory provides a large part of the foundation for the antithetic origin of the sporophyte. In outline the theory assumes that a sporophyte of simple structure, such as that of the liverworts, has been elaborated in form and structure; that its large, simple sporogenous mass has been broken up by sterilization so that only pockets of spore-producing cells (sporangia) remain; that the sporangia have been relegated to a superficial position; that enations of sterile tissue have appeared on the surface of the sporophyte, beside or beneath the sporangia; that the sporangia ultimately have become situated on the enations (which then became sporangiophores or sporophylls); that under further sterilization the sporangia have disappeared from part of the sporophylls, and these sterile appendages became leaves; that with great increase in size the central core (axis) became an extended stem with the leaves and sporophylls distributed over its surface, and the leaves and the sporophylls became large and complex; that roots were developed as appendages of the base and the sporophyte became independent of the gametophyte.

The strobiloid form is seen at the stage where the enations have appeared upon the surface of the globose or cylindrical sporophyte and the sporangia lie closely on the surface, or in the axils or upon the base of the enations—as do the sporangia in *Lycopodium* and *Selaginella*. At this stage the entire plant is a strobilus. Such a condition was seen in *Phylloglossum* especially —also in *Isoetes*, and a somewhat later stage in those species of *Lycopodium* where "every leaf is a sporophyll." Support for the interpretation of *Phylloglossum* as a sporophyte still in the strobilus stage was seen in its form, the apparently weak development of vascular tissue, the irregularly placed, simple leaves, and the lack of roots for one or more years. The strobilus-like form and the apparently simple structure of *Phylloglossum* and *Isoetes* are now known to be the result of reduction. The protocorm of *Lycopodium* is like that of other plants, merely a resting stage in early embryonic development. The fossil record of the lycopods shows that these plants as early as the Devonian period had sterile leaves and many were tree-like. The Silurian *Baragwanathia*, which in form and sporangium position suggests *Lycopodium*, was clothed with sterile leaves. The form of Silurian and Devonian plants in general indicates that the primitive sporophyte body had the form of a branching axis which was not small.

The Phyton Theory. Under this theory the leafy plant was seen to be a complex organism, to consist of individuals living somewhat as do individuals in colonial organisms. The individual members were the leaves. Either these alone constituted the plant body, the axis consisting merely of leaf bases, or the leaves plus axis segments (nodal regions) built up a leafy stem. Under these interpretations the leaf is the fundamental structure in the plant body, and the axis is secondary. The phyton theory is related to the strobilus theory in that at the stage where the sporophyte is in the form of a strobilus—a cluster of sporophylls (leaves) attached to a central core—the plant is a cluster of leaves and there is no axis as such. Later, an axis is formed from the sporophyll bases and is enlarged and elaborated. (The *peri-caulome* and *leaf-skin theories* are related to the phyton theory in that they assume the axis to be built up at least in considerable part from leaf bases.)

With the recognition of the sporophyte body of vascular plants as fundamentally an axis system, with leaf and root as secondary structures, these theories are without value. An old theory, which has been called the "*cauloid theory*" which assumes the plant body to have been differentiated from a "primeval cauloid," that is, an axis system, seems best to fit the facts of the history of the sporophyte as they are known today.

THE CLASSIFICATION OF VASCULAR PLANTS
(TRACHEOPHYTA)

In the earlier chapters the morphological basis for a classification which seems natural has been laid out, and that classification has been built up, piece by piece. It may now be looked upon as a whole and compared in major features with the classification commonly in use today (Table 5). The table covers the major groups of all vascular plants—those to be treated in the second part of this book, however, only in their relation to the great divisions of vascular plants. The characters of the various groups need not be repeated here; the mention of some of the more critical ones in connection with a comparison of the old and the new systems will suffice.

Vascular plants have long been divided into Pteridophyta and Spermatophyta. This classification represents in a measure the persistence of the much older system which separated plants into Cryptogamia and Phanerogamia—those in which reproduction was hidden (that is, by spores) and those in which it was open (that is, by seeds). In the elaboration of method of reproduction the attainment of the seed was considered the highest stage,

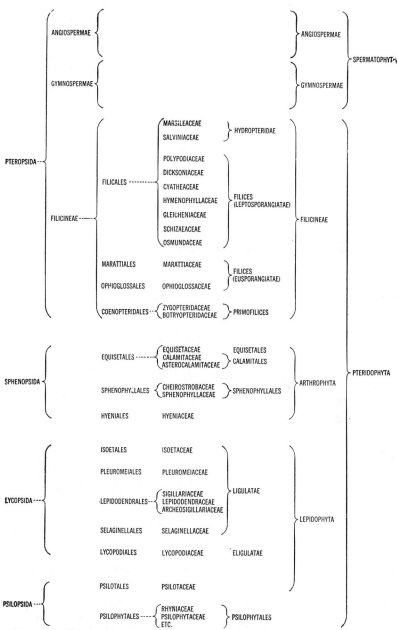

TABLE 5.—The classification of vascular plants.   On the left the newer grouping;
on the right the obsolete, unnatural arrangement.

and the possession of this structure determined therefore a major group. The discovery that certain ancient fern-like plants

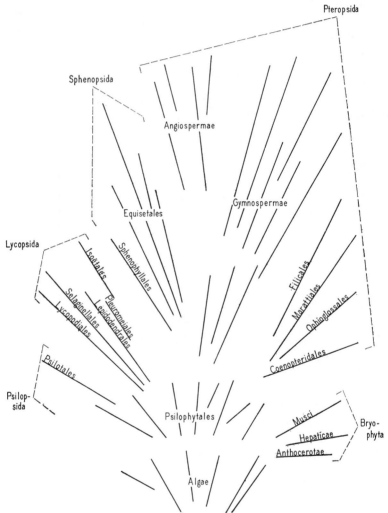

Fig. 214.—Diagram showing present day view of relationships among vascular plants.

(Pteridospermae) bore seeds broke down over 30 years ago the line between pteridophytes and spermatophytes. Since that time the fossil record has presented evidence that other groups of pteridophytes also possessed at one time a well-developed seed habit. The gap between "vascular cryptogams" and spermatophytes has been firmly bridged; the possession of seeds can no longer be considered a character which sets gymnosperms and angiosperms apart from ferns, club mosses, and horsetails. Another basis for the major division of vascular plants—one resting, as is necessary, not upon one, but upon several characters—has been found in fundamental features of body structure: the nature and relation of leaf and stem; the vascular anatomy; the position of the sporangia. On this basis vascular plants fall into four groups: Psilopsida, Lycopsida, Sphenopsida, and Pteropsida (Fig. 214). The detailed morphology of the groups, as far as it is known at present, fails to show definite connections between the last three of these groups; they represent distinct lines of vascular plants. The Psilopsida are, with little doubt, members of an ancestral stock—a large and most diverse one—from which probably arose the higher groups. They perhaps should not be considered a separate group, parallel with the others; they may be looked upon as merely early stages of the other groups, but in a system of classification they must be given a name and a position. Within this group or in still earlier, as yet unknown, forms are to be sought possible connections between the other groups. The diversity of the Psilophytales provides in form and structure ample variety from which the variety of type may have been derived. Today it can only be said that lycopsid, sphenopsid, and pteropsid lines all go back into the psilopsid complex. The variety of body type and sporangium position in the Psilopsida is to be seen in the higher algae from which the group appears to have arisen. If the Psilopsida be considered a group with a tremendously long history of development and diversification before Upper Silurian and Lower Devonian times, they may perhaps be considered monophyletic, and vascular plants therefore as also monophyletic; but, if the Psilophytales have arisen as several independent lines from algal groups—as their diversity suggests—vascular plants are polyphyletic, and pteropsid, sphenopsid, and lycopsid lines are wholly distinct, running back through the provisional (and doubtless unnatural) group Psilophytales to the algae. The possession of vascular tissue may as well represent the expression of an adaptive tendency appearing independently in

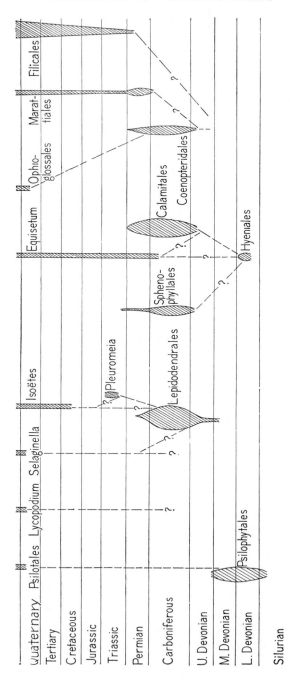

FIG. 215.—Diagram showing distribution of major vascular plant groups in geological time.

unrelated groups as does the development of heterospory, of the seed habit, of leaves, of vessels. Only from further evidence from the earliest land plants can this question be answered.

It is obvious that the division of vascular plants into Pteridophyta and Spermatophyta was highly unnatural; not only did it place together the lycopods, horsetails, and ferns (which show surely no relationship closer than that of possible common origin in ancestral Psilophytales), but it separates the ferns from their closest relatives the gymnosperms and angiosperms. The "fern allies" are not the club mosses and the horsetails. The older classification is obsolete and has been so for many years; general recognition was given by morphologists almost at once to the establishment of the "Pteropsida," uniting ferns, gymnosperms, and angiosperms. At first, on the new basis, all other vascular plants were placed in a parallel group, the "Lycopsida." From this group the horsetails and sphenophylls were soon set off as the Sphenopsida—a division of the Lycopsida now seen well justified; and the discovery of the Psilophytales seems to make necessary the formation of a fourth parallel group. This group supplies a place for the Psilotaceae which have long been anomalous members in whatever group they have been placed. The Psilopsida should of course be recognized as a provisional group. Complexity of form and variation in sporangium position indicate that its members will be distributed among other groups as relations are recognized, or that it will be maintained as a composite, low-level stage of development of all the groups.

Other important points of difference in the two schemes will be seen to be the following. The Psilotaceae have been thought to be lepidophytes, with *Lycopodium* as their closest relative. There is little doubt but that they belong with the Psilophytaceae.

Interrelationships among lycopsid forms are obscure, but a separation into "ligulate" and "eligulate" serves no useful purpose so far as can at present be determined. The number of cilia on the sperms is perhaps of as much value as the presence of a ligule. The orders Lepidodendrales, Pleuromeiales, and Isoetales are closer together apparently than any one of these is to the Lycopodiales or the Selaginellales, or than these are to one another.

The separation of the living ferns into "Eusporangiatae" and "Leptosporangiatae" served the purpose of setting apart the modern types; it brought together the Marattiaceae and Ophioglossaceae which, though they have in common many archaic characters, are apparently as distantly related as either of them is to the Leptosporangiatae. The separation is of value in that it contrasts the modern structure and method of growth with the ancient. The separation of the Filicineae into four main groups is comparable to that of the division of all vascular plants into four groups. The Coenopteridales represent the ancestral stock from which the higher groups arose. Relationships between the other groups are surely not close, and the Filicineae are best treated as four separate groups until early fossil ferns are better known.

An important difference in the division of the ferns is the fact that in the new scheme the Hydropteridae are not considered a separate major group. It is now recognized that heterospory, like the seed habit, has appeared independently in various groups, and that it does not in itself serve as a character distinguishing a major group. The water ferns have long been known to be a heterogeneous group, and detailed study and comparison of leptosporangiate ferns show that the two families are not so closely related to one another as they are to other ferns: the Marsileaceae are related to the Schizaeaceae, the Salviniaceae probably to the Hymenophyllaceae. The old group Hydropteridineae, therefore, must be discarded and its members distributed among the Filicales.

The classification of vascular plants as seen today is of course not to be considered final; it represents merely a stage in the development of a classification that will ultimately be as closely natural as a classification can be made when the actual course of change cannot be followed. There has been added in the last two or three decades a great deal of information from the fossil record—providing a knowledge of structure that actually existed, to support or to replace speculative structure. Comprehensive and detailed studies have been made of living groups (especially of the ferns). A better understanding has been obtained of such important aspects of modification as parallel development and reduction. All these give a more sure basis for a classification that goes a long way toward a natural one. Today's classification will of course not long stand without modification. Activity in the study of fossil plants will surely soon provide the basis for changes. In the light of what is known today, however, the major divisions seem pretty well marked out.

A view of the distribution, in time, of the various large groups demonstrates the fact that the orders thus far treated are primarily ancient; with the exception of the leptosporangiate ferns all can be considered primarily paleozoic groups. It is indeed for botanical science a most fortunate circumstance that most of them have members surviving to the present day. With these for comparison, morphology and taxonomy may be much more certain of their interpretation of the extinct forms.

Bibliography

The Plant Body

ARBER, E. A. N.: "Devonian floras: A Study of the Origin of Cormophyta," Cambridge, 1921.

BENSON, M.: The sporangiophore—a unit of structure in the Pteridophyta, *New Phyt.*, **7**: 143–149, 1908.

BOWER, F. O.: On medullation in the Pteridophyta, *Ann. Bot.*, **25**: 555–574, 1911.

———: On leaf-architecture as illuminated by a study of Pteridophyta, *Trans. Roy. Soc. Edinburgh*, **51**: 657–708, 1916.

BROWNE, I.: The phylogeny and inter-relationships of the Pteridophyta, *New Phyt.*, **7**: 93–102; 103–116; 150–166; 181–197; 230–253, 1908.

———: Some views on the morphology and phylogeny of the leafy vascular sporophyte, *Bot. Rev.*, **1**: 383–404; 427–446, 1935.

BUGNON, P.: L'origine phylogénétique des plantes vasculaires d'après Lignier, *Bull. Soc. Linn. de Normandie*, ser. 7, **4**: 196–212, 1921.

GOEBEL, K.: Morphologische und biologische Studien XII–XV. *Ann. Jard. Bot. Buitenzorg*, **39**: 1–232, 1928.

RUDOLPH, K.: Die Entwicklung der Stammbildung bei den fossilen Pflanzen, *Lotos*, **69**: 15–34, 1921.

TANSLEY, A. G.: Lectures on the evolution of the filicinean vascular system. I–X. *New Phyt.*, **6**: 25–35; 53–68; 109–120; 135–147; 148–155; 187–203; 219–238; 253–269, 1907; **7**: 1–22; 29–40, 1908.

ZIMMERMANN, W.: Der Baum in seinem phylogenetischen Werden. *Ber. Deut. Bot. Gesells.*, **48**: 34–49, 1930.

Alternation of Generations

Anonymous: Discussion on "alternation of generations" at the Linnean Society, *New Phyt.*, **8**: 104–116, 1908.

BLACKMAN, V. H.: Alternation of generations and ontogeny, *New Phyt.*, **8**: 207–218, 1909.

BOWER, F. O.: Studies in the morphology of spore-producing members—Equisetineae and Lycopodineae. *Phil. Trans. Roy. Soc. London*, **185B**: 473–572, 1894.

———: *Ophioglossum simplex*, Ridley, *Ann. Bot.*, **18**: 205–216, 1904.

———: A theory of the strobilus in archegoniate plants, *Ann. Bot.*, **8**: 343–365, 1894.

CAMPBELL, D. H.: The relationships of the Anthocerotaceae, *Flora*, **118**: 62–74, 1925.

CAVERS, F.: The interrelationships of the Bryophyta, *New Phyt.*, Reprint 4, 1911.

CHURCH, A. H.: Thalassiophyta and the subaërial transmigration, *Oxford Bot. Mem.* 3, 1919.

COULTER, J. M.: The origin of the gymnosperms and the seed habit, *Bot. Gaz.*, **26**: 153–168, 1898.

FARMER, J. B., and L. DIGBY: Studies in apospory and apogamy in ferns, *Ann. Bot.*, **21**: 161–199, 1907.

FRITSCH, F. E.: Thalassiophyta and the algal ancestry of the higher plants, *New Phyt.*, **20**: 165–178, 1921.

———: The structure and reproduction of the algae. Vol. I. Cambridge, 1935.

LANG, W. H.: On apogamy and the development of sporangia upon fern-prothalli, *Ann. Bot.*, **12**: 251–256, 1898.

———: Alternation of generations in the archegoniatae, *Ann. Bot.*, **12**: 583–592, 1898.

———: A theory of alternation of generations, based upon the ontogeny, *New Phyt.*, **8**: 1–12, 1909.

MIELINSKI, K.: Ueber die Phylogenie der Bryophyten mit besonderer Berücksichtigung der Hepaticae, *Bot. Archiv*, **16**: 23–118, 1926.

SCHIFFNER, V.: Die systematisch-phylogenetische Forschung in der Hepaticologie, etc. *Prog. Rei Bot.*, **5**: 387–520, 1917.

SMITH, G. M.: "The Fresh-water Algae of the United States," New York, 1933.

TANSLEY, A. G.: Professor Bower on the theory of antithetic alternation of generations (a review), *New Phyt.*, **7**: 117–129, 1908.

WALTON, J.: Carboniferous Bryophyta. I. Hepaticae, *Ann. Bot.*, **39**: 563–572, 1925; II. Hepaticae and Musci, *idem*, **42**: 707–716, 1928 .

WORSDELL, W. C.: The principles of morphology, *New Phyt.*, **4**: 124–133; 163–170, 1905.

ZIMMERMANN, W.: Phylogenie (der Bryophyten) *in* Verdoorn, Fr., "Manual of Bryology," The Hague, 1932.

CLASSIFICATION OF VASCULAR PLANTS

BOWER, F. O.: Studies in the morphology of spore-producing members. V. General comparisons and conclusions, *Phil. Trans. Roy. Soc. London*, **196B**: 191–257, 1903.

CAMPBELL, D. H.: The relationships of the Hepaticae, *Bot. Rev.*, **2**: 53–66, 1936.

CONRADI, A.: Das System der Farne unter Berücksicht der Morphologie, Entwicklungsgeschichte, Paläontologie und Serodiagnostic dargestellt, *Bot. Archiv*, **14**: 74–137, 1926.

FRITSCH, F. E.: The algal ancestry of the higher plants, *New Phyt.*, **15**: 233–250, 1916.

FRITSCH, K.: Die systematische Gruppierung der Pteridophyten, *Ber. Deut. Bot. Gesells.*, **47**: 618–622, 1930.

MÄGDEFRAU, K.: Die Stammesgeschichte der Lycopodiales. (Zugleich ein Beitrag zur Methodologie der botanischen Phylogenetik.), *Biol. Zentralbl.*, **52**: 280–294, 1932.

SAKISAKA, M., and Y. SINOTÔ: Critical considerations on the phylogenetic system of classification of plants, *Bot. Mag. Tokyo*, **44**: 285–293, 1930.

SCHAEDE, R.: Embryologische Untersuchungen zur Stammesgeschichte, *Beitr. zur. Biol. Pflanzen*, **14**: 87–143, 1920.

SCHAFFNER, J. H.: Phylogenetic taxonomy of plants, *Quar. Rev. Biol.*, **9**: 129–160, 1934.

SCOTT, D. H.: The early history of the land flora, *Nature*, **110**: 606–607; 638–640, 1922.

General Bibliography

BAKER, J. G.: "Handbook of the Fern-allies," London, 1887.

BAUER, F.: "Genera Filicum," London, 1842.

BOWER, F. O.: "The Origin of a Land Flora," London, 1908.

———: "The Ferns (Filicales)," 3 vols., Cambridge, 1923, 1928.

———: "Size and Form in Plants," London, 1930.

———: "Primitive Land Plants," London, 1935.

CAMPBELL, D. H.: "Mosses and Ferns," 3d ed., New York, 1918.

CLUTE, W. N.: "The Fern Allies of North America North of Mexico," New York, 1905.

ENGLER, A., and K. PRANTL: "Die natürlichen Pflanzenfamilien," Leipzig, 1887–1909.

GOEBEL, K.: "Organographie der Pflanzen," Pt. II, 3d ed., Jena, 1930.

HIRMER, M.: "Handbuch der Paläobotanik," vol. I, München and Berlin, 1927.

HOFMEISTER, W.: "The Higher Cryptogamia," Ray Soc. transl. by F. Currey, 1862.

JEFFREY, E. C.: "The anatomy of woody plants," Chicago, 1917.

LOTSY, J. P.: "Vorträge über botanische Stammesgeschichte," Jena, 1909.

MOORE, R. C.: "Historical Geology," New York, 1935.

POTONIÉ, K.: "Grundlinien der Pflanzenmorphologie im Lichte der Paläontologie," Jena, 1912.

SCHIMPER, A. F. W.: "Pflanzen-Geographie auf Physiologischer Grundlage," Jena, 1898.

SCOTT, D. H.: "Studies in Fossil Botany," 3d ed., London, 1923.

SEWARD, A. C.: "Fossil Plants," Cambridge, 1898.

———: "Plant Life through the Ages," Cambridge, 1931.

THOMAS, H. H.: The old morphology and the new, *Proc. Linn. Soc. London*, **145**: 17–32, 1932.

WARMING, E., and M. MÖBIUS: "Handbuch der systematischen Botanik," 4th ed., Berlin, 1929.

WARBURG, O.: "Die Pflanzenwelt," 3 vols., Leipzig and Vienna, 1913.

WETTSTEIN, R.: "Handbuch der systematischen Botanik," 4th ed., Leipzig and Vienna, 1933.

WILLIS, J. C.: "Flowering Plants and Ferns," 4th ed., Cambridge, 1919.

WINKLER, H.: Über Parthenogenesis und Apogamie im Pflanzenreiche, *Prog. Rei Bot.*, **2**: 293–454, 1908.

ZIMMERMANN, W.: "Die Phylogenie der Pflanzen," Jena, 1930.

INDEX

413